FOREWORD TO THE FIRST EDITION

This booklet is intended for farmers, advisers, students and everyone else who, frequently or infrequently, find themselves hunting for data relating to farm management - whether it is for blunt pencil calculations on the back of an envelope or for feeding into a computer. The material contained is based upon the sort of information which the author finds himself frequently having to look up in his twin roles as adviser and teacher in farm management. There are several excellent handbooks already in existence, but this pocketbook endeavours to cover a wider field and thus to be substantially more comprehensive. It is intended that most of the data herein contained will have a national application, although there is inevitably some bias towards conditions in the south-eastern half of the country.

The development of farm planning techniques in recent years has outstripped the quality and quantity of data available. It is hoped that this booklet will go a little further in supplying the type of information required. It cannot, however, claim to be the ultimate in this respect. For example, there are many variations in labour requirements according to farm conditions and sizes and types of machine used and there are many more variations in sheep and beef systems than are dealt with here. More detailed data on these lines are gradually becoming available from various sources. It is hoped further to refine the material in this booklet and to keep it up to date in subsequent editions, as the information becomes available. As a help towards this end, any comments or criticisms will be gratefully received.

The author wishes to thank his many friends and colleagues who have given him so much time and help in compiling this information.

John Nix
October, 1966

First published   October 1966
Forty Sixth Edition   September 2015

FOREWORD TO THE FORTY SIXTH EDITION

Not for the first time - nor, doubtlessly, the last - British farmers have had to contend with some very low output prices over the last year. The dramatic collapse in the milk price since its record peak in early 2014 is perhaps the most poignant example. Similarly, grain prices were around £40 per tonne higher at that time than at present and most livestock values were relatively buoyant, highlighting the degree of exposure that commodity producers have to market fluctuations.

The marginal principle, albeit a basic economic concept, has been used subconsciously by successful farmers for decades - often to a greater extent than they realise. The application of the principle is an intelligent response to volatile commodity prices, recognising that seemingly minor adjustments to various aspects of the business can deliver a synergistic effect across the whole.

Although the temptation to resist budgeting may be strong amidst such volatility, the need could not be greater. A farm plan, drawn up using a combination of experience, judgement and intuition and evaluated in financial terms, provides a vital glimpse into the future of the business. It is hoped that this book will assist in its preparation by providing some of the detailed analysis required for effective decision-making in the challenging environment in which today's farm business operates.

Figures in this book are estimated for 2016. Thus the crops data relate to the 2016 harvest. The livestock data relate either to the 2016 calendar year (e.g. for milk production) or to 2016/17 (e.g. for winter-finished beef). The yields and prices assume a 'normal' or average season, based on trends. Looking 6-18 months ahead to 2016/17, no one can know what the actual average yield and price for that particular year will be. *The figures should be adjusted as appropriate according to circumstances and price and cost differences.* Assumptions are set out to enable this to be done.

As always, I would like to thank all those who have contributed to the revision of this edition.

John Nix
August 2015

CONTENTS

I.   GENERAL

1.   THE USE OF GROSS MARGINS

DEFINITION

The data on the crop and livestock enterprises in the Pocketbook are based on gross margins. The gross margin of an enterprise is its output less its variable costs. Enterprise output includes the market value of production retained on the farm. The variable costs must (a) be specific to the enterprise and (b) vary in proportion to the size of the enterprise, i.e. number of hectares or head of stock. The main items of variable costs are: Crops: fertiliser, seed, sprays, casual labour and contract work specific to the crop. Non-Grazing Livestock: concentrate feed, vet. and med., marketing expenses. Grazing Livestock is as for non-grazing livestock, plus forage crop variable costs.

POINTS TO NOTE

1. The gross margin is not a profit figure. The 'fixed costs' (rent, labour, machinery, general overheads) have to be covered by the total farm gross margin before arriving at a profit.

2. The gross margin of an enterprise will differ from season to season, because of yield and price differences affecting output and also because variable costs will vary, e.g. the number and type of sprays required. Different soils and other natural factors, as well as level of management, will also cause differences between farms.

3. Items of variable cost vary from farm to farm, e.g. some farmers have greater weed control costs than others; some farmers employ a contractor to combine their cereals (a variable cost), others use their own equipment (a fixed cost); some employ a contractor to deliver their sugar beet to the factory (a variable cost), others have their own lorry (a fixed cost). These differences must be borne in mind in making inter-farm comparisons.

4. Provided points 2 and 3 are borne in mind, comparison of gross margins (particularly averages over several seasons) with standards can be a useful check on technical performance.

5. The other main usefulness of gross margins lies in farm planning. This is not simply a matter of substituting high gross margin enterprises in place of low ones. The gross margin is only one feature of an enterprise, albeit an important one. It says nothing about the call the enterprise makes on the basic farm resources - labour at different times of the year, machinery, buildings, working capital requirements, etc. All these factors and more have to be taken into account in the planning process.

6. This is not to argue that these other costs should be allocated. Complete allocation of many farm expenses is only possible on an arbitrary basis, since they are shared by two or more, possibly all farm enterprises. Allocation can therefore be completely misleading when making planning decisions. The same is true even when regular labour and machinery are employed specifically on certain enterprises, if such costs are calculated on a per-hectare or per head basis. This is because when enterprises are substituted, expanded, contracted or deleted, the variable costs for each enterprise will vary in proportion to the size of that enterprise, but other costs will not, except possibly some fuel and repair costs. Most 'fixed' costs may stay the same, others will change - but not smoothly in small amounts at a time. Either the same regular labour force will cope with a revised plan or a smaller or larger number of men will be needed. The same is true of tractors, other machines and buildings. Such cost changes must be taken into account, but allocating these costs on a per-hectare or per head basis

will not aid, and may positively confuse, planning decisions. The only point of making such calculations is for efficiency comparisons, e.g. labour cost per cow.

7. Allocating fixed costs at a flat rate (e.g. per hectare) for all enterprises, deducting this from the gross margin and hence calculating a 'net profit' from each enterprise can also be misleading. It ignores the whole problem of enterprise inter-relationships, differences between enterprises in total and seasonal requirements for labour, machinery and capital, and other factors such as different quality land on the same farm.

8. Changes in the scale of an enterprise may well affect its gross margin per unit, e.g. increasing the area of winter wheat from 30% to 55% on a farm will mean more second and third crop wheats being grown and a smaller proportion of the crop being drilled under the best conditions; hence yields may fall. Even if yields remain the same, variable costs (e.g. fertiliser) may be higher.

9. Gross margins used for planning future changes should also take account of possible changes in price, and the effect of changes in production techniques.

LOW, AVERAGE AND HIGH LEVELS

The levels of production given for most crop and livestock enterprises are meant to indicate differences in managerial skill or natural factors, soil productivity, etc., given the level of variable costs. They refer, to an average for each level over several years taking trends into account. Higher variable costs do not necessarily mean greater output, but depends on other factors too such as timing of applications.

The book is written with the progressive and business orientated farm manager in mind, those wanting to improve their businesses both technically and commercially. It therefore presupposes that the performance of the average Pocketbook user will exceed that of the national average farm performance, albeit only slightly. We therefore don't simply take Defra's average yields but, in most cases, a slightly higher yield. These figures are still thoroughly achievable in most farm businesses. The 'high' yields and performances are set out for those pushing the barriers of production slightly harder.

2.   COMPLETE ENTERPRISE COSTINGS

Gross margins are extremely useful for simple benchmarking and comparative tests. However, more than half of the variation in performance between farms (of all sectors) is in their overheads so won't show up on gross margin schedules. This means examining farm structure and overhead costs is crucial and understanding full costs of production is useful for business planning.

However, we must note that almost everybody will calculate the cost of production per tonne differently thereby giving different answers to the same question. Much arbitrary allocation of 'joint costs' is required to attempt fully costed net margins, and the results are often of limited use in making farm decisions. Another problem in 'complete enterprise costing' is where to stop. For example should interest on capital be included, whether borrowed or not? Further problems of asset valuation and allocation are involved if so. Variations between farms in their financial situations are considerable as, ranging from the farmer who owns all his land without any mortgage and has no other borrowings to the one with both a rent to pay for all his land and heavy borrowings in addition.

The above problems arise when 'costs per tonne' or 'costs per litre' are calculated. Wheat can be calculated to cost anything between £105 and £175 a tonne according to just what costs are included, how they are allocated and their yield.

It is natural to want to know 'unit costs' to compare, for example, with prices received. Sometimes these calculations clarify particular costs and therefore efficiency gains that could be made. For these reasons costs per litre of milk are included, although the calculation of some of the 'fixed cost' items is difficult. If a farm has only one enterprise such calculations on that farm are obviously straightforward. However, even on solely dairy farms followers are usually reared or forage grown, which are separate enterprises to milk production.

If required, a cost per tonne of combinable crops can be calculated by adding the fixed costs per hectare of mainly cereals farms (according to size range, given on page 220) to the variable costs per hectare given in the enterprise gross margin data and dividing by the selected yield. Such calculations need to be interpreted with caution because the allocation of fixed costs per hectare is inevitably crude. Often, the most successful allocation of labour and machinery is according to fuel use per hectare. This makes the resulting margins more comparable for example grass seed with potatoes. This is not a perfect science but attributes the various costs more accurately than per hectare or per unit of yield.

The allocation of specific labour (e.g. a full-time cowman), machinery (e.g. a potato harvester) and buildings (e.g. a grain store) is relatively simple and can provide useful information both for purposes of efficiency comparisons and partial budgeting. For some enterprises on many mixed farms, there are few such specific items and the question of the other so-called fixed cost items remains if a full costing is attempted.

3.   HISTORIC DATA

It is not the intention of The Pocketbook to include 'historical data', except for some of the material in the Agristats section. Hence total farm survey results, which are inevitably a year or two old by the time they are published, are not included, although some are used in some sections with interpretation for the forthcoming year. However the Pocketbook is gradually publishing spreadsheet tools with charted historical data on its website in the subscriber's section. This is not exhaustive and is anticipated to gradually increase. Let us know if there is a particular series that is not on the website.

4.   FARM BUSINESS SURVEY DATA

ENGLAND

The Farm Business Survey (FBS) is a key source of farm business data in England. It is carried out on behalf of DEFRA by a consortium of Universities. Its site; www.farmbusinesssurvey.co.uk holds a number of sets of FBS data and publications on specialist enterprises.

WALES

The Farm Business Survey in Wales is undertaken on behalf of the Welsh Assembly Government by the University of Aberystwyth.   The results are published at - www.aber.ac.uk/en/ibers/enterprise-kt/fbs/

SCOTLAND

In Scotland the data for the Farm Accounts Survey is collected by the Scottish Rural College.   It is available in the publication 'Farm Incomes in Scotland'.   See www.scotland.gov.uk/Topics/Statistics/15631/8884

NORTHERN IRELAND

The Department of Agriculture and Rural Development for Northern Ireland undertakes the Farm Business Survey in the province. Results can be found at http://www.dardni.gov.uk/index/statistics/statistical-reports/statistics-farm-incomes-in-ni.htm

5.   MAIN ASSUMPTIONS

Budgeting future prices, by necessity requires making several assumptions about how they are likely to move in the future from current levels (August 2014). This Edition of the Pocketbook uses the following key assumptions for 2015:

- The pound: euro exchange rate throughout the book is £1 = €1.40, equivalent to €1 = 71.5p. *Last year it was £1 = €1.25 (€1 = 80p).*

- Fertiliser prices for nitrogen (N), phosphate (P) and potash (K) are the same throughout. A full schedule of fertiliser valuations can be found on page 272. For calculating the gross margins, the following are used:

  - N: 69.6 p/kg (£240/t 34.5% N)   (UK Ammonium Nitrate)
  - P_2O_5:   68.5 p/kg (£315/t 46% P_2O_5) (Triple Super Phosphate)
  - K_2O: 44.2 p/kg (£265/t 60% K_2O) (Muriate of Potash)

- Farm machinery fuel price (red diesel) is taken to be 47ppl.

- Feed wheat price (from which many other commodity prices are benchmarked), is £135/tonne. This is an ex-farm price for 2016 harvest, delivery averaged throughout the year and typical marketing dates.

II.   ENTERPRISE DATA

1.   CROPS

Feed Wheat

Production level	Low	Average	High
Yield: tonnes per ha (tons per acre)	6.75 (2.7)	8.50 (3.4)	9.75 (3.9)
	£	£	£
Output	911 (369)	1,148 (465)	1,316 (533)
Variable Costs:			
Seed…………………………………		56 (23)	
Fertiliser…………………………..		199 (81)	
Sprays………………………………		236 (96)	
Total Variable Costs		491 (199)	
Gross Margin per ha (acre)	**420** (170)	**657** (266)	**825** (334)

Milling Wheat

Production level	Low	Average	High
Yield: tonnes per ha (tons per acre)	6.15 (2.5)	7.80 (3.2)	9.00 (3.6)
	£	£	£
Output	929 (376)	1,178 (477)	1,359 (550)
Variable Costs:			
Seed…………………………………		61 (25)	
Fertiliser…………………………..		235 (95)	
Sprays………………………………		245 (99)	
Total Variable Costs		541 (219)	
Gross Margin per ha (acre)	**388** (157)	**637** (258)	**818** (331)

1. *Prices*. The average feed wheat price for the 2016 harvest crop (i.e. 2016/17 marketing year) is £135 per tonne.

    The average milling price is £151/tonne. This is based on a 'full specification' premium of £28 over feed wheat, a 'biscuit' grade milling specification of £14 and a 25% failure rate of achieving the specification. The average premium achieved varies widely according to quality and season: see note 3. Full specification is defined as NABIM Group 1 wheat with a minimum Hagberg of 250, 13% Protein and a bushel weight of at least 76Kg/hl.

2. *Yields*. The average yield is for all winter wheat, i.e. all varieties and 1st and subsequent wheats. See over for more on First and Second Wheats. The overall yield used for feed and milling wheats combined calculates as 8.3t/ha.

3. *Straw* is costed as incorporated. Average yield and price is approx. 3·5 tonnes per hectare at £60/tonne (£5 more in small bales); variable costs (string) approx. £3.35 per tonne. Unbaled straw (sold for baling): anything from no value to £180/ha (£73/acre), national average around £38/ha (£15/acre).

4. *Seed*. Rates vary according to soil, season, variety, drilling date etc. Seed: £360 and £375 used for feed and milling respectively (C2) with a single purpose dressing; 175kg/ha in good conditions; Farm-saved included at 36% (feed) 25% (milling) as

according to pesticide survey 2010. Includes grain value, cleaning, dressing, testing and BSPB levy (refer to p 278). As many as a third of growers are finding an increasing requirement for additional seed treatments, in particular to supress BYDV. This can potentially add around £135 per tonne of seed to the cost (£24/ha). This has not been added in the gross margins so should be taken into account.

5. *Fertiliser* costs are based on P and K replacement cost for an average yield crop, with straw incorporated. RB209 suggests Phosphate and Potash is replaced at 7.8kg/t and 5.6kg/t of grain weight harvested respectively (66 and 48kg/ha respectively in this gross margin). Nitrogen is 190kg/ha for feed wheat and 250kg/ha for milling.

6. *Sprays*. Refer to Agrochemical Rates on page 278

7. *Milling v. Feed*. The yield of bread and biscuit wheat (generically known as milling) averages about 8% below that of feed wheat. Slightly higher seed, fertiliser and spray costs are normal for milling wheats. The price premium varies each season according to quality and scarcity. Also, not all deliveries achieve full specification. Grade 2 varieties normally achieve a premium of a few pounds a tonne (£14 used here) but their yields are higher than Grade 1 varieties. Full specification bread-making premium averaged £26/tonne from 2009 to 2015 with a range of £6.50 to £66.00 per tonne. The 2014/2015 bread-wheat premium averaged £38/tonne. NABIM wheat group 1 varieties account for about 21% of wheat area (2015), having risen sharply from 14% in 2014.

8. *First v. Second (Feed) Wheat*. Different types and lengths of rotational breaks affect subsequent wheat yields as well as weather, soils and varieties etc. The table below assumes a yield reduction of 10% for second wheats compared with first. Only average and high levels are shown. Third wheats could yield 10% below second wheats; variable costs are likely to be similar. Heavy, well-structured, well-drained clay soils are best suited to second wheats.

Comparison between First and Second Feed Wheat Crops

Production level	Average		High	
Year (after break)	First	Second	First	Second
Yield: tonnes per ha (tons/acre	8.93 (3.6)	8.22 (3.3)	10.24 (4.1)	9.42 (3.8)
	£	£	£	£
Output	1,206 (488)	1,110 (449)	1,382 (560)	1,272 (515)
Variable Costs:				
Seed............................	42 (17)	99 (40)	42 (17)	99 (40)
Fertiliser......................	209 (85)	192 (78)	209 (85)	192 (78)
Sprays..........................	231 (94)	252 (102)	231 (94)	252 (102)
Variable Costs	482 (195)	543 (220)	482 (195)	543 (220)
Gross Margin per ha (acre)	**724** (293)	**567** (230)	**900** (365)	**729** (295)

9. This schedule does not account for severe *grass weed infestations* such as Black Grass or Sterile Brome. The costs associated with managing such problems can amount to up to £155/hectare of additional agrichemical costs. Yield losses increase as infestation rises:

Yield losses from Black Grass Infestations

Grass plants/m^2	Yield loss t/Ha	% yield loss
8-12	0.2-0.4	2-5%
12-25	0.4-0.8	5-15%
100	1-2	15-25%
>300	+3	37%

References:
Roebuck, J.F. (1987).
B.C.P.C. and
Blair A, Cussans J,
Lutman P (1999).

SPRING WHEAT

Production level	Low	Average	High
Yield: tonnes per ha (tons per acre)	4.75 (1.9)	5.75 (2.3)	6.75 (2.7)
	£	£	£
Output	713 (289)	863 (350)	1,013 (410)
Variable Costs:			
Seed....................................		75 (30)	
Fertiliser................................		149 (60)	
Sprays....................................		140 (57)	
Total Variable Costs		364 (148)	
Gross Margin per ha (acre)	**349** (141)	**499** (202)	**648** (263)

1. *Price*: In general, see Winter Wheat (previous pages). A far higher proportion of spring wheat is sold for milling compared with winter wheat. Here we assume 90% making the average price £150/tonne for 2016 harvest.

2. *Straw*: See Winter Wheat but yields are considerably lower.

3. *Seed*: £390/tonne at 200kg/ha used. Home saved included at 15% including grain value, cleaning, dressing, testing and BSPB levy (refer to p 278).

4. *Fertiliser*: 150kg/ha N used, and P and K replacing off-take at 45kg/ha and 32kg/ha respectively.

5. *Sprays*. Refer to Agrochemical Rates on page 278

Normally, only about 3% of the UK wheat area is spring sown although survey data is unavailable. It is popular after root crops. The percentage is naturally higher after a particularly wet autumn. The percentage is even lower in Scotland (1% or less) than in England or Wales. The area has risen in recent years because of very hard 'Red Wheat' varieties grown to contract, Greening obligations and to manage grass weeds.

RED WHEAT

Production level	Low	Average	High
Yield: tonnes per ha (tons per acre)	4.00 (1.6)	5.00 (2.0)	6.00 (2.4)
	£	£	£
Output	840 (340)	1,050 (425)	1,260 (510)
Variable Costs:			
Seed....................................		90 (36)	
Fertiliser................................		179 (72)	
Sprays....................................		210 (85)	
Total Variable Costs		479 (194)	
Gross Margin per ha (acre)	**361** (146)	**571** (231)	**781** (316)

1. Red Wheat is a hard, high protein crop. It is used widely in bread-making, with imports of about 850,000 tonnes per year. It is solely grown on contract, and currently priced against the St Laurence (Canada) fob (free on board) price plus a margin of about £30/t. Here it is £210/tonne.

2. *Inputs*: *Seed* used here at £575/t at 155kg/ha, *Fertiliser* at 155:65:60 N:P:K accordingly and for *sprays*, see page 278.

WINTER BARLEY

Feed Barley

Production level	Low	Average	High
Yield: tonnes per ha (tons per acre)	5.5 (2.2)	6.9 (2.8)	7.9 (3.2)
	£	£	£
Output	688 (279)	863 (350)	988 (400)
Variable Costs:			
Seed………………………………		59 (24)	
Fertiliser……………………………..		152 (62)	
Sprays……………………………….		181 (73)	
Total Variable Costs		392 (159)	
Gross Margin per ha (acre)	**296** (120)	**471** (191)	**596** (241)

Malting Barley

Production level	Low	Average	High
Yield: tonnes per ha (tons per acre)	5.0 (2.0)	6.0 (2.4)	6.9 (2.8)
	£	£	£
Output	705 (286)	846 (343)	973 (394)
Variable Costs:			
Seed………………………………		61 (25)	
Fertiliser……………………………..		117 (47)	
Sprays……………………………….		181 (73)	
Total Variable Costs		359 (145)	
Gross Margin per ha (acre)	**346** (140)	**487** (197)	**614** (249)

1. *Prices.* The feed barley price for 2016 harvest (i.e. 2016/17 marketing year) is taken to be £125/tonne, an 8% discount to feed wheat (the average over 5 and 20 years is about 7.5%). The winter malting price (£141.00/tonne) assumes an average premium over feed of £16/tonne. This accounts for some that don't meet malting standards. For the best malting barleys the premium in the past has been £25 and in some years higher.

2. *Straw* is costed as being incorporated. Average yield is approx. 2·75 tonnes per hectare, value £65 per tonne baled ex-field, higher in the West, (£10 more in small bales); variable cost (string) approximately £3.35 per tonne. Prices rise in years of forage shortage.

3. *Seed.* Winter barley seed averages £365 for feed and £375 for malting at 175kg/ha. Seed includes 25% farm-saved including grain, dressing, testing and BSPB levy (see p 279).

4. *Fertiliser* costs are based on N at 160kg/ha for feed, 100kg/ha for malting crops. P and K replacement cost, with straw incorporated making 53:38kg/ha for feed and 45:32kg/ha for malting crops.

5. *Sprays.* Refer to Agrochemical Rates on page 278

SPRING (MALTING) BARLEY

Production level	Low	Average	High
Yield: tonnes per ha (tons per acre)	4.6 (1.9)	5.45 (2.2)	6.3 (2.6)
	£	£	£
Output	695 (281)	823 (333)	951 (385)
Variable Costs:			
Seed....................................		62 (25)	
Fertiliser................................		99 (40)	
Sprays...................................		140 (57)	
Total Variable Costs		301 (122)	
Gross Margin per ha (acre)	**394** (159)	**522** (211)	**650** (263)

1. *Prices.* Virtually all spring barley grown is malting varieties, grown for a premium. Spring malting premiums usually exceed those for winter varieties. Here the premium over feed barley is £26/tonne. Again, this allows for failed samples making £151.00/t.

2. *Seed.* Spring barley seed used is £390/tonne at a seed rate of 175Kg/ha. 35% is home saved (refer to p 279).

3. *Fertiliser* costs are based on N at 80kg/ha. P and K replacement cost, with straw incorporated making 43:31kg (P:K) per hectare.

4. *Sprays.* Refer to Agrochemical Rates on page 278

OATS

Winter Oats

Production level	Low	Average	High
Yield: tonnes per ha (tons per acre)	5.3 (2.1)	6.3 (2.6)	7.7 (3.1)
	£	£	£
Output	656 (266)	788 (319)	956 (387)
Variable Costs:			
Seed……………………………		58 (23)	
Fertiliser…………………………..		112 (45)	
Sprays…………………………		127 (51)	
Total Variable Costs		297 (120)	
Gross Margin per ha (acre)	**359** (145)	**490** (199)	**659** (267)

Spring Oats

Production level	Low	Average	High
Yield: tonnes per ha (tons per acre)	4.5 (1.8)	5.5 (2.2)	6.5 (2.6)
	£	£	£
Output Feed	563 (228)	688 (278)	813 (329)
Variable Costs:			
Seed……………………………		64 (26)	
Fertiliser…………………………..		92 (37)	
Sprays…………………………..		88 (36)	
Total Variable Costs		244 (99)	
Gross Margin per ha (acre)	**319** (129)	**443** (179)	**569** (230)

1. *Price* used is £125/tonne for the 2016 harvest crop, i.e. the 2016/17 movement year for milling oats. Milling specification requires a minimum bushel weight of 50Kg/Hl. Conservation grade milling oats may obtain a premium of £10-20/tonne.

2. *Straw* is not included above. Average yield is 3.5 tonnes per hectare; value £68 per tonne according to region and season; variable costs (string) £3.35 per tonne.

3. *Seed*: priced here at £390/tonne and £415/tonne, at 175kg/ha and 185kg/ha for winter and spring crops respectively, both with 40% home saved (refer to p 279).

4. *Fertiliser*; winter costs are based on N at 90kg/ha winter and 70kg/ha spring. P and K replacement cost, with straw incorporated making 50:36kg/ha for winter and 43:31kg/ha for spring.

5. *Sprays*. Refer to Agrochemical Rates on page 278

6. For *Naked Oats* refer to page 21

7. *Winter or Spring?* The majority of GB oats are winter crops although the popularity of spring oats has been rising in recent years; the proportion of spring oats increases further north with say 70% winter oats in England/Wales but less in Scotland.

OILSEED RAPE

Winter Rape

Production level	Low	Average	High
Yield: tonnes per ha (tons per acre)	2.40 (1.0)	3.40 (1.4)	4.40 (1.8)
	£	£	£
Output	672 (272)	952 (386)	1,232 (499)
Variable Costs:			
Seed..		52 (21)	
Fertiliser.................................		181 (73)	
Sprays.....................................		217 (88)	
Total Variable Costs		449 (182)	
Gross Margin per ha (acre)	**223** (90)	**503** (204)	**783** (317)

Spring Rape

Production level	Low	Average	High
Yield: tonnes per ha (tons per acre)	1.5 (0.6)	2.00 (0.8)	2.75 (1.1)
	£	£	£
Output	420 (170)	560 (227)	770 (312)
Variable Costs:			
Seed..		49 (20)	
Fertiliser.................................		85 (34)	
Sprays.....................................		141 (57)	
Total Variable Costs		275 (111)	
Gross Margin per ha (acre)	**145** (59)	**285** (116)	**495** (201)

1. *Prices.* The price assumed for the 2016 crop is £270/tonne, including oil bonuses at 42% oil content, (£260 before).

2. *Seed.* Winter price is 30% conventional merchant's seed (£40/ha), 40% hybrid (£70/ha) and 30% home saved conventional (refer to p 279 for home saving costs).

3. *Fertiliser* costs are based on N at 190kg/ha for winter, 80kg/ha for spring. P and K replacement cost, with straw incorporated making 45:35kg/ha for winter and 28:22kg/ha for spring crops.

4. *Sprays.* Refer to Agrochemical Rates on page 278

5. *Winter Versus Spring;* very little spring OSR is grown in the UK, maybe as little as 15,000 hectares which is 2-3 percent of the entire crop. As can be seen the financial reward is slim compared with winter crops.

LINSEED

Spring Linseed

Production level	Low	Average	High
Yield: tonnes per ha (tons per acre)	1.25 (0.5)	1.75 (0.7)	2.75 (1.1)
	£	£	£
Output	378 (153)	529 (214)	831 (337)
Variable Costs:			
Seed..		90 (36)	
Fertiliser.................................		81 (33)	
Sprays.....................................		64 (26)	
Total Variable Costs		235 (95)	
Gross Margin per ha (acre)	**143** (58)	**294** (119)	**596** (241)

Winter Linseed

Production level	Low	Average	High
Yield: tonnes per ha (tons per acre)	1.50 (0.6)	2.30 (0.9)	3.00 (1.2)
	£	£	£
Output	453 (183)	695 (281)	906 (367)
Variable Costs:			
Seed..		95 (38)	
Fertiliser.................................		139 (56)	
Sprays.....................................		77 (31)	
Total Variable Costs		311 (126)	
Gross Margin per ha (acre)	**142** (58)	**384** (155)	**595** (241)

1. The *price* for the 2016 crop is £292/tonne (OSR price plus 10%). Contract prices are normally tied to a standard 38% oil and 9% moisture. Some specialist contracts for specific varieties such as Yellow Linseed can be worth more.

2. *Seed*, 50kg/ha (sold in hectare bags) minimal home saved

3. *Fertiliser* N/P/K of spring 80/25/19 and winter 90:75:50

4. *Sprays*. Refer to Agrochemical Rates on page 278

5. Most *linseed is spring-sown*, drilling mid-March to mid-April, no more than 1 year in 5. Too much nitrogen (over 130 kg/ha) can cause lodging, delayed maturity and excessive weed growth and hence difficult harvesting, poor quality and lower yields; it should be applied early. Harvesting: spring normally end Aug-early Sept. Moisture content most likely 12-16%: must be dried to 9% for storage.

6. *Winter Linseed* area has plateaued at about 6,500ha grown in the UK. Yield is affected by frost heave, disease and thrips (thunder-bugs), most varieties susceptible to lodging; pigeons can be troublesome. Early sowing (early to mid-September) is best.

FIELD PEAS

Blue Peas

Production level	Low	Average	High
Yield: tonnes per ha (tons per acre)	3.0 (1.2)	3.75 (1.5)	5.0 (2.0)
	£	£	£
Output	570 (231)	713 (289)	950 (385)
Variable Costs:			
Seed..		88 (36)	
Fertiliser....................................		40 (16)	
Sprays......................................		146 (59)	
Total Variable Costs		274 (111)	
Gross Margin per ha (acre)	**296.3** (120)	**439** (178)	**676** (274)

Marrowfats

Production level	Low	Average	High
Yield: tonnes per ha (tons per acre)	2.7 (1.1)	3.40 (1.4)	4.5 (1.8)
	£	£	£
Output	675 (273)	850 (344)	1,125 (456)
Variable Costs:			
Seed..		182 (74)	
Fertiliser....................................		36 (15)	
Sprays......................................		181 (73)	
Total Variable Costs		399 (161)	
Gross Margin per ha (acre)	**276.3** (112)	**451** (183)	**726** (294)

1. *Price*. All peas are grown for a premium market (not stock-feed) with only a small proportion (20%) are compounded as feed peas. The high premium for food consumption justifies pea cleaning to remove discoloured and damaged peas. Feed value is therefore not relevant as a base price.

   The overall price for *Blue Peas* is £190/tonne, taking account of human consumption premiums (£200/tonne) and a 20% failure rate with feed price of £165. Most peas (70% in 2016) are Blues, used for micronizing (largely for pet food) and exports.

   Marrowfats can achieve higher prices. They are not priced with a premium over wheat, as the markets bear no relationship. They are used for canning, packets and export trade. They are almost entirely grown on a contract thus production is restricted by demand although this is growing. They yield about 10% less than Blue Peas. The average price in this gross margin is £250/tonne being £270/tonne for 80% £165 for the 20% that fails quality specification.

2. *Seed*: Blues, £500/tonne planted at 200kg/ha, Marrowfats £655/tonne at 300kg/ha. Home Saved rate of 30% for blues and 30% for Marrowfats (refer to p 279).

3. *Fertiliser*: based on 9kg phosphate and 10kg potash per tonne of pea harvested per hectare. No nitrogen is applied making 0:34:38kg/ha Blues and 0:30:34 Marrowfats.

4. *Sprays*. Refer to Agrochemical Rates on page 278

FIELD BEANS

Winter Beans

Production level	Low	Average	High
Yield: tonnes per ha (tons per acre)	3.0 (1.2)	4.0 (1.6)	5.0 (2.0)
	£	£	£
Output	540 (219)	720 (292)	900 (365)
Variable Costs:			
Seed....................................		91 (37)	
Fertiliser...............................		42 (17)	
Sprays...................................		122 (50)	
Total Variable Costs		255 (103)	
Gross Margin per ha (acre)	**285** (115)	**465** (188)	**645** (261)

Spring Beans

Production level	Low	Average	High
Yield: tonnes per ha (tons per acre)	2.8 (1.1)	3.7 (1.5)	4.6 (1.9)
	£	£	£
Output	518 (210)	685 (277)	851 (345)
Variable Costs:			
Seed....................................		96 (39)	
Fertiliser...............................		39 (16)	
Sprays...................................		120 (49)	
Total Variable Costs		255 (103)	
Gross Margin per ha (acre)	**263** (106)	**429** (174)	**596** (241)

Winter Bean Notes
1. *Price*. The 2016 harvest price for winter feed beans is budgeted at £180 per tonne. This is based on a Human consumption price of £185/tonne achieved by 70% and feed specification for the rest at £165/tonne.

2. *Fertiliser*: 9kg phosphate and 10kg potash/t bean harvested/ha. No nitrogen is applied making 0:36:40kg/ha.

3. *Seed*: 185-220 kg per hectare (200kg used here) at £485/tonne. About 60% is farm-saved as in this gross margin (refer to p 279).

4. *Sprays*. Refer to Agrochemical Rates on page 278

Spring Bean Notes
5. *Price*. Spring beans are all grown for the human consumption market. It is only the poor quality beans (predominantly Bruchid beetle damaged) that are rejected and redirected to feed compounders. Damaged samples can be cleaned if the premium justifies it. A large proportion of the crop is exported (to North Africa). Average spring bean price is budgeted here at £185/tonne comprising 60% at £195/tonne and the rest at £165/tonne.

6. *Fertiliser*: 9kg phosphate and 10kg potash/t bean harvested/ha. No nitrogen is applied making 0:33:37kg/ha.

7. *Seed*: 185-220 kg per hectare (200kg/ha here) at £485/tonne. About 50% is farm-saved. Sprays: as for winter beans.

8. *Sprays*. Refer to Agrochemical Rates on page 278

Winter versus Spring Beans.

The key determinant between which to crop is soil type. Winter beans are more suited to heavy soils and springs on lighter land. As the schedules illustrate, there is little real difference between the gross margins. Spring crops are retained in many rotations to help manage grass weed problems.

Peas or Beans?

For the last decade the area of peas was about 20% of the UK combinable pulse area having fallen from 50% in 1997. High quality and good yields can return high gross margins and offer wider benefits to the farming system although they can be difficult to grow and the unpredictability of pulses had put several growers off in previous years.

Beyond the Gross Margin

Page 1 explains that the gross margin is only a partial measure of crop contribution and cost to the farm business. Amongst the combinable crops this is particularly true for the legumes such as peas and beans. They fix nitrogen into the soil which is then available for uptake by subsequent crops either saving input costs of the following crop or raising its yield. The amount fixed is very difficult to predict but varies from almost nothing to over 200kg/ha in the extreme cases based on soil type, crop health, growing conditions and other factors too. A useful average figure used by the PGRO for additional nitrogen available for the following crop after a pulse crop is 50kg/ha. The associated input savings from the following crop, or the additional yield it achieves should therefore, for management purposes be attributed to the leguminous crop.

LUPINS

The table refers to spring sown *white lupins*:

Production level	Low	Average	High
Yield: tonnes per ha (tons per acre)	2.25 (0.9)	3.00 (1.2)	3.75 (1.5)
	£	£	£
Output	495 (200)	660 (267)	825 (334)
Variable Costs:			
Seed …………………………….....		130 (52)	
Fertiliser…………………………..…		62 (25)	
Sprays ……………………………..…		80 (32)	
Total Variable Costs	272 (110)	272 (110)	272 (110)
Gross Margin per ha (acre)	**223** (90)	**388** (157)	**553** (224)

1. *Price* used here is £220 per tonne. Few lupins are traded on the open market, but the value tends to be slightly higher than the feed bean price (closer to soya values).

2. *Inputs; Seed;* £740/tonne at 175kg/ha, *Fertiliser;* N,P,K, 25:40:40

3. A leguminous spring crop traditionally associated with light land. Their protein content is about 40 to 50% higher than peas and beans, making lupins a good substitute for soya bean meal in livestock feed compounds. They are a non-GM source of high quality digestible protein. Most is whole-cropped for silage but can be crimped or milled and fed directly to stock or the grain traded as a cash crop.

4. The area grown is around 4,000 hectares (10,000 acres). About 65% of the UK lupin area is white (mostly in South and East), 15-20% blue and the remainder yellow (North and Scotland due to their shorter growing season).

5. Lupins need a good cereal seedbed and pre-emergence weed control. Nitrogen fertiliser is not necessary. Replacement P and K at 30-50kg per ha is assumed. There are no serious crop pests. Anthracnose is a potentially serious threat but plant health measures have so far kept it under control.

6. Appropriate variety choice is important depending on area of the country, soil pH, intended end use and growth habit required. There are three distinct species of spring lupins; white (*lupinus albus*), blue (*l. angustifolus*) and yellow (*l. luteus*). White lupins have higher protein and potentially greater yield than blues but require a longer growing season. Yellow lupins fall between blue and white on both counts.

Lupin characteristics

	White *Lupinus Albus*	**Yellow** *Lupinus Luteus*	**Blue** *Lupinus Angustifolius*
Flower Colour	white or blue	yellow	white or blue
Growth habit	semi-determinate	semi-determinate	fully or semi-determinate
pH tolerance	5 to 7.6	4.6 to 6.8	5 to 6.8
Protein	36-40%	38-42%	31-35%
Oil content	10%	5%	6%
Yield	3.0-3.5 t/ha	2.5-3.0 t/ha	3.0-3.5 t/ha

Acknowledgement: Thanks to - Soya UK, Tel: 02380 696922.

HERBAGE SEEDS

	Italian Ryegrass		Early Perennial Ryegrass	
	Average	High	Average	High
	£	£	£	£
Yield (tonnes per ha)	1.4	1.8	1.30	1.60
Price per 50 kg (£)	50		55	
Output	1,400	1,800	1,430	1,760
Variable Costs:				
Seed	115		105	
Fertiliser	238		238	
Sprays	125		130	
Cleaning / Certification............	236	296	221	266
Total Variable Costs	714	774	694	739
Gross Margin per ha	**686**	**1,026**	**736**	**1,021**
Gross Margin per acre	278	415	298	413

	Intermediate Perennial Ryegrass		Late Perennial Ryegrass	
	Average	High	Average	High
	£	£	£	£
Yield (tonnes per ha)	1.3	1.6	1.10	1.50
Price per 50 kg (£)	60		65	
Output	1,560	1,920	1,430	1,950
Variable Costs:				
Seed	100		100	
Fertiliser	238		238	
Sprays	135		135	
Cleaning / Certification............	221	266	191	251
Total Variable Costs	694	739	664	724
Gross Margin per ha	**866**	**1,181**	**766**	**1,226**
Gross Margin per acre	350	478	310	496

	Hybrid Ryegrass		Kent Wild White Clover & Kent Indig. Peren. R'grass	
	Average	High	Average	High
	£	£	£	£
Yield (tonnes per ha)	1.3	1.6	0.09 (Clover)	0.11 (C)
			0.6 (R'grass)	0.8 (R)
Price per 50 kg (£)	60		350 (C)	60 (R)
Output	1560	1,920	1,350	1,730
Variable Costs:				
Seed	105		70	
Fertiliser	226		95	
Sprays	135		115	
Cleaning / Certification............	221	266	143	179
Total Variable Costs	687	732	423	459
Gross Margin per ha	**873**	**1,188**	**927**	**1,271**
Gross Margin per acre	353	481	375	514

1. *Prices* in are for certified seed for 2016 harvest. Current markets for grass seed are well-supplied after good recent harvests. Demand has weakened from the livestock sector. High sugar varieties command a premium of £5-£10 over the values quoted. Amenity ryegrasses and fescues also command a premium for high quality sports use, and some yield nearly as much as agricultural varieties.

2. No allowance has been made above for *by-products*. Some crops produce 4 to 5 tonnes of threshed hay, which is of low feeding value, potentially worth £300 per hectare. Some grasses, especially spring-sown ryegrass, also provide good autumn and winter grazing. Clovers can be grazed or cut for hay or silage and do not have to be 'shut up' until late May.

3. *Yields* are for cleaned certified seed. The crop is risky, i.e. yields are highly variable, depending especially on the weather at, and precise timeliness of, harvesting. The use of growth regulators and stripper headers reduces the risk. Most grasses give their highest yield in their first harvest year, assuming good establishment. Yields can be increased by up to 30% with a combination of higher nitrogen applications along with a growth regulator (e.g. Moddus). This would add £15 per ha (£6 per acre) to the chemical figure in the margins, with a similar cost increase for extra nitrogen.

4. *Inputs: Seed* 10kg per hectare for autumn sown Italian ryegrass. Spring planted seed rates are lower. If the seed crop is undersown, specialist growers often reduce the seed rate for the cover crop by up to half and restrict nitrogen dressing: the cereal yield may thus be reduced by up to 0.6 tonnes per hectare. *Fertiliser: N:P:K 155:100:140*

5. *Chemical* costs. Autumn sown crops have higher costs than spring sown ones. The margins assume an autumn-sown crop.

6. The following were the number of hectares grown for certified seed production for the main grasses and clovers in the UK for the 2013 harvest;

Italian / Westerwold Ryegrass ..	147	Cocksfoot	89
Early Perennial Ryegrass	66	Timothy..................................	0
Inter. Perennial Ryegrass	1,881	Red Fescue	179
Late Perennial Ryegrass	2,549	White Clover	128
Amenity Perennial Ryegrass.....	388	Red Clover..............................	184
Hybrid Ryegrass	699	Common Vetch......................	86

The ryegrasses total 5,730 ha (*14,160 acres*).
All herbage seeds total 6,396 ha (*15,800 acres*).

7. *Labour*: see page 173.

Acknowledgement: Thanks to - British Seed Houses, Tel: 01522 868 714; Herbage Seed Services, Tel: 01962 774 432; NIAB, Tel: 01223 342 238.

RYE

Production level	Low	Average	High
Yield: tonnes per ha (tons per acre)	4.90 (2.0)	6.20 (2.5)	7.50 (3.0)
	£	£	£
Output	711 (288)	899 (364)	1,088 (440)
Variable Costs:			
Seed		95 (39)	
Fertiliser...................................		153 (62)	
Sprays		105 (43)	
Total Variable Costs	353 (143)	353 (143)	353 (143)
Gross Margin per ha (acre)	**358** (145)	**546** (221)	**734** (297)

1. The *price* assumed is £145 per tonne for 2016 harvest. This is based on a £10 per tonne premium over the prevailing feed wheat price at the point of movement and Oct-Dec delivery. The price assumes the milling specification is achieved. Deductions are made for low quality, and if it is feed grade, price then falls between feed wheat and feed barley. Only a very small percentage of the crop is grown for the free market.

2. *Seed:* 150kg per hectare at £650 per tonne.

3. *Fertiliser:* based on 120kg Nitrogen per hectare, with P and K at replacement levels of 50 and 80 kg per hectare respectively

4. Rye is autumn-sown, drought tolerant and very hardy. It can withstand low temperatures and starts growing early in the spring. It has all-round resistance to wheat and barley diseases, e.g. eyespot, and suffers less from take-all than wheat – hence it is a possible replacement for third or fourth wheat. Its vigour keeps weeds down. Its *herbicide, fungicide* and *fertiliser* requirements are lower than for other cereals, except for growth regulators. Rye is harvested earlier than winter wheat (useful for following with oilseed rape).

5. Largely grown on light, low fertility, sandy or stony soils, not suited to other cereals. Yields would clearly be higher on better soils, but then rye has difficulty competing with wheat and barley; it doesn't on good land. The average yield in the UK in the five years 2010 to 2014 was 5.6 tonnes per hectare.

6. The area grown in the UK has ranged between 6,000 and 7,000 ha for several years, but saw an uplift to over 10,000 hectares for 2014. It remains to be seen whether this growth will be maintained. Rye crisp-bread is the major outlet. It is also milled into flour, used in mixed-grain bread and muesli. About two-thirds of UK requirements are imported, mainly from Canada (which produces the highest quality), Denmark, Germany and Spain. Demand for UK-grown rye has been falling in recent years, owing to increased competition in the crisp-bread market.

7. Drawbacks: it sprouts in a wet harvest: must therefore harvest early, at relatively high moisture content. It grows very tall and lodges easily: hence high levels of nitrogen are not possible; but growth regulators help. Its heavy straw crop means very slow combining (takes about twice as long per hectare as wheat and barley), and difficult straw incorporation. Hybrid varieties, with shorter, stiffer straw, are being developed; these would improve the comparative profitability of rye on better soils.

8. Drilling: 2nd and 3rd weeks September. Harvesting: by mid-August at relatively high moisture content, then dry to 14-15% (no drying costs included in margin).

TRITICALE

Production level	Low	Average	High
Yield: tonnes per ha (tons per acre)	4.00 (1.6)	5.00 (2.0)	7.20 (2.9)
	£	£	£
Output	520 (211)	650 (263)	936 (379)
Variable Costs:			
Seed		54 (22)	
Fertiliser..................................		147 (59)	
Sprays		70 (28)	
Total Variable Costs	270 (110)	270 (110)	270 (110)
Gross Margin per ha (acre)	**250** (101)	**380** (154)	**666** (270)

1. The price is usually £4 or £6 per tonne below feed wheat, but this tends to vary from season to season; £130 per tonne is assumed above for the 2016 harvest crop.

2. A 'man-made' cross between rye and hard wheat. It combines the hardiness of rye and the marketability of feed wheat. It is used in livestock feed, particularly pig and poultry rations, having high levels of lysine (an amino acid). It is not widely used by feed compounders though. The cropped UK area has risen in recent years to around 15,000ha, largely because of the new spring varieties (see below).

3. *Yields* in the five years 2010 to 2014 averaged 4.0 tonnes/ha. But between 1996 and 2000, yields (apparently) averaged 5.90 tonnes per hectare. Low yields are a result of it mainly being grown on light land. In these circumstances, it frequently out-yields wheat or barley, especially the former, and with lower input requirements. Its yields tend to be more consistent on such soil than those of barley. Triticale tends to do well compared with second and subsequent wheats owing to its resistance to drought and fungal diseases. It is also less prone to damage than other cereals where rabbit grazing is a problem.

4. Lower levels of fungicide are needed because of its good disease resistance, except for ergot, but including take-all (making it a good replacement for a third or fourth wheat). It is a tall crop, which helps to suppress weeds, but it is susceptible to lodging; growth regulators are beneficial. New semi-dwarf varieties are being developed, to overcome straw strength weakness and susceptibility to rust infections.

5. The crop is best drilled early (September) on very light, drought-prone soils; otherwise October is satisfactory. Harvesting is at approximately the same time as wheat. There is more straw, which slows combining, and incorporation is difficult; this is less of a problem on poor soils as there is less straw.

Spring Triticale

New spring varieties of this crop have been introduced in the last few years. These have been taken up strongly in livestock areas – the north and west of England, as well as western Scotland, Wales and N. Ireland. Being a spring crop means that winter water logging is not an issue, and it can be grown on a wider range of soils. In total up to 5,000 hectares of spring triticale is grown in the UK: either on its own or as part of a mixture.

It has lower yields than winter triticale if it is harvested for grain in the conventional way. However, most is whole-cropped to produce an 'arable forage'. Often it is grown in a mixture with a proteins crop – peas or lupins for example. Inputs for spring triticale will be lower than those for winter varieties.

NAKED OATS

Production level	Low	Average	High
Yield: tonnes per ha (tons per acre)	4.50 (1.8)	5.50 (2.2)	6.50 (2.6)
	£	£	£
Output	824 (334)	1,007 (408)	1,190 (482)
Variable Costs:			
Seed		60 (24)	
Fertiliser..............................		122 (50)	
Sprays		100 (41)	
Total Variable Costs	282 (114)	282 (114)	282 (114)
Gross Margin per ha (acre)	**541** (219)	**724** (293)	**907** (367)

1.   The 2016 harvest crop *price* assumed is £183 per tonne, based on contracts offering premiums 35% above the average feed wheat price. The premium can be reduced according to husk content. Contracts require a maximum moisture content of 14%, which is also recommended for long-term storage.

2.   *Inputs* are lower than for wheat or barley. The agronomy is similar to that of husked oat varieties. Traditionally, high nitrogen use has not been possible due to the risk of lodging, however, new semi-dwarf varieties with stiff straw have been introduced. As well as increasing the scope for higher fertiliser applications, this means the crop is also suited to more fertile soils, and growth regulators may be avoided. Oats provide a break in the take-all cycle.

3.   Naked oats have a higher protein, energy and oil content than 'traditional' oats, but the fibre content is lower – as the husk is removed during harvesting.

4.   The area being grown continues to increase steadily. Naked oats account for in excess of 10% of the traded tonnage of UK oats (i.e. excluding those grown for on-farm use). The traditional markets such as racehorse feed, dog food, and bird feed markets are all increasing. Over recent years the human consumption market has developed so that at least half the crop is now sold for health foods, artisan breads and breakfast cereals. In future, a further growth area is likely to be for inclusion of the crop in monogastric animal feeds. The poultry industry in particular is looking into setting up supply chains.

5.   Around a third of plantings are spring and this proportion rises after a wet autumn. The margin above is winter cropping. Past NIAB survey results have suggested that spring yields average 20%-25% less than conventional oats. The actual difference will depend on the particular season, but are likely now to be in the range 15%-20%.

6.   Harvest is early (just after winter barley). New varieties are less susceptible to shedding than in the past, however care needs to be taken with both the timing of harvest, and the set-up of the combine, to ensure a clean, saleable, sample.

Naked Barley

Naked barley, suitable for roasting, flaking or milling as pearl barley, is now rarely heard of. It is grown like normal barley, but yields are reckoned to be some 15% lower. It could be either autumn or spring sown.

BORAGE

Production level	Low	Average	High
Yield: tonnes per ha (tons per acre)	0.10 (0.0)	0.40 (0.2)	0.70 (0.3)
	£	£	£
Output	340 (138)	1,360 (551)	2,380 (964)
Variable Costs:			
Seed		189 (77)	
Fertiliser.....................................		95 (39)	
Sprays		40 (16)	
Total Variable Costs	324 (131)	324 (131)	324 (131)
Gross Margin per ha (acre)	**16** (6)	**1,036** (420)	**2,056** (833)

1. Borage is indigenous to Britain (or at least here since Roman times); it has both grown in the wild, and been cultivated for centuries. It is produced principally for use as a dietary supplement, but it may also be used in cosmetics and pharmaceuticals. The oil has a high gamma linolenic acid (GLA) content.

2. It was first grown as a field crop in the UK in the early 1980's. The last few years have usually seen around 5,000 hectares (12,500 acres) planted per year. However, due to a world-wide surplus of GLA, few, if any, contracts were offered in the years 2009 to 2011. The area has recovered since, partly due to the high quality of the UK crop compared to other sources. The usual area should be contracted for 2016.

3. The harvest crop price assumed is £3,400 per tonne. This reflects better demand prospects and the quality of the UK crop. The market tends to be volatile, it is essential for a grower to have a buy-back contract with a reputable company. The crop should not be grown speculatively.

4. The crop is spring sown (March-April) into a good seedbed. Its aggressive growth gives good weed control with a high plant density. There are no significant pests and diseases, except for powdery mildew. Low rainfall areas are preferred owing to harvesting difficulties in wet conditions. It is combined in late July/early August, after swathing and drying, which takes a minimum of two weeks. The costs of swathing is not included in the margin above. Harvesting can be difficult and seed shedding at maturity is a problem. Seed should be promptly dried to 10% for safe storage. Cleaning may be necessary.

5. Borage should only be considered by those prepared to invest sufficient time in the crop's husbandry, harvest and storage. Borage is a low yield / high risk crop – yields are from virtually nothing to 0.75 tonnes per ha (6cwt per acre); average 0.4 (3.2).

Acknowledgement: Thanks to – Frontier, Tel: 01522 556600; Fairking, Tel: 01206 212330; Premium Crops, Tel: 023 9263 2883.

MINORITY CROPS

Camelina Sativa

Camelina, Gold of Pleasure, or False Flax is a fast growing spring (or occasionally winter) sown crop. It is easily grown and harvested and is drought tolerant. The oil contains a range of essential fatty acids. It can be used as a food supplement or in industry as a drying oil. There is currently no commercial scale production in the UK that the authors are aware of. It is thought that current domestic usage requirements could support around 1,000 ha of the crop in the UK. Yields are in the 1.0-2.5 tonne per ha range. Price is uncertain due to the absence of a domestic market but an indicative price is likely to be around £250-£300 per tonne.

Crambe - Abyssinian Mustard

Crambe is an industrial oilseed that contains high levels of erucic acid. Converted into erucamide it is used as a slip agent in plastics and is a constituent of heat sensitive dyes. The area of crambe in the UK had grown to around 5,000 ha in the early 2000's.. However, the major promoter/buyer of the crop went into receivership and little or none is being currently grown commercially.

Crambe is a cruciferous spring crop managed in a similar way to spring oilseed rape. It has a short growing season, requiring only 100-120 days to reach maturity after emergence. As with oilseed rape, timely harvesting is important. Crambe can be combined direct, desiccated and combined or swathed. The crop should be stored and marketed at a moisture content of 9% or less. Yields are in the 2.5 tonne per ha range. Contract prices offered in the past were £180 per tonne. Growing costs are likely to be around £300 per tonne.

Durum Wheat

As well as pasta, durum is used to produce ethnic foods, semolina, biscuits, etc. Domestic demand is relatively small; UK consumption per head is approx. 4% that of Italy and 10% that of France.

The crop started to be grown in England in the late 1970s and reached a high-point of 11,000 ha (*27,000 acres*) in 1984. The area has fluctuated since then, but had declined to well below 1,000 hectares (*2,500 acres*). At present there are no contracts being offered to produce durum in the UK. In the past, an ex-farm premium for 'Grade A' durum of £50 per tonne over feed wheat was offered.

On average the crop should yield 75%-80% of conventional feed wheat in the same situation. As with milling wheat, there is a risk of rejection if contaminated with excess foreign seeds, especially self-set cereals from previous crop; thus safer as a first cereal crop. A poor price is obtained if quality is too poor for pasta and thus has to go for feed.

Durum Wheat Gross Margin Schedule

	£/ha	(£/ac)
Yield 6.2t/ha (2.5t/acre), Price £185/t ex-farm		
Output	1,147	(465)
Variable Costs:		
Seed	95	(38)
Fertiliser	168	(68)
Sprays	150	(61)
Total Variable Costs	350	(142)
Gross Margin per ha (acre).................................	**797**	(323)

The crop is likely to be grown only in the driest parts of the east/south east, where it can best compete with second and third wheats. It may be either autumn or spring sown; around two-thirds is currently autumn sown and this is assumed in the table above. The crop is very sensitive to stress and frost-kill in severe winters; the spring-sown crop is more reliable, and cheaper to grow, but the yield is usually 15-20% lower. Spring crops also allow more opportunities for black grass control. The crop has a higher disease resistance than other wheats, except for eyespot and ergot.

Harvesting is a critical operation; it needs to be done as soon as the crop reaches 20% moisture content, or at most 18%: it is very prone to sprouting and the quality for semolina is reduced if harvest is delayed. Durum must be dried (slowly) to 15%. It is easier and quicker to dry than normal wheat. The straw is of poorer quality and lesser quantity than conventional wheat straw and is therefore rarely baled.

Echium

Echium is a relatively new commercial plant to the UK. It has been cultivated on contract for less than a decade. It is a member of the Boraginacea family and is rich in stearidonic acid, which is used in cosmetic creams to reduce skin wrinkling and the effects of sunburn.

In past years there has been around 1,000 ha or so grown in the UK. A global glut of the active ingredient led to no contracts being offered in the years 2009 to 2015. It is believed that few if any contracts will be offered for 2016 as there is currently little to no demand for Echium oil as it is uncompetitive against marine oil alternatives. It is essential for a grower to have a buy-back contract with a reputable company, and the crop should not be grown speculatively. In the past prices have collapsed to almost nothing due to over-supply in the market.

The crop can be grown as far north as Yorkshire. It has a husbandry programme similar to that of borage but does not shed its seed as readily as borage. The seed is relatively small in size. Echium is suitable for light to medium land whereas borage performs better on a wider range of soil types.

The crop is sown in April and should come to harvest in July/August. There appear to be no significant pests of the crop. Harvesting is carried out with the use of a swather. Yields are approximately 250kg per ha (100kg per acre). Contract prices have been around £3,500 per tonne of clean seed.

Evening Primrose

This crop is an important source of gamma linolenic acid (GLA), but it is no longer grown in the UK and very little is cultivated elsewhere in Western Europe – it has been largely superseded by borage, which is easier to grow. The crop is still widely grown in China where the climate is more suitable, and labour costs are lower. Previous editions have given details of the crop and possible gross margin data.

Flax (cut flax for industrial fibre)

Flax was re-introduced into the UK during the 1990s, not as the traditional, pulled, long fibre variety used for linen textiles but as a cut, combinable crop producing shorter fibres for industrial uses – 'short-fibre flax'. As a natural, biodegradable fibre and a renewable resource it was promoted as a 'green' alternative to synthetic fibres and plastics. New markets were developed and several processing plants set up – the area of flax expanded to 20,200 ha in 1996. Following low prices and reform of the subsidy regime, the area fell to less than 2,000 ha by 2003, and the one remaining processing facility in Wales was closed. Little, if any, is currently grown.

The agronomy of flax is similar to that of linseed but it is harvested earlier. It is spring sown, suitable for most soil types although lighter soil is preferred. It is a low input crop but weed control is essential. It grows best in areas of high rainfall such as Wales and the South-west. There are several harvesting options (described in earlier editions). Currently the preferred option is desiccation followed by combining. The straw is left to rett in the field and then baled. Retting takes 10-21 days, depending on weather conditions. The price paid for straw will reflect quality. The fibre content of a reasonable crop is 20-30%.

Hemp

The traditional use for hemp was in canvas and rope manufacture. New uses have developed over recent years in building materials and producing internal car panels for the automotive industry. The core or pith of the plant is used for horse or poultry bedding.

The area grown had be stable at around 1,000 ha have been in recent years. However, the UK's sole commercial processor of the crop went into administration in autumn 2013. With no buyer for the company, the processing factory has ceased operation, and no contracts will be available in the UK for the foreseeable future.

Hemp is drilled in late April/May and the fibre crop grows 3 to 3.5m (10-12 feet) tall. Hemp Technology suggests a minimum area of 10 ha. A well-grown crop should have no weed or pest problems. The crop is mowed in mid to late August, and then baled when it is dry, bleached, and partially retted after 2-3 weeks. Average yields should be around 7.5 tonne per ha (*3.0t per acre*), with target yields at 9.5 tonnes per ha (*3.8t per acre*). The margin below assumes that the grower will undertake the cutting and baling operations. If contractors are used then the variable costs will obviously be higher. The crop must be stored under cover.

The margin below is based on the past contract price of £160 per tonne delivered. Transport costs need to be taken into consideration. A figure of £15 per tonne is used in the table below.

Hemp Gross Margin Schedule

Yield 7.5t/ha (3.0t/acre), Price £160/t delivered	£/ha	(£/ac)
Output	1,200	(486)
Variable Costs:		
Seed	135	(55)
Fertiliser	171	(69)
Sprays	20	(8)
Haulage to factory (£15/tonne)	113	(46)
Total Variable Costs	438	(177)
Gross Margin per ha (acre)................................	**762**	(309)

Dual Hemp

Hemp may also be grown as a dual-purpose crop. In recent years, up to 10-15% of the national hemp crop was of this type. The crop is left to mature longer, and then the top can be combined for the seed before the straw is mown and retted. A yield of 1.0-1.2 tonne per ha (*0.4-0.5t per ac*) of seed is possible. The seed was worth around £500 per tonne. However, the yield of straw is lower at 5-6 tonnes per ha (*2.0-2.4t per ac*), with the price being the same as 'conventional' hemp. The seed is cold-pressed to produce high-value cooking oil, and is also used for bird feed, fishing bait and in nutritional supplements and cosmetics. Agronomy and costs are likely to be similar to a fibre crop. Because of the time needed to let the seed heads mature, an earlier-maturing variety is used. The later harvest also means that this crop is more suitable for early land in the East and South.

Grain Maize

Maize is one of the major global grains – with world output being higher than that for wheat. However, the climate of the UK has made it difficult to ripen the crop and most maize is grown for forage rather than grain. A combination of earlier varieties, the development of machinery that copes with wet conditions, and even possibly the effects of warmer summers has improved the prospects of this crop.

There is market potential, as well over a million tonnes of grain maize are imported annually. It is used in animal rations, human foods, and in industrial processes. Marketing the UK crop is a problem at present as consignments are generally not big enough to interest the major buyers. The animal feed market is the likeliest outlet for domestic production - a specialised or local market can be developed, for example feed for pigeons or corn-fed chickens. The basis of pricing in the margin is a £10-£20 per tonne premium over feed wheat. This assumes sale into a 'niche' premium market.

There is no fundamental difference between forage and grain maize – the same varieties are simply left in the field for 3-6 weeks longer to let the cobs mature. It is difficult to know how much of the total UK maize area is taken for grain but it could be around 3,000 ha (out of circa 180,000 ha grown in total). The crop can be grown south of a line from Bristol to East Anglia, excluding the far south-west. Fields should be below 500ft in elevation and south-facing. To maximise heat units, the crop should be drilled as soon as soil temperatures are above 8°c – usually late April/May. Harvest by conventional combine with an adapted header in October/November. In UK conditions grain maize seldom drops below 30% moisture. The crop needs to be dried to 15% for storage which can be expensive and time-consuming. On good land the crop can yield 8-10 tonnes per ha but the average is not likely to be so high.

Grain Maize Gross Margin Schedule

	£/ha	(£/ac)
Yield 7.5t/ha (3.0t/acre), Price £150/t ex-farm		
Output	1,125	(456)
Variable Costs:		
Seed	155	(63)
Fertiliser	107	(43)
Sprays	70	(28)
Total Variable Costs	332	(134)
Gross Margin per ha (acre)................................	**793**	(321)
But note high drying costs:		
£15-25/t on-farm; £20-30/t off-farm	113-225	(46-91)

The majority of grain maize is currently stored as a crimped product. This sees the crop cut at 30-35% moisture from mid-October to early November with the 'wet' grain being processed, and an additive added (usually an organic acid). The overall cost of crimping and preservative is around £12-£15 per tonne. The grain is clamped or put into large bales or bags. It provides a very digestible dairy feed of high nutrition content. Yields can be 11-13 tonnes per ha and it sells for £150-£200 per tonne ex-farm.

Acknowledgement: Thanks to - Maize Growers Association, Tel: 01363 775040.

Millet

Millet describes a range of small-seeded grain plants covering a number of different species. The most commonly grown type in the UK is proso (also called white or common) millet. Millet has been cultivated since prehistoric times. It is a major food source in arid and semi-arid parts of the world; predominantly India, China, and parts of Africa. The crop has been grown in the UK for game cover for many years, but it has recently been commercialised to supply grain to the bird seed market.

Millet Gross Margin Schedule

Yield 3.0t/ha (1.2t/acre), Price £235/t ex-farm	£/ha	(£/ac)
Output	705	(286)
Variable Costs:		
Seed	100	(41)
Fertiliser	106	(43)
Sprays	60	(24)
Total Variable Costs	266	(108)
Gross Margin per ha (acre).................................	**439**	(178)

The UK currently imports approximately 25,000 tonnes of millet for bird and pet feed each year. Domestic plantings in 2013 were in the region of 1,000 ha, but dropped substantially for 2014. There is the potential to raise this to around 5,000 ha. Full import substitution is unlikely to be possible as UK seed cannot match the quality of the best imported millet.

The crop can be grown on a range of soil types, but as it is drought tolerant, it is often planted on lighter land. It does not grow well in heavy or very chalky soils. The crop requires warm temperatures to ripen and is therefore best suited to the South of England.

The crop is late drilled, usually in May once the soil has warmed up sufficiently. It can be planted as late as June. It requires a fine seedbed. The crop grows to about a metre high and is ready to harvest after 4½ months in mid to late September. The crop is usually desiccated before harvesting with a conventional combine harvester.

Yields are in the range 2.5-4.0 tonnes per ha. The contract price for 2016 is not known at the time of writing. However, contract values have historically been around £100 per tonne above the feed wheat price and a price of £235 per tonne is assumed.

Acknowledgement: Thanks to - Premium Crops, Tel: 02392 632 883. Soya UK, Tel: 02380 696922.

Navy Beans

Navy beans are the basis for the familiar canned 'baked beans'. Over 100,000t of these are consumed annually in the UK – with the vast majority of these being imported from North America. A few years ago there was some interest in the crop, as varieties adapted to the soil types and climate of the UK were introduced. However, disappointing prices, variable yields, and the lack of area aid discouraged growers. It seems unlikely that the economics will encourage a resurgence of production in the foreseeable future.

The crop requires good fertile land and some care in growing. Sowing is in mid-May when there is no further frost risk. Harvesting is late August/early September. The target yield is 3.0 tonnes per ha but the average is likely to be substantially less. When budgeting, an average of around 2.0 tonnes per ha (*0.8t per acre*) could be assumed. There is very little market information available on price, but it is likely to be in the region of £250-£300 per tonne. Variable costs are likely to be in the range £300-£350 per ha.

Poppies

Commercial growing of poppies in the UK began in the early 2000's. The poppy heads are processed to produce morphine for pharmaceutical purposes. The seeds are sold into the culinary market. A bit less than 3,000 ha of the crop are currently grown – all on contract to the sole UK processor.

The crop needs free-draining alkaline soils; it is planted in the second half of March, and is harvested in early to mid-August. The processor undertakes the harvesting operation with a specialised machine. Seed is included as part of the contract, as is agronomy advice (the processor specifies the pesticides to be used). The grower needs to be able to offer on-floor drying facilities.

The contract for the 2016 harvest has not yet been finalised. In previous years a basic fee of £200 per ha was paid by the processor, which was then topped-up by a bonus based on the yield of the alkaloid from the crop.

Poppy Gross Margin Schedule

	£/ha	(£/ac)
Fixed Area Payment	200	(81)
Alkaloid Bonus Payment	1,000	(405)
Output	1,200	(486)
Variable Costs:		
Seed	0	(0)
Fertiliser	163	(66)
Sprays	170	(69)
Total Variable Costs	333	(135)
Gross Margin per ha (acre)...............................	**867**	(351)

Acknowledgement: Thanks to – Macfarlan Smith, Tel: 01225 793 679.

Soya Beans

Soya is a sub-tropical crop in origin, grown mainly in North and South America, but also to a small extent in southern Europe. The UK imports three quarters of a million tonnes each year as beans and almost a further 2 million tonnes as meal, all for animal feed, so there would appear to be a ready market for the home grown product.

Various attempts have been made to commercialise the crop in the UK. In the late 1990's new varieties were introduced and by the early 2000's the area expanded to 1,700 ha. But after several difficult years the planted area declined. In recent years, less than 100 ha were being grown. However, the plant breeding process has continued and further varietal improvements yield and earliness have been made. Importantly, the soya price has been at high levels, making the economics more attractive. An expansion in area has been seen in the last couple of years, although the amount grown in the UK is still likely to be well below 500 ha.

Soya Bean Gross Margin Schedule

Yield 2.5t/ha (1.0t/acre), Price £370/t ex-farm	£/ha	(£/ac)
Output	925	(375)
Variable Costs:		
Seed	145	(59)
Fertiliser	57	(23)
Sprays	75	(30)
Total Variable Costs	277	(112)
Gross Margin per ha (acre)...............................	**648**	(263)

The crop is sown in late April or early May, depending on soil temperature, into a fine moist seedbed. The crop has a requirement for high temperatures and cumulative day-degrees of heat (similar to maize). This effectively restricts the crop to the southern half of England. The crop is combine harvested in September, usually after desiccation. The crop should be cleaned and dried to 14% moisture and 2% admixture.

As a legume, soya is a good alternative break crop, largely fixing its own nitrogen. Maintenance P and K is required plus 10-20kg of N to get the crop started. Spray costs also tend to be low.

Target yield is 3.0 tonnes per ha but the average is likely to be less; an average of 2.5 tonnes per ha (*1.0t per acre*) can be assumed. The price is largely determined by the price of imported crop. The UK crop is GM free, for which a premium is paid. A further premium may be paid for Identity Preserved UK crop which goes into human consumption or for organically grown soya. For 2016 harvest the price is estimated to be £370 per tonne.

Sunflower

The UK imports the equivalent of 400,000 tonnes of sunflower seed each year, mainly as sunflower oil. None is commercially crushed in the UK. There has been continued interest in sunflower, but late harvests and low yields have restricted the development of the crop. It is unclear how much of the crop is currently been commercially grown in the UK, but it is likely to be less than 500 ha. This would produce some 1,000 tonnes of seed. Almost all UK production goes into pet-food or bird seed. Producers should satisfy themselves of the end-market before planting the crop. The birdseed market takes 20,000 tonnes of sunflower seed annually, so there is scope for import substitution. Some attempts have been made to cold-press sunflowers to produce a UK-sunflower oil, but this market is still restricted to local and small-scale production.

Extra-early maturing semi-dwarf hybrid varieties are the most suitable to conditions in the UK. The crop needs a relatively mild climate and is best grown south-east of a line from the Wash to east Dorset. Sowing is from April to early May when the soil temperature is 7-8°C. Although sunflower will grow on a broad range of soil types its capacity to do well in dry and sandy soils and areas of low rainfall is a recommendation. Pre-emergence weed control may be necessary; at the right plant density weeds should not subsequently be a problem. As it is a broad row crop, chemical or mechanical weed control is possible. Sclerotina and botrytis, in a wet season, may affect the crop; on areas of less than 6 ha bird damage can be serious. Sunflower has a low nitrogen requirement.

Harvesting is from mid-September by combine harvester. Yields of up to 2.5 tonnes per ha with oil content of 44% are possible. The crop is dried to 8-9% for safe storage, which can be expensive. The price is usually based on a premium over the price of oilseed rape (around £40-£50 per tonne), but other pricing mechanisms may be used in specialist markets. Growing costs will be in the region of £300-£350 per ha.

Others

Other crops that have been in the news in recent years as possible new crops for the future (or present crops capable of substantial development) include the following: chickpeas and lentils, ahiflower, fenugreek, meadowfoam, cuphea, peppermint, quinoa, buckwheat, honesty and herbs for their essential oils. At present there are no reliable data for these crops on average yield expectations and little on prices or variable costs, when grown on a commercial scale in this country. A number of them are either for the health food market or are sources of oil for industry as replacements for marine oils and light mineral oils. Research continues on many of them. More details may be available from the contact listed below;

Contact: National Non-Food Crops Centre (NNFCC): www.nnfcc.co.uk

VINING PEAS

Production level	Low	Average	High
Yield: tonnes per ha (tons per acre)	3.80 (1.5)	4.75 (1.9)	5.46 (2.2)
	£	£	£
Output	874 (354)	1,093 (442)	1,256 (509)
Variable Costs:			
Seed.....................................		220 (89)	
Fertiliser................................		87 (35)	
Sprays....................................		146 (59)	
Total Variable Costs		453 (183)	
Gross Margin per ha (acre)	**421** (171)	**640** (259)	**803** (325)

1. The table above relates to vining peas grown on contract for 2016 where harvesting (approx. £78/tonne) and haulage (approx. £30/tonne) are paid for separately;

2. The *price* ranges from £200 to £370/tonne depending primarily on quality. Here we use an average of £230/tonne. The average yield is taken as 4.75 tonnes per hectare; the national average (fresh weight) for the last five years has ranged between 3.6 and 5.1 although growers are paid on frozen weight. Top quality ('150 minute') peas have to be grown within 40 miles of the factory. More distant 'long haul' peas will be in the lower price range. A pea viner costs in the region of £400,000.

   The average yield of petit pois is lower but the price averages 12 to 15% more.

3. *Fertiliser*. Many growers use no fertiliser; but RB209 suggests P&K. Here $P_2O_5:K_2O$ = 85:65kg/ha respectively.

4. *Sprays*. Both herbicide and aphicide are commonly used with fungicides being used dependant on seasonal requirements.

5. Total Area: Around 32,000 ha are grown in the UK annually with a view to vining a 140,000-tonne crop for frozen and canned use. A small surplus might be grown that exceeds contracted requirements

MAINCROP POTATOES

Production level	Low	Average	High
Yield: tonnes per ha (tons per acre)	37.0 (15)	45.0 (18.2)	53.0 (21.5)
	£	£	£
Output	4,884 (1978)	5,940 (2406)	6,996 (2833)
Variable Costs:			
Seed…………………………………		845 (342)	
Fertiliser…………………………..		372 (151)	
Sprays…………………………….		726 (294)	
Casual lab. (harvest & grading)……….	722 (292)	878 (355)	1034 (419)
Sundries (levy, sacks, etc.)…………..	377 (153)	459 (186)	541 (219)
Total Variable Costs	3,042 (1232)	3,279 (1328)	3,517 (1424)
Gross Margin per ha (acre)	**1,842** (746)	**2,661** (1078)	**3,479** (1409)

1. *Prices*. The price assumed above is £140 per tonne for ware and £30 for stock feed (assumed to be 7½%), which is £132 per tonne for the whole crop. Variations according to quality and market (as well as season) are considerable. The average GB price for wares between 2010 and 2014 was £160/tonne if the extreme highs of 2012 are included (averaging £240/t), £129 if not.

2. *Seed*: 60% planted with certified seed: 3 tonnes per hectare at £320 per tonne (the price varies widely from season to season); 40% with once-grown seed: 2.8 tonnes per hectare at £240 per tonne.

3. *Fertiliser*: N:P:K application of 160:170:271 as recommended in RB209. £25 Magnesium is also added.

4. *Sprays*: herbicide, blight control, and haulm destruction. Includes Nematode (PCN) spray, which accounts for about 60% of potato land. This accounts for £430/ha. Refer to Agrochemical Rates on page 278

5. *Casual Labour*. The figure in the table above is for assistance during (machine) harvesting and for grading/riddling (approx. £19.70/tonne); it is assumed that most of the labour for the latter is supplied by casuals.

6. *Contract mechanical harvesting*: £610-620/hectare (excl. pickers, carting, etc.), £1,000/hectare incl. carting. Other contract work see page 196.

7. *AHDB-Potatoes levy*: £42.62/ha (£17.25/acre) for growers to April 2016; exempt from levy if less than 3ha grown. 2016 rates as yet unpublished.

8. *Sacks*. Approx. £8.50 per tonne, plus the cost of wire ties or stitching.

9. *Potato Land Rentals* range depending on the year, location, soil and water availability, ranging from over £650/ha (£260/acre) to as much as £1,200/ha (£500/acre), depending on terms as well as soil type such as irrigation maintenance. The late harvested potatoes depress following crop yields. As a result some have tried to increase potato rents on back of increased cereal prices.

10. *Specialised Equipment Prices*: see page 190.

11. *Potato Store Costs*: see page 228.

12. *Labour*: see p. 173.

EARLY POTATOES

Production level	Low	Average	High
Yield: tonnes per ha (tons per acre)	18.0 (7)	23.0 (9.3)	28.0 (11.3)
	£	£	£
Output	4,140 (1677)	5,290 (2142)	6,440 (2608)
Variable Costs:			
Seed…………………………………		850 (344)	
Fertiliser…………………………..		269 (109)	
Sprays……………………………		377 (153)	
Casual labour………………………	334 (135)	388 (157)	442 (179)
Sundries (levy, sacks, etc.)…………..	230 (93)	293 (119)	357 (145)
Total Variable Costs	2,060 (834)	2,178 (882)	2,295 (930)
Gross Margin per ha (acre)	**2,080** (842)	**3,112** (1261)	**4,145** (1679)

1. *Prices* and *Yields*. The price assumed above is an average of £230 per tonne for a 23 tonne/ha yield. However, yields increase and prices fall as the season progresses. Thus both depend on the date of lifting, e.g. late May to early June, 7 to 12t/ha; July, 20 to 30 t/ha. Prices in late May to mid-June can be up to three times those in July; the very earliest crops (early May) can even fetch more than £1,000 per tonne, but the price could be down to £500 by mid-May and to £250 or even £200 by early June. Thus the average output of £5,290 given above could be obtained from 10 tonnes at £529 per tonne, 15 at £353, 20 at £265 or 30 at £176.

2. *Seed*: 100% certified seed: 3.4 tonnes per hectare at £255 per tonne (the price varies widely from season to season).

3. *Fertiliser*: N:P:K application of 100:170:143 plus £20 Magnesium as recommended in RB209.

4. *Sprays*: herbicide, blight control, and haulm destruction. Includes Nematode (PCN) spray, which accounts for about 60% of potato land. This accounts for £430/ha. Refer to Agrochemical Rates on page 278

5. *Casual labour for planting*: £145 per hectare, plus help with harvesting/grading (£11.40/tonne). Sprays. Refer to Agrochemical Rates on page 278

6. *AHDB-Potatoes levy*: £42.62/ha (£17.25/acre) for growers to April 2016; exempt from levy if less than 3ha grown. 2016 rates as yet unpublished.

7. *Labour*: see p. 173.

Early and Maincrop Potatoes

The percentages of the total potato area in Great Britain planted in early and main crop, respectively are approximately 35 and 65 in England, 72 and 28 in Wales, 40 and 60 in Scotland and 38 and 62 of the total GB potato area. Some people differentiate semi-earlies as a separate gross margin although this is not done here.

SUGAR BEET

Production level	Low	Average	High
Yield: tonnes per ha (tons per acre)*	59.5 (24)	70.0 (28.4)	80.5 (32.6)
	£	£	£
Output	1,545 (626)	1,818 (736)	2,090 (847)
Variable Costs:			
Seed.....................................		194 (79)	
Fertiliser.................................		214 (87)	
Sprays....................................		232 (94)	
Contract Harvest........................		247 (100)	
Transport (Contract)....................	324 (131)	382 (155)	439 (178)
Total Variable Costs	1,211 (490)	1,268 (514)	1,326 (537)
Gross Margin per ha (acre)	**334** (135)	**549** (222)	**765** (310)

* *'Adjusted tonnes' at standard 16% sugar content*

1. Note, these figures are for the 2016/17 harvest crop, meaning cultivation in 2016, delivery in 2016/17.

2. *Prices.* The 'all-in' delivered price is falling in 2016/17 to £25.97 per adjusted tonne. This is based on 90% sold 'in contract' 5% industrial contract entitlement (ICE) and 5% non-contract. The 'in-contract' and ICE beet price is set at 20.30 plus average transport of £6.00 and £5.50 per tonne and late delivery allowances of 40p/tonne. Non-contract beet price is projected at £12.00/tonne with a £4.50 transport allowance.

    Late delivery bonus. 26 December - 7 January: 0.8% of price; thereafter, the rate rises by 0.3% per day and at 0.4% per day from 1 March onwards.

    An Inter-Professional Agreement between the NFU and British Sugar has historically been the process for negotiating the sugarbeet price. This is currently in place for 2016/17 but is no longer mandatory. The global sugar price has fallen sharply and there is ample sugar in Europe and the UK with export restrictions, hence the expected fall in prices.

3. *Seed*; priced for 2016, including a standard seed dressing.

4. *Fertiliser*: 140 kg N, 58kg P, 117kg K and Sodium

5. *Sprays*. Refer to Agrochemical Rates on page 278

6. *Contract*. Excludes carting or £296 per hectare including carting.

7. *Transport*. Contract haulage charges vary according to distance to factory. The figure assumed above is £5.40 per (unadjusted) tonne of unwashed beet including loading and cleaning (dirt and top tare assumed at 14% in total).

TOP FRUIT

The figures indicate a range within which the performance of most (established) orchards falls. The gross margin is calculated as lower yields less lower costs/higher yields less higher costs. In practice yields are not necessarily so directly linked to costs.

	Dessert Apples		Culinary Apples		Pears	
	Low	High	Low	High	Low	High
Yield: tonnes/ha	15	55	25	50	15	30
Price (£/tonne)	535	915	270	535	485	700
	£		£		£	
Output	8,025	50,325	6,750	26,750	7,275	21,000
Variable Costs*						
Orchard Depreciation	315	2,067	177	1,304	143	335
Fertilisers/Sprays	870	1,455	675	1,260	675	1,110
Crop Sundries	165	655	215	545	165	440
Harvesting	968	3,548	1,325	2,650	968	1,935
Grading/Packing	2,060	7,550	3,435	6,865	2,060	4,120
Packaging	796	8,755	796	3,714	637	3,820
Transport	946	5,201	788	3,678	709	2,207
Commission/Levies	720	4,530	610	2,410	650	1,890
Variable Costs*	6,839	33,760	8,021	22,426	6,007	15,857
Gross Margin	1,186	16,565	-1,271	4,324	1,268	5,143

* Excludes Storage

1. *Price*: Average of all grades. Price is influenced by grade-out, and also by variety, customer and pack format (which in turn may affect packing, packaging costs).

2. *Orchard Depreciation*: Establishment costs written off over lifetime of orchard. Establishment includes trees and stakes and, in newer plantings, support structures and irrigation. Total establishment costs of £6,300 - £31,000 per hectare at planting densities of 750 – 4,000 trees per hectare, 2,850 being a typical density.

3. *Orchard Duration*: Traditional dessert apples around 20 years, with culinary and pears frequently 30 years plus. More recently planted denser apple and pear systems likely to be nearer 15 years, with full cropping reached in years 3-5 (6-9 for traditional systems). Figures above include an allowance for 5% immature trees.

4. *Crop Sundries*: Including tree ties, stake replacement, tree replacement, bee hire, picking hods, bin depreciation etc.

5. *Harvesting*: Based on £64.50 per tonne average (including supervision, Employer's NI & holiday allowance) for dessert apples and pears and £53.00/tonne for culinary. In practice can vary significantly with variety, yield, fruit size and quality, etc.

6. *Grading and Packing*: Based on £137.30 per tonne. Can vary considerably, particularly with crop quality.

7. *Packaging*: Typical average of between £56 and £163 per tonne, although may be higher with specialist formats (e.g. overwrapped packs). Considerable variations arise from both crop quality (i.e. grade-out), customer and pack format.

8. *Transport*: allowance for farm to packer, as well as delivery to final customer.

9. *Commission/Levies*: Including both marketer's and retailer's commission, as well as levies (e.g. English Apples and Pears, AHDB). A total of 9% has been used, although charges can vary considerably. N.B. This category does not include levy payments under the Producer Organisation regime.

SOFT FRUIT

The figures – for both soil-grown and a tabletop substrate crop - indicate a range within which the performance of many, but not all crops is likely to fall. The gross margins are lower yields less lower costs/higher yields less higher costs. In practice, yields are not necessarily linked to costs.

	Strawberries Raised Bed June bearers (Soil)		Strawberries Ever bearers (Substrate-Tabletop)		Raspberries (Soil)	
	Low	High	Low	High	Low	High
Yield: tonnes/ha	18.0	23.0	28.0	44.0	8.0	15.0
Price (£/tonne)	2,575	3,445	2,575	3,445	5,370	7,245
	£		£		£	
Output	46,350	79,235	72,100	151,580	42,960	108,675
Variable Costs						
Planting	3,085	3,950	11,905	19,480	1,515	1,840
Structures	5,410	8,655	7,575	10,820	5,410	8,655
Fert.s/Sprays/Predators	1,115	1,860	1,675	2,795	840	1,305
Fieldwork	1,915	4,245	3,180	8,490	3,180	5,305
Harvesting	14,700	19,220	16,585	26,060	15,832	29,680
Grading/Packing	4,770	6,095	7,420	11,660	3,815	7,155
Packaging	6,680	8,535	10,390	16,325	5,945	11,145
Transport	3,220	4,115	5,010	7,875	1,865	3,495
Commission	4,170	7,130	6,490	13,640	3,870	9,780
Variable Costs	45,065	63,805	70,230	117,145	42,272	78,360
Gross Margin	1,285	15,430	1,870	34,435	688	30,315

Strawberry June bearers Notes
1. *Planting* - including plants, substrate and wirework. *Plants* –35,000 per hectare with 60-day cropping in year 1 followed by 2 further years in main season production. *Plants/planting/sterilisation* written off over crop life of 3 years. Bed making not included as a variable cost.

2. *Structures* – average cost per year. Annual cost of poly-tunnels including both metalwork (w/o 10 years) and plastic (w/o 3 years). Costs also included for erection, dismantling and venting.

3. *Fertiliser, Sprays, Predators*. Relatively small component of gross margin.

4. *Fieldwork* – weeding, runner removal, leaf thinning etc.

5. *Harvesting*- including supervision, Employer's NI & holiday allowance.

6. *Grading/Packing* at £265/t. *Packaging* at £371/t, *Transport* at £179/t.

7. *Commission/Levies*: Including both marketeer's and retailer's commission, as well as levies (e.g. AHDB). A total of 9% has been used, although charges vary considerably. N.B. This does not include levy payments under the Producer Organisation regime.

Strawberries – Tabletop Ever Bearer Notes:

1. *Plants* – assumes 40,000 per hectare. Plants/planting written off over crop life of one year. Cost of substrate bags w/o 3 years.

2. *Structures* – poly-tunnel cost as for June-bearers, together with annual cost of tabletop system (estimated as £21,000 w/o 10 years, tabletop system costs vary considerably)

3. *Fertiliser, Sprays, Predators.* Relatively small component of gross margin.

4. *Fieldwork* – weeding, runner removal, leaf thinning and tucking, truss support etc.

5. *Harvesting-* including supervision, Employer's NI & holiday allowance.

6. *Grading, Packing / Packaging / Transport / Commission* - as for June bearers.

Raspberries Notes:

1. *Plants* – 8000/ha at 43p per plant. Planting at 13p per plant.

2. *Structures* – as for strawberries.

3. *Wirework* – to include material and labour.

4. *Plants/planting/wirework* written off over crop life of, say 5 years (crop life typically 4 to 7 years).

5. *Harvesting* (including supervision, employer's NI & holiday allowance) – £1,980 per tonne (£1.98 per kilo).

6. *Grading/Packing* – at £477 per tonne (48 pence per kilo).

7. *Packaging* – at £743 per tonne (74 pence per kilo).

8. *Transport* – at £233 per tonne (23 pence per kilo).

9. *Commission/Levies*: Including both marketeer's and retailer's commission, as well as levies (e.g. AHDB). A total of 9% has been used, charges can vary considerably. N.B. This does not include levy payments under the Producer Organisation regime.

Blackcurrants

Although a soft fruit, this crop is much more of a field crop grown on arable farms with machine harvesting. The majority of the UK blackcurrant crop is grown for processing into cordial drink. Typical output is 6-7 tonnes/ha sold at £650-£750 per tonne = £3,900-£5,250/ha, with annual variable costs of say £1,470/ha (principally share of crop establishment, fertilisers and sprays) leaving a gross margin of £2,300-£3,750/ha. Establishment costs approximately £7,250/ha for bushes with full production in year 2 followed by up to 10 years cropping. Contracts with processors required,

Acknowledgement (Top & Soft Fruit): Thanks to - Andersons Midlands

FIELD-SCALE VEGETABLES

In order to grow field vegetable crops commercially, certain resources are necessary, the key being good quality land. The overhead structure of the farm is somewhat different to that of combinable crops as is crop marketing. These are more like products than commodities so a market is necessary in advance of cultivation. In some cases major costs such as harvesting, packing and marketing expenses are borne by the produce company taking the crop, although the pricing structure of the product will reflect this.

Per Hectare (acre)	Dry Bulb Onions		Cauliflower		Calabrese	
(tons/acre)	41	(16.6)	12	(4.9)	10	(4.1)
Net Price (£/tonne)	145		375		384	
	£		£		£	
Output	5,945	(2,408)	4,500	(1,823)	3,840	(1,555)
Variable Costs:						
Seed	768	(311)	990	(401)	856	(347)
Fertiliser	359	(145)	475	(192)	417	(169)
Sprays	641	(260)	217	(88)	250	(101)
Casual Labour			1523	(617)	1525	(618)
Packaging/consumables			271	(110)	270	
Total Variable Costs	1,768	(716)	3,476	(1,408)	3,318	(1,344)
Gross Margin	4,177	(1,692)	1,024	(415)	522	(211)

The unit sale of cauliflower and calabrese can differ according to retailer supplier arrangement. For example some might be sold on a pence per head basis, pounds per tray, or pound per tonne and therefore a general output calculation has been provided. Sizes of heads and percentages harvested vary enormously and therefore yield so an average yield and price calculation is also ambiguous.

Dependant on the system, field scale vegetables have a high working capital requirement relative to other cropping alternatives, and bear considerable risk (both yield of saleable product and price vary enormously according to production and also demand factors). It is therefore necessary to carefully research the potential end market in terms of its expectations and cost structure.

Cauliflower and Calabrese give an example of brassica production. The majority of fresh produce crops such as carrots, parsnips, leeks, lettuce, rhubarb, and brassicas are now grown by a few highly specialised growers with in-house marketing departments. These growers supply the multiple retailers with high volumes and work to exacting specifications. The other key market for fresh produce is the local market, usually on a smaller scale and often tied into a local food chain such as a farm shop.

HOPS

Output Data

Hops are sold to contracts and on the open market, the latter varying greatly in price. They are sold per kilogram or in 50kg lots, (historically known as Zentners). The national area of hops has recently dropped below 1,000 hectares, most of which is in Hereford and Worcestershire. Recent average national yields have been at the low end of this gross margin, but top producers can achieve more.

This gross margin spreads the establishment costs over 11 years and wirework structure over 40. There is no harvest in year 1 but substantial investment.

Hop Gross Margin Schedule

Production level	Low	Average	High
Yield: Kg per ha (Kg/Acre)	1,400 (567)	1,500 (608)	1,600 (648)
	£	£	£
Output	9,184 (3720)	9,840 (3985)	10,496
Variable Costs:			
Establishment		1040 (421)	
Growing Costs		2450 (992)	
Harvesting		3270 (1,324)	
Total Variable Costs		6760 (2,738)	
Gross Margin per ha (acre)	**2,424** (982)	**3,080** (1,247)	**3,736** (1,513)
Overheads		2,925 (1,185)	
Return	**-501** -(203)	**155** (63)	**811** (328)

Establishment Costs

	£/ha		£/ha
Ground Preparation	255	Ties & Strings	306
Plants	2,448	Fert/Spray	255
Wirework Structure	7,013	Labour	305
Planting	510	Sundries	310
Total	**11,402**	**Cost per Year**	**1,040**

Growing Costs; Fertiliser & sprays £1,100, crop sundries £200, labour £1,150/hectare

Harvesting: labour £1,400, drying fuel £500 per hectare

Overheads: general labour £500, power and Machinery £1,950 inc. harvesting machinery, admin & property costs £475 (rent not included). Costs per hectare

A new hop garden (erecting the poles, wiring and planting) could cost in the order of £25,500 per hectare (£10,300 per acre), which would be expected to last 40 years. About 4,000 plants per hectare (61p each) are planted in a new hop garden, which would be expected to last 10-12 years.

Acknowledgement: Thanks to – Ali Capper, British Hops Association alicapper@mac.com

VINEYARDS

The total planted area under vines in England and Wales in 2015 is estimated to be 2,250 ha; an almost trebling of the vineyard area since 2003 when it was 773 ha. This had fallen from a previous high of 1,065 ha in 1993 when the UK was growing mainly Germanic grape varieties which then fell out of fashion. There are 470 vineyards of 0.10 hectare or more registered with the Wine Standards Branch (WSB) of the Food Standards Agency as at August 2014, plus several smaller ones run as hobbies and not selling wine. The average size of vineyards in the UK is now around 4 ha. However, there are several vineyards of over 100 hectares and the 50 largest vineyards account for around 75% of total production; more if you only consider sparkling wine. There is no EU restriction on planting vines in the UK, and in 2008 it was confirmed that there will not be one in the future, whatever level production reaches. Changes to the vine variety legislation also meant that, from August 2009, almost any variety may be legally planted in the UK.

2014 was another good year for UK vineyards, with a total of 6.32 million 75 cl bottles of wine, both still and sparkling, being produced. This is the highest number of bottles ever produced. If 2015 (which is currently looking like it is going to be a good yielding year) is factored in, it means that the total yield over the last three vintages will probably be more than the previous seven added together. Although the five-year average yield is only 2,200 litres per hectare, this is because there are many young vineyards and under-performing and poorly managed vineyards included in the official WSB figures. Yields in well-run, favourably sited vineyards would be several times these levels.

Most UK wines used to be white, but the proportion of red (and mainly) rosé has risen to around 25% of the total. Industry estimates suggest that at least 60% of the total amount produced is destined to be made into sparkling wine; a figure that will increase as many of the newer (and larger) sparkling-only vineyards start cropping. Since the very warm year of 2003, plantings of Champagne-style varieties (Chardonnay, Pinot Noir and Meunier) have increased significantly, and it is estimated that the majority of plantings in the last decade have been for the production of sparkling wine. Chardonnay and Pinot Noir are now the most widely planted varieties (about 450 ha each) and these, together with Meunier (125 ha), account for around 55% of the total vine area. Bacchus, the most widely planted still wine variety is becoming recognised as one from which excellent top-quality wines can be made and is expanding, accounting for around 10% of the UK vineyard area.

The amount of UK sparkling wine available for sale is by definition smaller than the amount being produced. This is because bottle-fermented sparkling wines take 2 to 5 years to mature after bottling and many new vineyards are still building up stocks or only just releasing their first vintages. Still wines come to market faster than sparkling wines – wine for sale ought to be available within 4 years of planting – whereas sparkling wine producers typically have 3-4 years' worth of stock to store (and more importantly, finance) before they can start selling wines. Although UK-grown wines only account for around 0.3% of the UK wine market, sales through the off-trade i.e. supermarkets and wine merchants and the on-trade i.e. hotels, restaurants and pubs, can be slow. Many producers find that at least initially, before they have built up a reputation for the quality of their wines, selling from the 'farm-gate' is their best route to market and helps introduce the public to their wines. However, over the last twenty years, the reputation of UK-grown sparkling wines has considerably improved and with the rising availability of these wines, more and more outlets, both on-trade and off-trade, are now willing to stock them. All wines sold in the UK bear the same level of VAT and duty irrespective of their origin, and the duty on sparkling wines is higher than for still wines.

The overall UK market for sparkling wines is around 100 million bottles a year, of which around two-thirds is Cava, Prosecco, Asti Spumante and other less expensive wines. Champagne (for which the UK is the biggest export market) accounts for about 35m bottles and it is into this sector of the sparkling wine market that UK producers need to sell their wines if their enterprises are to be profitable. Although the amount of sparkling wine available for sale today is still quite small, given the amount of land in the UK already planted with Champagne varieties, this will rise from today's estimated 2.0 million bottles to around 4 million by 2018 and 6 million by 2013. What impact this increase in supply will have upon prices, currently matching those of Champagne and other top-quality sparkling wines, is anyone's guess, although most of the major producers feel that increased availability will result in more wine-buyers being exposed to the wines, resulting in increased sales. Some of the larger producers have also started exporting their wines and this may be a route to additional sales.

A Quality Wine Scheme for England and Wales was introduced in 1991 and a Regional Wine Scheme in 1997, but in 2010 these were replaced with a new system of wine classification based upon the terms Protected Designation of Origin (PDO) and Protected Geographical Indication (PGI). PDO wines are broadly the same as Quality Wines and PGI wines the same as Regional wines. All PDO and PGI wines have to go through a testing and tasting procedure before they can use the relevant names. There are also 'Varietal Wines' which have to be 'certified' and can then can be labelled with the name of the grape variety and vintage, but not vineyard name. Wines outside of these three categories are known as 'UK Wines' and may not bear vintage or variety names, although they can state their origin. There is also a PDO for sparkling wines made from certain vine varieties which allows the term 'English Quality Sparkling Wine' to be used. The UK Vineyards Association (UKVA) has a marketing arm, English Wine Producers (www.englishwineproducers.com) to promote all English wines and organise tastings and events such as the 'St. George's Day' trade tasting (usually held in early May) and English Wine Week (late May).

The quality of any wine depends on the site and, in a cool climate like the UK's, considered 'marginal' by many non-UK growers, the best sites are to be found on south-facing, well-drained land, with shelter from the prevailing south-westerly winds and less than 100 metres above sea level. Sites too near to the sea are best avoided. In the UK, these are to be found in the southern half of England or Wales. Tthe counties of Kent, East and West Sussex, Hampshire and Surrey, the traditional fruit and hop growing counties, are home to the most successful vineyards. Success needs to be defined not only in terms of wine quality, but also by the level of yields, the most important factor in the sustainability of any agricultural business. Low to very low yields in many vineyards, whilst they might contribute positively to wine quality, do not help the viability of the business. Most of the longest-established and most successful UK vineyards sell a good proportion of their wine direct to the consumer and often have tea-rooms, restaurants and even small hotels as part of the enterprise. They also make money from guided tours, weddings, parties and corporate entertaining. Therefore any suitable site for vines should be selected with these activities in mind.

High quality vineyard management and marketing ability is essential for a successful enterprise. There is no minimum area for profitable production and a small vineyard selling wine at the farm gate and locally may be just as profitable per pound invested or per hectare as a larger one selling wine (at a considerable discount) through wholesalers and retailers. Quite a few vineyards grow grapes under contract for other wineries who wish to spread the source of their grapes for both financial and diversity of supply reasons. Grape supply contracts vary, but prices can be up to £1,500 per tonne for grapes for still wine and £2,500 per tonne for sparkling, although these prices have softened recently. There is also an annual 'spot' market for grapes and prices fluctuate according to demand which is very vintage dependent. Given the last three higher-than-average harvests plus the increase in plantings, many in the industry think that prices for grapes (and wines) must fall at some stage.

Most UK vineyards are now planted with a row width of between 1.75 m and 2.25 m, an intervine distance of between 1.0 m and 1.4 m and use the Double Guyot cane-pruned system. It is considered that vine density of around 4,000 vines/ha gives the best quality and chances of an economic yield in UK conditions. Cane-pruned vines, with good establishment, should be partially cropping at the end of their third summer and fully cropping at the end of their fourth summer in the ground, although much will depend on how they establish.

Investment capital (including planting materials and labour for establishment but not the land) of £21,000 to £30,000/ha is typically required for the vineyard. A suitable tractor, mower, sprayer etc. is required to manage the vines and together these would cost at least £40,000-£50,000. There are currently 135 wineries in the UK (August 2014) and whilst many of them are small and housed in modest buildings, there are several which are as modern and as well-equipped as any in the world and will have cost many millions to build and equip. Many smaller vineyards take their grapes to be made into wine under contract at one of the established wineries which gives them access to state-of-the-art equipment and experienced winemakers. Temperature controlled storage space for sparkling wines is required, whether or not you have your own winery. The recent improvement in the Sterling to Euro rate has helped lessen the capital costs of both vineyards and wineries given that a substantial proportion of these use materials from the Eurozone.

Depending on the quality of the site, the vine varieties being grown and the style of wine being produced, a well-sited, well-managed vineyard should yield on average at least 7.5 tonnes/ha (*3 tonnes/acre*) of grapes, with higher average yields possible. For still wine production, around 950 x 75cl bottles will be produced from 1 tonne of grapes. For sparkling wine production will be between 675 and 800 bottles per tonne, depending on quality, with some additional juice/wine available which will not be suitable for sparkling wine, but might be acceptable for blending into still wine, depending on the vintage.

The costs below refer to a commercial enterprise on a suitable site with a broad variety range. Establishment costs could be more if the site has to be drained and provided with windbreaks and rabbit and deer fencing. Annual growing costs can also be significantly greater, depending on planting density, variety, yield and management.

	Double Guyot	
	per ha	per acre
Number of Vines . . . . 3,000 - 5,000		(1,210 - 2,020)
	£ per ha	£ per acre
Establishment Costs:	over two years	
Materials	14,700	5,950
Labour	12,500	5,059
Total Establishment Costs	**27,200**	**11,009**
Subsequent Annual Costs:		
Materials	1,500	607
Labour (growing)	6,250	2,529
Harvesting*	1,600	648
Total Variable Costs	**9,350**	**3,784**

* Harvesting costs are very yield dependent. Growers without wineries will also have transport costs.

Prices: Grape prices will vary according to the variety and the vintage and whether growers are under contract or not. Prices range from £1,500 to £2,500 per tonne delivered to a winery, with still varieties being less valuable and good Pinot Noir or Chardonnay for sparkling wine at the higher end.

A retail price for still wine of at least £9.40 per bottle is necessary to cover outgoings, let alone pay for the capital or any profit, assuming a grower is using a contract winery and selling wine at full price direct to the consumer with no sales costs. Larger producers, having their own wineries and selling wines via wholesalers and/or retailers and into the on-trade (hotels, bars and restaurants) will have a different cost structure to the one below. Minimum prices for sparkling wine would have to take account of higher costs of production, higher excise duty and costs of finance and storage for 2-5 years of production.

Retail price of £9.40 less 20% VAT and £2.05 ① duty = £5.78 ②

Less winery costs (materials and labour) £4.50 per bottle③ = £1.28

At 7.50 tonnes per ha and 950 bottles per tonne = £9,120/ha (£3,691/acre).

① Sparkling wine of 8.5% and up to 15% or more has a duty rate of £2.63 per 75cl bottle; still wines of the same alcoholic strength, £2.05 per 75cl bottle

② If wines are sold via a wholesaler and/or retailer, gross profit margin of at least 10% (wholesaler) and 30% (retailer) on duty-paid prices must be allowed for.

③ Having still wine made under contract costs at least £4.50 a bottle. Sparkling wine will be at least £6 per bottle, plus storage costs.

Acknowledgements: Thanks to:

Stephen Skelton MW, Viticultural Consultant, 1B Lettice Street, London, SW6 4EH. Tel: 07768 583 700 www.englishwine.com

United Kingdom Vineyards Association, Mrs Jo Cowderoy, UKVA, PO Box 819 Haywards Heath RH16 9LW. Tel: 07904 011331. www.ukva.org.uk

2. GRAZING LIVESTOCK

DAIRY COWS

General Notes:

The notes below are intended to act as an introduction to the dairy section, detailing some of the general points that are pertinent to completing costings for dairy enterprises. A number of gross margins are then presented with more specific detail given relating to each type of dairy production system.

1. *Yield per cow:* Increases in this are usually (though not necessarily) associated with more intensive farming operations. Intensification focuses on higher gross margins per hectare, although more intensive systems will incur higher overhead costs (specifically machinery and labour requirements). Higher milk yields require improved cow genetics (usually Friesian / Holstein's) and increases in concentrate feeding (kg/litre), as well as other inputs.

2. *Yield*: The yield is annual herd production divided by the average number of cows and calved heifers in the herd. The average yield given for each type of production system is an estimated national figure for sizeable herds of black and white cows in 2016.

3. *Milk Price:* the average milk price for 2016 is 23p per litre for black and white cows' milk. The prices used for each gross margin are an average for the 2016 calendar year, after deducting transport costs. It incorporates adjustments for milk composition and seasonality assuming an average-size herd. Payments are lower in the spring but constituents higher, making prices per litre similar for each system. Currently (Summer 2015), prices between contracts are more diverse than at any time in many years. Some fresh milk suppliers are receiving near to 30ppl, whilst others beneath 20ppl. A few suppliers who are not on supply contracts will on occasions be receiving less than that.

Smaller herds achieve a lower price due to smaller volume bonuses / larger transport charges and *vice versa*. The average price received by individual producers also depends on seasonality of production and compositional quality.

Seasonality Price Adjustments: These are diverse between the various dairy companies. An increasing number of companies no longer operate 'conventional' seasonal adjustments but instead have payment systems that encourage a level monthly production, with a range of deductions and bonuses related to the individual producer's spring and autumn deliveries. The average adjustments for a selection of companies operating conventional adjustments are as follows in 2016/17 in pence per litre:

April	May	June	July	Aug	Sept	Oct	Nov	Dec	Jan– Mar
–2.8	–3.5	–2.75	0	+1.1	+2	+2.5	+2.25	+1.0	0.0

Some companies also offer a premium for a level delivery option if supplies in a calendar month are within 10% of an agreed daily volume. Spring calving herds will produce more milk in the spring and summer, therefore receiving a lower price on average, whereas autumn calving herds will receive a higher average price as a result of producing more milk in the autumn and winter.

Milk Quotas ended in April 2015, meaning a dairy's production controls over the farms are more difficult. This has led to some dairies introducing an 'A' and 'B' production payment system. This is a reduced payment for deliveries greater than an agreed percentage of the previous year (possibly 100%). This means that if production from one farm increases, the payment per additional litre will be reduced.

Compositional Quality Payments: How milk prices are derived depends on the buyer and its end market. For example, cheese-makers derive the majority of the milk price from payments per percentage of butterfat and protein; whereas a liquid processor pays largely on a set base price per litre with small adjustments for butterfat and protein. As a result, constituent values vary widely between buyers. A *standard litre* is typically 4·10% butterfat and 3·40% protein.

Within Breed Quality Variation: For Holstein Friesians without going to extremes, the range can easily be: 3.5% to 4.1% butterfat and 3.1% to 3.4% protein. The difference in value between these levels combined can be up to 3.5p per litre depending on milk contract. This is being achieved by both breeding and feeding for milk quality to meet varying contractual requirements.

Proportional Split of Dairy Breeds and milk Compositions:

	Cows %	Butterfat %	Protein %
Holstein Friesian.........................	96	4.01	3·22
Jersey......................................	1·3	5·4	3·9
Guernsey.................................	1·0	4·7	3·6
Ayrshire..................................	1·4	4·1	3·3
Dairy Shorthorn........................	0·3	3·9	3·3
All Breeds.................................		4.08	3·25

Data from Dairy Co.

Hygiene Price Adjustments: These vary widely between the different dairy companies. A typical 2016/17 example is as follows:

A. *Bactoscan (bacteria measure)*

Bactoscan Reading	Price Adjustment (ppl)
0- 50,000	+0.5
51-100,000	-0.50
101-200,000	− 2.00
Over 200,000*	− 7.00

   *1st month, -10p subsequent months.

B. *Somatic Cell Count (Mastitis)*

Count	Price Adjustment (ppl)
0-200,000	+ 1.00
200 - 250000	+0.25
251-325,000	0
326-400,000	− 4.00
Over 400,000	− 15.00

Several milk buyers have no bonus for top hygiene bands; they expect suppliers to deliver top quality milk in order to receive the standard litre price.

C. *Antibiotics.* Milk in a consignment that fails an antibiotics test is usually worth 1p/litre.

4. *Concentrate Price:* An average of £200/t has been used for dairy concentrate. This includes blends and straights which are typically cheaper than compounds. Spring calving herds tend to have lower protein concentrate as fresh grass has more protein than preserved feeds; conversely, autumn calvers receive higher protein concentrate. An average of £190/t has been used for spring calving herds and £210/t for autumn calving herds.

5. *AI / Bull Costs:* AI is assumed in the gross margins with no bull. However bull depreciation would be approximately £140 a year (£1,500 purchase price less £800 cull

value, 5-year herd life); tight calving pattern: average 40 cows per bull; 10 to 15 tonnes silage per year, 0·15 tonnes concentrates a year. Very high yielding herds may use more expensive (dairy) bulls above £2,500 purchase price. Most herds now use AI but rely on bulls as sweeper bulls.

Spring Calving Friesians (per cow per year)

	Average	High
Yield Per Cow (litres)	5,250	6,000
Milk Output @ 23 ppl	1,208	1,380
Calf Value	129	129
Cull Value	77	77
Less, Replacement Cost @ 20% per year	-240	-240
Total Output	**1,174**	**1,346**
Variable Costs:		
Concentrate Costs £190/t @ 0.8t & 1.02t/cow	152	194
Purchased Bulk Feed	0	0
Vet & Med	54	55
Bedding	44	45
AI	33	34
Recording, Parlour Consumables, Sundries	66	66
Total Variable Costs	349	394
Gross Margin per cow Before Forage Costs	**825**	**952**
Forage Costs @ 2.4 Cows Per Forage Hectare	108	108
Gross Margin per Cow After Forage Costs	**717**	**844**
Gross Margin Per Forage Hectare	1,720	2,026
Margin of Milk Over Concentrates	1,056	1,186
Sensitivity Analysis per cow		
Concentrate Price +/- £10/tonne	+- 8.0	+- 10.2
Concentrate Price +/- £20/tonne	+- 16.0	+- 20.4
Milk Price +/- 0.25 ppl	+- 13.1	+- 15.0
Milk Price +/- 0.50 ppl	+- 26.3	+- 30.0

Spring calving herds (80% or more calvings between February and May) typically have a much lower annual average yield than other systems due to a smaller, hardier cow type. As a result, replacement rates will be lower than other production systems. Spring calving herds will normally produce high milk constituents and aim to sell on a cheese/manufacturing based contract to maximise their price, despite the reductions incurred through seasonality. These systems often have lower overhead costs (labour, buildings and machinery) and are often focused on milk from grass. Lower costs reflect the lower milk price received.

See notes on page 47.

Autumn Calving Friesian/Holsteins (per cow per year)

	Average	High
Yield Per Cow (litres)	*7,000*	*8,500*
Milk Output @ 23 ppl	1,610	1,955
Calf Value	129	129
Cull Value	88	88
Less, Replacement Cost @ 23% per year	-276	-276
Total Output	**1,552**	**1,897**
Variable Costs:		
Concentrate Costs £210/t @ 1.68t & 2.635t/cow	353	553
Purchased Bulk Feed	42	42
Vet & Med	64	65
Bedding	59	59
AI	38	39
Recording, Parlour Consumables, Sundries	66	66
Total Variable Costs	622	824
Gross Margin per cow Before Forage Costs	**930**	**1,072**
Forage Costs @ 2.2 Cows Per Forage Hectare	122	122
Gross Margin per Cow After Forage Costs	**808**	**951**
Gross Margin Per Forage Hectare	1,778	2,092
Margin of Milk Over Concentrates	1,257	1,402
Sensitivity Analysis per cow		
Concentrate Price +/- £10/tonne	+- 16.8	+- 26.3
Concentrate Price +/- £20/tonne	+- 33.6	+- 52.7
Milk Price +/- 0.25 ppl	+- 17.5	+- 21.3
Milk Price +/- 0.50 ppl	+- 35.0	+- 42.5

Autumn calving herds (80% or more calvings between August and November) tend to have much higher overhead costs than spring calving herds, mainly associated with winter housing and feeding – buildings, greater silage requirements, slurry and muck handling, plus labour. Autumn calving herds will benefit from a marginally greater milk price than spring or all-year-round calving herds because of seasonality, and will typically (but not always) sell milk to a liquid buyer. The decision between being a spring or autumn calving producer will depend largely upon specific circumstances, such as building facilities available, the ability of the farm to grow forage (wet or dry land) and the nearby milk buyers' requirements.

See notes on page 47.

All-Year-Round Calving Friesian/Holsteins (per cow per year)

	Average	High
Yield Per Cow (litres)	*8,000*	*9,500*
Milk Output @ 23 ppl	1,840	2,185
Calf Value	115	115
Cull Value	96	108
Less, Replacement Cost @ 25% & 28% per year	-325	-378
Total Output	**1,726**	**2,029**
Variable Costs:		
Concentrate Costs £200/t @ 2.56t & 3.61t/cow	512	722
Purchased Bulk Feed	42	43
Vet & Med	75	78
Bedding	62	62
AI	41	43
Recording, Parlour Consumables, Sundries	76	76
Total Variable Costs	808	1,024
Gross Margin per cow Before Forage Costs	**918**	**1,005**
Forage Costs @ 2.2 Cows Per Forage Hectare	125	125
Gross Margin per Cow After Forage Costs	**793**	**880**
Gross Margin Per Forage Hectare	1,744	1,936
Margin of Milk Over Concentrates	1,328	1,463
Sensitivity Analysis per cow		
Concentrate Price +/- £10/tonne	+- 25.6	+- 36.1
Concentrate Price +/- £20/tonne	+- 51.2	+- 72.2
Milk Price +/- 0.25 ppl	+- 20.0	+- 23.8
Milk Price +/- 0.50 ppl	+- 40.0	+- 47.5

All-year-round calving herds have higher costs of production than seasonal producers and so will aim to sell their milk on a liquid premium based (supermarket supply) contract. However, these contracts are limited. Both vet and med and A.I. costs tend to increase with higher milk yield due to greater pressure on the cow and poorer fertility. As a result, herd replacement rates are also considerably higher.

Gross Margin Notes:

1. *Value of Calves:* Average annual value per cow at 10-20 days old, allowing for 5% mortality and an average calving index of 385 days. Average value assumed for spring and autumn calving herds is comprised equally as follows per year

2. *Calf Value*:

		Spring & Autumn	AYR
Dairy bull calf	(dairy x dairy)	£55	*45*
Dairy heifer calf	(dairy x dairy)	£65	*55*
Cross bred bull	(beef x dairy)	£245	*220*
Cross bred heifer	(beef x dairy)	£185	*165*
5% mortality, 385 day calving interval			
Average		***£109***	***£124***

* Calves for all-year-round calving herds with higher milk yields normally have less beef genetics meaning dairy bull calves and beef cross animals are less valuable.

3. *Replacement Costs:* The table below demonstrates herd replacement costs.

	Spring	Autumn	AYR	
Yield per cow	5,250	7,000	8,000	9,500
Value of new heifers (a)	1,200	1,200	1,300	1,350
Replacement Rate (b)	20%	23%	25%	28%
Herd Depreciation (a x b =c)	**240**	**276**	**325**	**378**
Cull Cow Value (d)	400	400	400	400
Casualty Rate (e)	4%	4%	4%	4%
Annual Cull Value (b x d x e = f)	**77**	**88**	**96**	**108**
Calf Values (g)	**129**	**129**	**115**	**115**
Net Replacement Cost (c-f-g)	**34**	**58**	**114**	**156**

Herd depreciation is the annual cost of replacing the herd i.e. the cost of a down-calving heifer divided by its life expectancy in years (or multiplied by the annual replacement rate). When the value of cull cows and calves are added (both adjusted for casualty and mortality allowance), the net replacement cost can be derived.

4. *Concentrate Costs:*

	Spring		Autumn		AYR	
Yield per cow	5,250	6,000	7,000	8,500	8,000	9,500
Tonnes / Cow	0.80	1.02	1.68	2.64	2.56	3.61
Kg feed / Litre	0.15	0.17	0.24	0.31	0.32	0.38
Concentrate Cost (ppl)	2.90	3.23	5.04	6.51	6.40	7.60
Conc. cost p/marginal L		5.57		13.37		14.00

This table gives the costs of concentrate feed per litre of milk and crucially, the costs of concentrate feed per litre of *additional* milk. In other words, the cost of the extra feed required to move from the first yield to the second yield bracket in each category. The yield difference in the spring and autumn groups is small, but the yield rise for all-year-round (AYR) herds is considerable, the cost of the last litre (to 9,500 in this instance) is always dearest, and will be more than the figure shown.

5. *Feeding:* Typically, specialist spring calving herds use 0.09 kg per litre / 850 kg per cow per year less concentrates than autumn calving herds. The table below is an example of annual concentrate use for an all-year-round calving herd.

Typical Monthly Variation in Concentrate Feeding (kg per litre, 8,000 litre herd)

Winter		Summer	
October	0.30	April	0.23
November	0.32	May	0.14
December	0.33	June	0.14
January	0.33	July	0.20
February	0.32	August	0.24
March	0.28	September	0.27
Average winter: 0.31		Average summer: 0.21	
Weighted average whole year: 0.26kg/l			

The distribution on farm varies according to factors such as seasonality of calving, milk yield, summer grazing productivity, the quantity and quality of winter forages and bulk feeds, as well as turnout and housing dates. The March figure in particular will be affected by type of soil and seasonal rainfall.

Yield with no concentrates and good quality silage can be 4,000 litres for spring calvers.

6. *Margin over Concentrates (MOC) and Concentrates per litre:* It is important to highlight in the above gross margins the differences between the margin (of milk value) over concentrates per cow; the same large variation can occur with widely differing combinations of milk yield and quantity of concentrates fed.

In the following table, for each production system, figures are given for *(a) margin of milk value over concentrates* per cow (£) and (b) *concentrates per litre* (kg).

Margin Over Concentrates (MOC) and Concentrates per Litre (C/L)

| Milking System | Spring Calving | | Autumn Calving | | All-Year-Round Calving | | | |
| Milk Yield (litres) | 5,250 | | 7,000 | | 8,000 | | 9,500 | |
	MOC	C/L	MOC	C/L	MOC	C/L	MOC	C/L
Concentrates per cow	£	kg	£	kg	£	kg	£	kg
0.65 tonne (£124)	1084	0.12	-	-	-	-	-	-
0.75 tonne (£143)	1065	0.14	-	-	-	-	-	-
0.90 tonne (£171)	1037	0.17	-	-	-	-	-	-
1.05 tonne (£200)	1008	0.20	1,410	0.15	-	-	-	-
1.60 tonne (£336)	-	-	1,274	0.23	-	-	-	-
1.75 tonne (£368)	-	-	1,242	0.25	-	-	-	-
1.90 tonne (£399)	-	-	1,211	0.27	1,441	0.24	-	-
2.10 tonne (£420)	-	-	-	-	1,420	0.26	-	-
2.25 tonne (£450)	-	-	-	-	1,390	0.28	-	-
2.40 tonne (£480)	-	-	-	-	1,360	0.30	1705	0.25
2.85 tonne (£570)	-	-	-	-	-	-	1615	0.30
3.00 tonne (£600)	-	-	-	-	-	-	1585	0.32
3.15 tonne (£630)	-	-	-	-	-	-	1555	0.33

7. *Stocking Rate and Forage Costs:* The stocking rates given assume that nearly all requirements of forage/bulk foods – both winter and summer – are obtained from the forage area, i.e. little is bought in. The stocking rates of 2.2 cows per forage hectare (autumn and AYR calving) and 2.4 cows per forage hectare (for spring calving herds) assume good grassland management. Greater stocking rates are achievable, particularly in the West of the UK where natural conditions favour forage production. On average about 55 per cent of the forage area (or production) is grazed and 45 per cent conserved for an all-year-round calving herd. Spring calving herds rely much less on conserved forage. Some high yielding herds are housed all-year-round.

The forage costs are taken from the *Forage Variable Costs* on page 87 as follows:

	Intensive Grass	Maize	Intensive Grass	Maize	Intensive Grass	Maize
£ Cost /Ha	260	332	£/Ha		£/cow	
Spring calving	100%	0%	260	0	108	0
Autumn calving	89%	11%	231	36	105	17
All year round calving	78%	22%	203	73	92	33

An increase in stocking density can be obtained not only by intensifying grassland production, but also by buying in bulk fodder (assuming the same level of concentrate feeding in both cases). Theoretically, a zero-grazed farm buying in forage needs no land. In this situation, the gross margin per hectare would be extreme (and meaningless), although the cost of hauling in forage would be high.

Overheads such as labour and buildings depreciation are likely to increase per hectare and fall per cow as stocking density rises. Management challenges occur with higher stocking rates such as poaching which can be alleviated with good cow tracks. Cross Compliance and Nitrate Vulnerable Zone regulations must still be adhered to.

7. *Labour*: see page 185.

8. *Building Costs*: see page 228.

Costs of Milk Production Summary (Pence per Litre)

Production type	Spring Calving	Autumn Calving	AYR Calving
Litres per cow	5,250	7,000	8,000
	Pence Per Litre		
Concentrates	2.90	5.04	6.40
Forage and Bought Bulk Feed	2.06	2.34	2.09
Other Variable Costs	3.75	3.24	3.18
Total Variable Costs	**8.71**	**10.62**	**11.67**
All Labour (inc. unpaid)	5.38	4.78	4.51
Power and Machinery*	6.35	5.86	6.09
General Overheads	1.37	1.17	1.22
Rent/Rental Equivalent & Finance	4.22	3.16	2.77
Total Fixed Costs	**17.32**	**14.98**	**14.59**
Less, Net Replacement Cost	0.64	0.83	1.43
Total Costs of Production	**26.67**	**26.43**	**27.68**

* inc electricity & parlour repairs

1. This schedule only compiles the costs of milk production. Adding milk price to it does not constitute a profit or loss as other components of the farm should be included such as BPS, calf and cull cow sales, youngstock enterprises, finance, rent and so on.

2. The *Variable Costs* per litre are derived from the data (and therefore the assumptions made) under average performance in the dairy gross margin tables for each system.

3. The *Fixed Costs* assume average financial performance. The average fixed costs are taken from the medium-sized 'mainly dairying' farm data in the Fixed Costs Section on page 218. Within each system, there will be a marked difference between the costs achieved by the top 10% and the bottom 10% of producers. The difference is due to improved management ability. *Labour* includes the farmer and any unpaid family labour. However, there is no management charge included. *Power and machinery* cover all machinery and equipment costs, including the use of farm vehicles, etc. *General overheads* similarly relate to the whole farm, including electricity and property repairs. *Rent/Rental Equivalent and Finance* assumes a modest rental charge on all land plus interest charges on a modest amount of working capital. No long-term debt is included.

4. All-year-round calving herds will have the highest overheads in absolute terms. However, well-managed high yielding herds can compete with block calving systems due to higher output. Block calving herds will have lower overheads due to lean times of the year i.e. periods when all cows are dry, and the economies of scale of managing animals in batches. Spring calving herds will have the lowest overheads due to a shorter housing period, less demand for winter forage and lower muck

handling costs. Rental costs, in pence per litre terms, will be higher though due to the fixed land charge and lower output (litres) per unit area of land.

Channel Island Breeds (per cow per year)

Performance level (yield)	S. Calving	A. Calving	AYR Average	AYR High
Milk Yield per Cow (litres)	*4,150*	*5,000*	*5,550*	*6,250*
	£	£	£	£
Milk Value per Cow	1,370	1,650	1,832	2,063
Calf Value	100	100	100	100
Cull Value	35	40	43	43
Less, Replacement Cost	-193	-222	-241	-241
Total Output	**1,311**	**1,568**	**1,733**	**1,964**
Variable Costs:				
Concentrate Costs	180	294	359	492
Purchased Bulk Feed	35	35	35	35
Vet & Med	32	36	40	44
Bedding	37	42	42	42
AI	30	32	32	34
Parlour Consumables, Sundries etc.	56	56	56	56
Total Variable Costs	**370**	**495**	**564**	**703**
Gross Margin Before Forage Costs	**941**	**1,073**	**1,170**	**1,261**
Forage Costs @ 2.5 Cows Per Forage Ha	104	104	139	139
Gross Margin After Forage Costs	**837**	**969**	**1,031**	**1,123**
Gross Margin Per Forage Hectare	2,093	2,422	2,577	2,806
Margin of Milk Over Concentrates	1,190	1,356	1,473	1,571

1. *Yield.* Average of Jerseys and Guernseys. See Note 1 and 2 for Holstein Friesians (page 43). Guernsey yield averages slightly higher than Jerseys and Jerseys achieve a higher butterfat and protein (see page 44).

2. *Milk Price.* This is 33p per litre (average of Jerseys and Guernseys for a level profile). This is based upon a channel island milk contract, for which a premium is usually paid.

3. *Concentrate Costs.* The average price taken (for 2016) is £205 per tonne (for all-year-round calving herds), £200 per tonne average for spring calving herds and £210 per tonne for autumn calving herds.

Amounts:	Milk Group	Spring	Autumn	AYR ave.	AYR High
	kg/litre	0.217	0.280	0.315	0.384
	tonnes/cow	0.90	1.40	1.75	2.40
	pence / litre (ppl)	5.20	7.00	7.73	9.41
	pence/ marginal litre*		13.0		20.4

* *This is the additional cost of feed between yield groups, and the cost of the additional feed divided by the additional litres of production.*

4. *Net Annual Replacement Cost*: Calculated as follows (replacement rates vary by system, 20% for spring, 23% for autumn, 25% for higher yielding all-year-round calving herds):

	£ per cow in herd
Cost of replacements: 25% of herd per year @ £965	241
Less Value of culls: 25% of herd per year @ £250	
(allowing for casualties)*	63
Herd Depreciation	179
Annual Value of Calves**	80
Net Annual Replacement Cost	**99**

*Cull cow prices for Guernseys are about £40 higher than for Jerseys.

** Allowing for calving index of 385 days and calf mortality; mixture of pure bred calves and beef crosses. Guernsey calves, especially crosses, fetch more than Jersey calves, averaging perhaps £10 more per head and substantially more for some Guernsey beef crosses.

5. *Forage Costs and Stocking Rate.* See, in general, Note 6 for Holstein Friesians (page 49). A small amount of purchased bulk fodder is assumed at £35/cow (purchased forage) for the higher yielding herds based upon the average stocking rate of 2.5 cows per forage hectare. (See forage section for details of improved temporary grass used here).

At the average stocking rate given above for combined Channel Island breeds (2.5 cows per forage hectare) the average figure for Jerseys would be approximately 2.60 and that for Guernseys 2.40 cows per forage hectare.

DAIRY FOLLOWERS

(per Heifer reared)

Performance Level	Low	Average	High
	£	£	£
Value of heifer (allowing for culls)	1080	1080	1080
Less Value of calf	168	168	168
Output	912	912	912
Variable Costs:			
Concentrate Costs	278	253	227
Miscellaneous Variable Costs	152	138	124
Total Variable Costs (excluding Forage)	430	391	352
Gross Margin per Heifer, before deducting Forage Costs	482	521	560
Forage Variable Costs	166	127	101
Gross Margin per Heifer	317	394	459
Forage Hectares (Acres) per Heifer reared	0.95 (2.3)	0.73 (1.8)	0.58 (1.4)
Gross Margin per Forage Hectare	333	540	792
Gross Margin per Forage Acre	135	219	321

B. Channel Island Breeds

Performance Level	Low	Average	High
	£	£	£
Value of heifer (allowing for culls)	869	869	869
Less Value of calf	90	90	90
Output	778	778	778
Variable Costs:			
Concentrate Costs	236	215	193
Miscellaneous Variable Costs	137	124	112
Total Variable Costs (excluding Forage)	373	339	305
Gross Margin per Heifer, before deducting Forage Variable Costs	405	439	473
Forage Variable Costs	149	115	91
Gross Margin per Heifer	256	325	382
Forage Hectares (Acres) per Heifer reared	0.68 (1.7)	0.58 (1.4)	0.50 (1.2)
Gross Margin per Forage Hectare	377	560	764
Gross Margin per Forage Acre	153	227	310

N.B. on average Channel Island heifers calve about three months younger than Holstein Friesian Heifers

1. *Heifer values* are based on the purchase price of down-calving heifers with an allowance for culls and barren animals. Most heifers are home-reared. If heifers are reared for sale, the price of whole batches is likely to be lower than the values given in the tables, by 10 or 15 per cent. On the other hand the purchaser will often take the batch a few months before the average expected calving date, thus reducing the costs incurred by the rearer.

2. *Calf Value*; is based on the cost of a heifer dairy calf, increased to account for mortality of 5%.

3. Lower levels of *concentrate costs* are the combined result of more economical feeding and a lower average calving age. (Other things being equal, including the overall level of management, a lower calving age requires higher levels of feeding.) Average (Holstein Friesians) = £74 to 3 months (see Calf Rearing on page 56) plus 290 kg calf concentrates @ £245/tonne and 500 kg @ £215/tonne = £254 per (average) calf.

4. *Miscellaneous* variable costs include bedding (£48): straw requirements average approx. 0.7 tonnes per heifer reared, but are variable, depending on time of year and age when calved, as well as system of housing and extent of out-wintering. Vet. and med. approximately £47 per heifer reared, and other sundry items £43.

5. *Forage variable costs*. Grass for both grazing and conservation, at £174/ha, assuming all home produced. This is the variable costs for long term leys and improved permanent pasture (combined in equal parts) in the forage section on page 87, thus assuming that less productive grassland is used to rear dairy heifers with the best pasture being retained for the dairy cows.

6. A *"replacement unit"* (i.e. calf + yearling + heifer) equals about 1·25 livestock units with an average calving age of 2 years 4 months. The three stocking rates used above are equivalent to approximately 0.75, 0·6 and 0·5 forage hectares (1.85, 1.48, 1.24 acres) respectively per Holstein Friesian cow (Livestock Unit). Note, this is a 2-year gross margin. It can be treated as a gross margin over a longer period of time or a margin per replacement unit, not per animal on the farm per year.

7. *Higher gross margin per hectare* figures can be achieved by intensive grazing methods, particularly if combined with alternative winter feeding systems, such as out-wintering on forage crops such as Fodder Beet or Kale.

8. *Contract Rearing*: see page 72.

9. *Labour*: see page 185.

SELF-CONTAINED DAIRY HERD: COWS AND FOLLOWERS

At average annual replacement rates (25 per cent of the milking herd), nearly one-third of a replacement unit is required for each cow in the herd, i.e. roughly one calf, yearling and heifer for every three cows (including calved heifers), allowing for mortality and culling. At average stocking rates for both, this means more than 1 hectare devoted to followers for every 3 hectares for cows. Since surplus youngstock are often reared and frequently the stocking rate is less intensive, the ratio often exceeds this in practice. 1:3 is about the minimum where all replacement heifers are reared, unless their winter feeding is based largely on straw and purchased supplements, or unless there is a combination of long average herd life and early calving, i.e. all at 2 years old.

The table below shows the combined gross margin per forage hectare (acre) for the whole herd (i.e., Cows and Followers combined) for four different farming systems assuming the same stocking rate for the dairy cows and three levels of performance, including different stocking rates, for the followers. This assumes a 3:1 land use ratio (dairy cow area: followers area) and relates to the dairying systems (gross margins) shown earlier in this section. It is important to note, however, that these are only a guide as the figures (ratio of land areas assumed) do not take account of the different herd replacement rates for each dairying system. In practise, it is likely that the amount of land required for the followers for a block spring calving herd would be less than that for a high yielding all-year-round calving herd; this is due to the fact that typically a high yielding herd would have a higher herd replacement rate and as such require more heifers and therefore land on which to rear them.

Gross Margin per Forage Hectare for Cows and Followers Combined

			G.M per Forage Hectare (acre) Dairy Cows			
	System Litres		Autumn 7,000 £	Spring 5,250 £	AYR Ave. 8,000 £	AYR High 9,500 £
G.M. per			1778 (720)	1720 (696)	1744 (706)	1936 (784)
Forage Hectare (acre) Followers	Low	333 (135)	1417 (574)	1373 (556)	1391 (563)	1535 (622)
	Ave.	540 (219)	1469 (595)	1425 (577)	1443 (584)	1587 (643)
	High	792 (321)	1532 (620)	1488 (603)	1506 (610)	1650 (668)

As an example, the above table indicates that at the average level of performance and stocking rate for an all-year-round 8,000 litre dairy herd (AYR Average) and followers, the whole farm-system gross margin per hectare (acre) figure is £1,958 (793) compared with £2,350 (952) for the dairy cows alone, a reduction of 17%.

BEEF

There are numerous different systems for producing beef in the UK which are heavily influenced by factors such as feed and forage, breeds, housing, sale weights, market outlets, labour availability, enterprise scale and personal choice. Thus, the financial performance of beef enterprises are infinitely variable. The enterprise gross margins shown on the following pages represent the 'standard' systems with output prices and costs based on 2016 budgets.

Calves

The values in the table below are for 2016 and relate to dairy bulls or beef cross calves of average quality, less than three weeks old. These values have been used in the budgets for the following beef systems. There is large regional and seasonal variation in calf prices.

Calf values of various beef cattle

	Bulls	Heifers
Holstein Friesians	75	-
Hereford Cross	250	195
HF/Continental Cross	310	260

Calf Rearing
Early Weaning - Bucket Rearing (per calf)

	3 months	6 months
	£	£
Value of Calf	390	475
Less Calf Purchase	270	270
Output	120	205
Variable Costs:		
Milk Substitute	35	35
Concentrates	39	85
Hay	4	18
Vet & Med.	17	19
Bedding	7	12
Miscellaneous	3	6
Total Variable Costs	105	175
Gross Margin per Calf Reared	14	29

1. *Calf Purchase*: Equal number of male and female calves (Holstein Friesian/ Continental beef cross, 1-2 weeks old). £270 average price plus 4% mortality, mainly in first 3 weeks.

2. *Milk substitute:* 20 kg @ £1,750/tonne = £35.00.

3. *Calf concentrates:* to 3 months, 160 kg @ £245/tonne = £39.20, *Rearer Feed* to 6 months, additional 270kg @ £170/tonne = £85. Calves fed on machine or lib milk systems will use more milk powder.

4. *Hay:* 50kg to 3 months, 230kg to 6 months (£62/tonne) See page 89.

5. *Miscellaneous:* Ear Tags etc.

6. *Weights*: at start = 45 to 50 kg; at 3 months = 115 kg; at 6 months = 245kg.

7. *Contract rearing charge* (both 0 to 3 months and 0 to 6 months): £14 per week. *Direct labour cost:* approximately £28 per head to 3 months, £42 per head to 6 months.

8. *Labour requirements (all beef systems):* see page 185.

Suckler Cows

Single Suckling (per Cow): Lowland

System	Spring Calving		Autumn Calving	
Performance Level	Average	High	Average	High
	£	£	£	£
Value of Calf Sold	*517*	*587*	*685*	*732*
Calf Sales / Calf Value per Cow	471	546	624	680
Less Cow and Bull Depreciation	164	164	185	185
Calf Purchases	8	8	10	10
Output	**298**	**374**	**428**	**485**
Variable Costs:				
Concentrate Costs (Cow and Calf)	38	32	66	60
Vet & Med	28	28	30	30
Bedding	43	43	50	50
Miscellaneous	20	21	23	26
Total Variable Costs (excl. forage)	**130**	**124**	**169**	**166**
Gross Margin per Cow, before				
deducting Forage Variable Costs	169	250	260	319
Forage Variable Costs	112	92	122	101
Purchased Bulk Feeds	12	10	20	16
Gross Margin per Cow	**45**	**148**	**118**	**203**
Cows per Hectare	1.80	2.20	1.65	2.00
Forage Hectares (Acres) per Cow	0.56	0.45	0.61	0.50
	(1.37)	*(1.12)*	*(1.50)*	*(1.24)*
Gross Margin per Forage Hectare (Acre)	**81**	**326**	**194**	**405**
	(33)	*(132)*	*(79)*	*(164)*

1. *System*: Relates to performance per cycle, i.e. for the production period. Assumed 390 days average calving interval.

2. *Performance level*: relates to variations in both outputs and inputs.

Calving Period	Spring Calving		Autumn Calving	
Performance Level	Average	High	Average	High
Calf Sale Weights (kg)	280	309	371	385
Sale Age (Days)	250	240	365	340
Sale Prices (£/kg)	£1.85	1.90	£1.85	1.90
Calves reared per 100 cows mated	91	93	91	93

3. *Cow & Bull Depreciation:*

	Spring C.	Autumn C.	Bull
Purchase Price - £	£1,700	£1,700	£4,200
Cull Price - £	£550	£550	£600
Animal Life (Years)	8	7	5
Depreciation £/cow	£144	£164	£21

4. *Calf Purchases:* £260 each, 3 per 100 cows mated (spring calving) 4 per 100 cows mated (autumn calving).

Dairy cross beef cows have better fertility performance than continental pure bred cows, but lower cull sale prices. Average 35 cows per bull.

5. *Concentrate feed:*

Concentrates	Spring Calving		Autumn Calving	
	Average	High	Average	High
Cow kg's	120	100	190	165
Cow - £/t	200	200	200	200
Calf kg's	60	50	120	115
Calf - £/t	235	235	235	235
Total Concentrate	£38	£32	£66	£60

6. *Straw:* where yarded in winter, straw requirements average 0.7 tonnes per cow for spring calvers and 0.8 tonnes for autumn calvers at £62/tonne.

7. *Forage Area:* includes grazing and conserved grass (silage and hay). Higher stocking rates imply better use of grassland or can be achieved by buying in more winter fodder, or feeding more arable by-products, including straw. Purchased bulk fodder and/or straw balancer concentrates will reduce gross margin per cow but increase gross margin per hectare. Forage cost from Long Term Ley in Forage at £201/ha on page 87.

8. *Headage Payment:* A payment is made in Scotland on three-quarter bred beef calves from Suckler Cows. From 2015 this is a flat rate payment, on all eligible calves, in the region of €100 per calf on the mainland and €160 per calf on the islands. Actual rates will depend on the number of calves claimed on each year. See Top-up Schemes in Chapter III.

9. *Multiple calves:* In lowland conditions rearing two or more calves per cow is an option, but needs substantially greater labour input. Output is raised by fostering a second purchased calf onto a cow soon after calving, with little impact on costs of keeping the cow. The cow breed needs to be of a quiet temperament and have enough milk to rear two calves.

System	Spring Calving		Autumn Calving	
Performance Level	Average	High	Average	High
	£	£	£	£
Value of Calf	504	532	672	703
Calf Sales / Valuation per Cow	454	489	605	647
Less Cow and Bull Depreciation	169	169	190	190
Calf Purchases	8	8	10	10
Output	**446**	**482**	**595**	**636**
Variable Costs:				
Concentrate Costs (Cow and Calf)	39	33	64	58
Vet & Med	28	28	30	30
Bedding	48	48	54	54
Miscellaneous	20	21	23	26
Total Variable Costs (excl. forage)	**135**	**130**	**172**	**169**
Gross Margin per Cow, before				
deducting Forage Variable Costs	311	352	423	468
Forage Variable Costs	92	78	118	98
Purchased Bulk Feeds	14	12	22	18
Gross Margin per Cow	**205**	**263**	**283**	**352**
Cows per Hectare	1.60	1.90	1.25	1.50
Forage Hectares (Acres) per Cow	0.63	0.53	0.80	0.67
	(1.54)	*(1.30)*	*(1.98)*	*(1.65)*
Gross Margin per Forage Hectare (Acre)	**328**	**499**	**354**	**527**
	(133)	*(202)*	*(143)*	*(213)*

1. *System:* Relates to performance per cycle, i.e. for the production period. Assumed 390 days average calving interval. Performance level: relates to variations in both outputs and inputs.

2. *Performance Level*

Calving Period	Spring Calving		Autumn Calving	
Performance Level	Average	High	Average	High
Calf Sale Weights (kg)	273	280	364	370
Sale Age (Days)	250	240	365	330
Sale Prices (£/kg)	£1.85	1.90	£1.85	1.90
Calves reared per 100 cows mated	90	92	90	92

3. *Cow & Bull Depreciation:*

	Spring C.	Autumn C.	Bull
Purchase Price - £	£1,700	£1,700	£4,200
Cull Price - £	£550	£550	£600
Animal Life (Years)	8	7	4
Depreciation £/cow	£144	£164	£26

4. *Calf Purchases*: £260 each, 3 per 100 cows mated (spring calving) 4 per 100 cows mated (autumn calving).

Dairy cross beef cows have better fertility performance than continental pure bred cows, but lower cull sale prices. Average 35 cows per bull.

5. *Concentrate Feed:*

Concentrates	Spring Calving		Autumn Calving	
	Average	High	Average	High
Cow kg's	130	110	195	170
Cow - £/t	200	200	200	200
Calf kg's	60	50	120	115
Calf - £/t	210	210	210	210
Total Concentrate	£39	£33	£64	£58

6. *Straw:* where yarded in winter, straw requirements average 0.75 tonnes per cow for spring calvers and 0.85 tonnes for autumn calvers at £64/tonne.

7. *Forage Area:* includes grazing and conserved grass (silage and hay). Higher stocking rates imply better use of grassland or higher can be achieved by buying more winter bulk fodder, or by winter feeding more arable by-products, including straw. Purchased bulk fodder and/or straw balancer concentrates will reduce gross margin per cow but increase gross margin per hectare. Forage cost from Improved Permanent Pasture in Forage page at £147/ha on page 87.

8. *Headage Payment:* A payment is made in Scotland on three-quarter bred beef calves from Suckler Cows. From 2015 this is a flat rate payment, on all eligible calves, in the region of €100 per calf on the mainland and €160 per calf on the islands. Actual rates will depend on the number of calves claimed on each year. See Top-up Schemes in Chapter III.

Store Cattle

Maintenance / Keeping of Young Dairy Store Cattle **(per head)**

	Summer Keeping		Winter Keeping
	£		£
Store Sales	744		736
Less Purchased Store (incl. mortality)	461		461
Output	**283**		**275**
Variable Costs:			
Concentrates	'		54
Vet & Med	10		12
Bedding	0		50
Miscellaneous	15		19
Total Variable Costs (excluding Forage)	**25**		**135**
Gross Margin per Head, before			
deducting Forage Variable Costs	258		141
Forage Variable Costs	35		74
Gross Margin per Head	**223**		**67**
Animals per Hectare	5.75		
Forage Hectares (Acres) per Head	0.17	*(0.43)*	
Gross Margin per Forage Hectare (Acre)	**1,281**	*(519)*	

1. *System*: Buying dairy cross steers and heifers at 6 months old for keeping / rearing. Animals spend 6 months in system before sale / transfer to a finishing enterprise.

2. *Sales*: at 402kg summer, 398kg winter (liveweight), both at £1.85/kg.

3. *Purchases*: Both systems 245kg purchase weight @ £1.90, plus 1% mortality.

4. *Concentrates*: Winter 270kg concentrates (1.5kg/day for 180 days) @ £200 per tonne. Summer, 100g/day.

5. *Forage Costs:* Summer Keep based on 'Long Term Ley' in forage section (page 87) at £201/ha gross margin. Winter Keep: 2.9 tonnes per head grass silage consumption. Full costs of grass and ensiling are included here at contract rates making £25.48/tonne silage. Similarly, bought in silage will increase the forage costs over those shown. *This means that the two gross margins are not comparable as different levels of overheads are included in the calculation. Be sure what is included in the forage calculation when working out the costs.*

Finishing Cattle

Finishing of Dairy Bred Store Cattle **(per head)**

	Summer Finishing		Winter Finishing	
	£		£	
Finished Sales	1,087		1,100	
Less Purchased Store (incl. mortality)	744		751	
Output	**344**		**349**	
Variable Costs:				
Concentrates	63		154	
Vet & Med	11		19	
Bedding	0		43	
Miscellaneous	35		42	
Total Variable Costs (excluding Forage)	**109**		**258**	
Gross Margin per Head, before				
deducting Forage Variable Costs	235		90	
Forage Variable Costs	67		94	
Gross Margin per Head	**168**		**-4**	
Animals per Hectare	3.00			
Forage Hectares (Acres) per Head	0.33	*(0.82)*		
Gross Margin per Forage Hectare (Acre)	**503**	*(204)*		

1. *System*: Finishing of dairy bred store cattle (as shown in previous margin – summer finishing cattle will have been winter stores and *vice versa*). Purchased / transferred in at 12 months old and finished over 7 months (210 days for summer finishing, 220 days winter finishing). Summer finishing takes place entirely at pasture whilst winter finishing is a housed system for the production period.

2. *Sales*: Finished sale liveweights of 598kg for summer finishing and 604kg for winter finishing. Sale price £1.82/kg in both systems.

3. *Purchases*: Purchase / transfer-in weight of 398kg and 402kg for summer and winter finishing respectively. Cost in both cases £1.85/kg plus 1% mortality allowance.

4. *Concentrates*: Summer finishing 1.5kg/day (=315kg); winter finishing, 3.5kg/day (=770kg) at £200 per tonne.

5. *Forage Costs*: Based on 'Long Term Ley' in forage section (page 87) at £201/ha. Winter Finishing: 3.7 tonnes per head grass silage consumption. Silage production costs are considered, (equivalent to purchasing the silage at cost) so relevant overheads are included in this calculation. Similarly, bought in silage will increase the forage costs. *This means that the two gross margins are not comparable as different levels of overheads are included in the calculation. Be sure what is included in the forage calculation when working out the costs.*

Finishing of Suckler Bred Store Cattle (per head)

	Summer Finishing		Winter Finishing
	£		£
Finished Sales	1,189		1,071
Less Purchased Store (incl. mortality)	557		715
Output	**632**		**356**
Variable Costs:			
Concentrates	72		126
Vet & Med	12		20
Bedding	0		48
Miscellaneous	46		51
Total Variable Costs (excluding Forage)	**130**		**245**
Gross Margin per Head, before			
deducting Forage Variable Costs	502		111
Forage Variable Costs	154		87
Gross Margin per Head	**348**		**24**
Animals per Hectare	3.00		
Forage Hectares (Acres) per Head	0.33	*(0.82)*	
Gross Margin per Forage Hectare (Acre)	**1,044**	*(423)*	

1. *System*: Beef suckler progeny purchased / transferred in at 8 months old for summer finishing and 12 months old for winter finishing (summer finishing cattle will be from spring calving suckler cows, with winter finishers from autumn calving suckler cows). Summer finishers = 300 days in system, winter finishers = 180 days in system.

2. *Sales*: Summer finishing 639kg liveweight, winter finishing 576kg liveweight. Sale price of £1.86/kg in both systems.

3. *Purchase Price*: Summer and winter bought in at 294 and 378kg respectively, both at £1.88/kg and allowing 1% mortality

4. *Concentrates*: Summer finishers consuming 360kg (1.2kg/day), winter finishers 630kg (3.5kg/day). Concentrate price of £200 per tonne.

5. *Forage Costs*: Based on 'Long Term Ley' in forage section (page 87) at £201/ha. Winter Finishing: 3.4 tonnes per head. Only silage variable costs are considered and therefore overhead costs of silage production need to be considered (inc. contracting). Similarly, bought in silage will increase the forage costs over those shown.

Maize & Grass Silage Beef Finishing (per Head Produced)

System	Dairy X Progeny		Suckler Progeny	
Performance Level	Average	High	Average	High
	£	£	£	£
Finished Sales	1,177	1,264	1,201	1,333
Less Purchased Store (incl. mortality)	461	461	531	587
Output	**716**	**803**	**669**	**746**
Variable Costs:				
Concentrates	131	124	85	79
Misc Variable Costs	113	110	129	125
Total Variable Costs (excl. Forage)	**244**	**234**	**214**	**204**
Gross Margin per Head, before				
deducting Forage Variable Costs	472	569	455	542
Forage Cost	84	76	78	71
Gross Margin per Head	**387**	**493**	**377**	**471**

1. *System*: An intensive finishing system utilising a housed forage-based system of grass silage and maize silage with heavy finished weights. Dairy cross progeny bought or transferred in at 6 months and suckler progeny at 8 months. Dairy-cross finishing period of 365 days and suckler progeny at 305 days. The gross margins are higher than in other finishing enterprises but overhead costs (fixed costs) will also be high in comparison.

2. *Sales*:

   Dairy cross = average 647kg liveweight at £1.82/kg, high 683kg at £1.85/kg.

   Suckler progeny = average 646kg liveweight at £1.86/kg, high 706kg at £1.89/kg.

3. *Purchases*:

   Dairy cross = average 245kg liveweight at £1.90/kg, high 683kg at £1.90/kg.

   Suckler progeny = average 280kg lwt at £1.92/kg, high 309kg at £1.92/kg.

4. *Mortality*: 1% mortality assumed.

5. *Concentrates*: Dairy cross = average 657kg (1.8kg/day), high 621kg (1.7kg/day), suckler progeny = average 427kg (1.4kg/day), high 397kg (1.3kg/day). All concentrates £200 per tonne.

6. *Miscellaneous* Variable Costs: assumed to be proportionally higher than the store and suckler finishing enterprises shown previously. Assumed 8% premium for average performance and 5% for high performance.

7. *Forage Costs:*

Maize Cattle (per head)	Dairy Cross		Suckler	
	Average	High	Average	High
Tonnes Maize Silage	1.90	1.71	1.80	1.62
Total Silage Cost £/t	£20	£20	£20	£20
Tonnes Grass Silage	1.85	1.7	1.70	1.5
Total Silage Cost £/t	25	25	25	25
Total **Per Cow**	**84**	**76**	**78**	**71**

The silage costs relate to the total operational cost of growing and harvesting the forage, but not the costs incurred in preparing/mixing rations as shown in page 87.

Cereal Bull Beef (per Head)

System	Continental Cross Holstein/Friesian Bulls		Holstein Friesian Bulls	
Performance Level	Average	High	Average	High
	£	£	£	£
Finished Sales	986	1032	860	932
Less Calf Purchase	296	294	51	51
Output	**690**	**738**	**809**	**881**
Variable Costs:				
Concentrates	406	393	406	393
Other Feed	22	20	22	20
Vet & Med	20	18	20	18
Bedding	54	54	54	54
Miscellaneous	48	48	48	48
Total Variable Costs	**550**	**533**	**550**	**533**
Gross Margin per Head	**140**	**205**	**259**	**348**

1. A traditional cereal based system for finishing cattle. Animals are housed throughout the production period and fed on a barley concentrate and straw based ration. Production period typically from 2 weeks to 14 months old. This system is highly exposed to swings in cereal commodity prices. A £10 per tonne feed price movement equates to a margin change of £22 per head.

2. *Sales:*

   Cont. cross bulls = average 530kg, high 555kg; average at £1.86/kg lwt;

   Dairy bulls, average 475kg, high 515kg average, at £1.81/kg

   All year round production is assumed. Average slaughter age is 15 months, with killing out percentages ranging from 54% to 59%, with the better conformation continental cross bulls achieving higher percentages.

3. *Purchases:* £290 for continental cross male calves at 3 weeks of age plus mortality; £50 for dairy bulls plus mortality. Mortality, average 2%, high 1.5%.

4. *Concentrates:* £74 calf rearing (to 12 weeks inc. milk powder: see page 56) + finishing ration. Finishing ration: 17 parts barley @ £120 per tonne, 3 parts concentrate supplement at £200 per tonne; plus £17 per tonne milling and mixing cost. Total, £149 per tonne.

   Barley ration quantity; average 2,225kg, high 2,140kg (excluding calf feed to 12 weeks – see page 56).

5. *Bedding:* 0.9 tonnes at £60 per tonne

Veal

Veal consumption is low in the UK - a small fraction of the per capita consumption of France for example. Continental demand is mainly for white veal, produced in individual veal crates, a system that is illegal in the UK. There is no live calf export activity from the UK to the continent for veal production owing to animal welfare concerns and the risk of spreading Bovine Tb. There is some activity in UK 'welfare friendly' domestic veal production where calves are kept in groups in straw yards producing heavier calves with 'pink' meat known as 'Rose Veal'. This is a premium product and is considerably more expensive to produce than imported 'white veal'.

SHEEP

Spring Lambing Flocks

Lowland Spring Lambing per Ewe (selling lambs off grass)

Performance Level	Low	Average	High
Average Price per Lamb (£)	63.2	66.7	70.2
Sales per ewe:	£	£	£
Lamb sales	80	103	123
Wool	2.4	2.4	2.4
Cull Ewes and Rams	13.5	13.5	13.5
Sub Total	95.6	119.2	138.6
Less Ewe and Ram Replacements	36.4	36.4	36.4
Output per Ewe	**59.2**	**82.8**	**102.2**
Variable Costs:			
Concentrates	17.9	13.3	11.9
Vet and Med	10.4	10.9	13.1
Miscellaneous	14.1	14.1	14.1
Total Variable Costs (excluding Forage)	**42.38**	**38.3**	**39.15**
Gross Margin per Ewe, before			
deducting Forage Variable Costs	**16.8**	**44.5**	**63.1**
Forage Variable Costs (inc bought-in			
Forage and Keep)	19.7	14.7	13.4
Gross Margin per Ewe	**-2.9**	**29.8**	**49.7**
Stocking Rate (Ewes with Lambs per forage			
Hectare (acre))	7.5 (3.0)	10 (4.0)	11 (4.5)
Gross Margin per Forage Hectare	-22	298	546
Gross Margin per Forage Acre	-9	121	221

1. *Rearing Performance Data:*

	Low	Average	High
Ewes in Lamb	90%	93%	95%
Lambing Percentage	160%	185%	201%
Lambs born per 100 ewes	144	172	191
Young Lamb Deaths	8%	6%	5%
Older Lamb Deaths	4.5%	4.0%	3.5%
Total Lamb Losses	13%	10%	9%
Lambs sold per 100 ewes put to ram	126	155	175

      These performance figures are assumed for flocks of mature ewes, i.e. shearlings and older. Where ewe lambs or mainly shearlings are included in flock performance adjustment needs to be made. The breed will have a large effect on performance data.

2. *Lamb Sales.* Prices for lambs sold for slaughter are based on the projection for the 2016 season. Average sale liveweight of 41kg, averaging £1.70.kg for 85% and 15% sold as stores at £50/head. 'Low' and 'High' have a £3.50/head adjustment.

3. *Wool:* 2kg/ewe at £1.20/kg

4. *Cull Ewes and Rams:* Here, 20% of the ewe flock is culled each year at £65 each and that, allowing for 4% mortality,

5. *Replacements:* 23% are purchased or home-reared at £145 each. Rams: 1 per 45 ewes, 3.5 year life, purchased @ £480, sold @ £75. The net cost (flock depreciation) is £23.1 per ewe per year.

6. *Concentrate Feeding:* Concentrate finishing of late season lambs has been common, but there has been a swing to sell as stores (for finishing on winter forage crops) rather than finish on high cost concentrates. Late season grass availability influences the store trade. 54kg per ewe at £210 per tonne and 8kg lamb creep at £240 per tonne.

7. *Veterinary and Medicine:* includes allowance for wormer (ewes and lambs), vaccines, fly strike chemicals and foot treatments.

8. *Miscellaneous Costs:* include contract shearing @ £1.49/ewe, scanning £1.00/ewe and ewe and lamb tags £1.49/ewe (assuming slaughter batch tags are used), carcase disposal £0.56/ewe, straw £1.47/ewe, minerals and licks etc. £2.05/ewe, marketing, levy and transport £6.10/ewe.

9. *Forage Costs:* Based on Improved Permanent Pasture (£147/ha) refer to forage section, page 87. Only variable costs are included and therefore overhead costs of forage production need to be considered. Similarly, bought in grass keep and forage may increase the forage costs over those shown.

10. *Other Costs:*

   a. *Prices of Specialised Equipment*

Troughs (2.75 m)	£30 to £43
Racks (2 to 3 m)......................	£210 to £235
Foot Baths (3 m)	£100 to £165
Shearing Machines..................	£460 to £1,000
Lamb Creep Feeders	£370 to £785
Weigh Crate...........................	£500 to £775
Mobile Handling System	£2,600 to £8,700

   b. *Fencing:* Approximately £6.10 per metre *for posts, sheep netting, 2 strands of barbed wired and labour inclusive. Refer to page 267.*

   c. *Labour:* see page 173.

Upland Spring Lambing per Ewe (selling lambs off grass)

Performance Level	Low	Average	High
Average Price per Lamb (£)	58.5	62.0	65.5
Sales per ewe:	£	£	£
Lamb sales	71.5	87.3	104.1
Wool	1.9	1.9	1.9
Cull Ewes and Rams	9.0	9.0	9.0
Sub Total	82.4	98.2	114.9
Less Ewe and Ram Replacements (4)	34.1	34.1	34.1
Output per Ewe	**48.3**	**64.1**	**80.8**
Variable Costs:			
Concentrates (60kg ewes, 10kg lambs)	20.25	15.0	12.00
Vet and Med	9.57	10.1	12.08
Miscellaneous	13.68	13.7	13.68
Total Variable Costs (excluding Forage)	**43.50**	**38.8**	**37.76**
Gross Margin per Ewe, before			
deducting Forage Variable Costs	**4.9**	**25.3**	**43.1**
Forage Variable Costs (inc bought-in			
Forage and Keep)	21.9	9.7	8.2
Gross Margin per Ewe	**-17.1**	**15.7**	**34.9**
Stocking Rate (Ewes with Lambs per forage			
Hectare (acre))	4 (1.5)	9 (3.4)	10 (4.0)
Gross Margin per Forage Hectare	-64	133	349
Gross Margin per Forage Acre	-26	54	141

1. *Rearing Performance Data:*

	Low	Average	High
Ewes in Lamb	90%	93%	95%
Lambing Percentage	158%	172%	190%
Lambs born /100 ewes	142.2	160.0	180.5
Young Lamb Deaths	9%	7%	7%
Older Lamb Deaths	5%	5%	5%
Total Lamb Losses	14%	12%	12%
Lambs sold / 100 ewes put to ram	122	141	159

These performance figures are assumed for flocks of mature ewes, i.e. shearlings and older. Where ewe lambs or mainly shearlings are included in flock performance adjustment needs to be made. The breed will obviously have a large effect on lambing percentage, liveweight gains and carcase grades.

2. *Lamb Prices.* Average market price of £1.68/kg liveweight (equivalent to £3.65/kg deadweight) has been assumed giving £65.52 per finished lamb at an average liveweight of 39kg for 82% of crop. 18% sold as stores for £46 per head. Performance variation is £3.50 variation each way caused by differences in weights, time of marketing and proportion sold finished or retained as stores.

3. *Wool:* Wool price assumed for upland flocks is £1.87 per ewe, based on a price of £1.10/kg at 1.7kg/ewe. Upland sheep wool is harsher than lowland which is softer and therefore dearer. Variations between breeds affect wool quality and ewe size affecting weight of wool produced.

4. *Cull Ewes and Rams:* Here, 19% of the ewe flock is culled each year at £45 each and that, allowing for 4% mortality,

5. *Replacements:* 23% are purchased or home-reared at £135 each. Rams: 1 per 45 ewes, 3.5 year life, purchased @ £480, sold @ £75. The net cost (flock depreciation) is £25.1 per ewe per year.

6. *Concentrate Feeding:* Concentrate finishing of late season lambs has been common, but there has been a swing to sell as stores (for finishing on winter forage crops) rather than finish on high cost concentrates. Late season grass availability influences the store trade.

7. *Veterinary and Medicine:* includes allowance for wormer (ewes and lambs), vaccines, fly strike chemicals and foot treatments.

8. *Miscellaneous Costs:* include contract shearing @ £1.51/ewe, scanning £1.00/ewe and ewe and lamb tags £1.43/ewe (assuming slaughter batch tags are used), carcase disposal £0.72/ewe, straw £1.37/ewe, minerals and licks etc. £1.55/ewe, marketing, levy and transport £6.10/ewe.

9. *Forage Costs:* Based on Low Input Pasture (£82/ha) refer to forage section, page 87. Only variable costs are included and therefore overhead costs of forage production need to be considered. Similarly, bought in grass keep and forage may increase the forage costs over those shown here.

Rearing Ewe Lambs

Purchasing ewe lambs and rearing over winter & summer for breeding

Sales:	£ Per Ewe
Sale Price / Transfer Value	145.00
Wool	1.80
Sub Total	146.80
Less Purchase Price / Transfer Value	80.00
Losses & Culling	5.00
Output per Ewe	**61.80**
Variable Costs:	
Vet and Med	7.10
Miscellaneous	3.34
Total Variable Costs (excluding Forage)	**10.44**
Gross Margin per Ewe, before	
deducting Forage Variable Costs	**51.36**
Forage Variable Costs (inc bought-in	
Forage and Keep)	11.80
Gross Margin per Ewe	**39.56**
Stocking Rate (Ewe lambs per forage	
Hectare (acre))	12.5 (5.1)
Gross Margin per Forage Hectare	495
Gross Margin per Forage Acre	200

1. *System*: Involves rearing or purchasing ewe lambs suitable for further breeding. Animals are purchased / transferred in late summer / autumn, grazed and outwintered, grazed on in the following summer before sale / transfer out in the autumn (i.e. 12 month system). The terminology for this system varies between regions; gimmers, thieves, shearlings and tegs all relate to the same age of female sheep.

2. *Sales*: wool, 1.5kg at £1.20/kg

3. *Purchase Price*: Assumes better quality ewe lambs are acquired at £80 per lamb than sold to market.

4. *Losses and Culls*: 4% losses of purchase and 3% culled at £60 (for meat as unsuitable for breeding).

5. *Veterinary and Medicine*: includes wormer, fly strike chemicals, vaccines and miscellaneous treatments.

6. *Miscellaneous Costs*: Shearing at £1.37/head, minerals at £1.65/head, carcase disposal at £0.32/head. No marketing costs are included as it is assumed the ewes are retained for home use.

7. *Forage Costs:* Based on Improved Permanent Pasture (£147/ha) refer to forage section, page 87. Only variable costs are included and therefore overhead costs of forage production need to be considered. Similarly, bought in grass keep and forage may increase the forage costs over those shown here.

Finishing Store Lambs

Purchasing store lambs and finishing late autumn & winter

Sales:	£ Per Lamb
Sale Price	73.10
Less Purchase Price / Transfer In Value	50.00
Losses	3.00
Output per Lamb	**20.10**
Variable Costs:	
Concentrates	2.94
Vet and Med	3.00
Miscellaneous	5.64
Total Variable Costs (excluding Forage)	**11.58**
Gross Margin per Lamb, before deducting Forage Variable Costs	**8.52**
Forage Variable Costs (inc bought-in Forage and Keep)	4.73
Gross Margin per Lamb	**3.80**
Stocking Rate (lambs per forage Hectare (acre))	28 (11.3)
Gross Margin per Forage Hectare	106
Gross Margin per Forage Acre	43

1. *System:* lambs are batch bought in the autumn at or shortly after weaning in September or October, then drawn out and sold as they are ready in smaller groups from then through to March the following year.

2. *Sales:* Assumes 43kg liveweight @ £1.70/kg.

3. *Losses:* assumed at 6% of transfer price

4. *Concentrates:* 14kg per lamb @ £210 per tonne

5. *Veterinary and Medicine:* Allows for wormer and scab injection, clostridial vaccines and miscellaneous treatments.

6. *Miscellaneous:* Including transport, marketing, minerals, carcase disposal.

7. *Forage Costs:* Based on Low Input Permanent Pasture (£82/ha) and Stubble Turnips (£157/ha) refer to forage section, page 87. Only variable costs are included and therefore overhead costs of forage production need to be considered. Similarly, bought in grass keep and forage may increase the forage costs over those shown.

GRAZING AND REARING CHARGES: CATTLE AND SHEEP

Grazing charges vary greatly according to the quality of the pasture, access, fencing and infrastructure. Local supply and demand also affect the value of grazing charges. The following figures are estimated for 2016:

Summer Grazing (per head per week)

Store Cattle and in-calf heifers over 21 months, dry cows, and fattening bullocks over 18 months...........................	£2.00 - £3.00
Heifers and Steers, 12-21 months	£2.00 - £3.00
6-12 months Cattle	£1.00 - £2.25
Cattle of mixed ages	£1.00 - £2.50
Ewes (with lambs).......................................	£0.45 - £0.70

Winter Grazing (per head per week)

'Strong' Cattle	£1.75 - £3.00
Heifers	£1.50 - £2.50
Sheep..	£0.30 - £0.50

Note: the above figures assume the farmer on whose land the livestock are present does all the fencing. The livestock owner remains their keeper, else the land owner would become liable for all the livestock based cross compliance such as tagging. If the stock owner does the fencing, the figures may be much less. Prices vary on local demand.

Grass Keep

Most typically around £100-£175 per ha (£40-£70/acre), with the best £185-£275 per ha (£75-£110/acre) and lower quality keep making £62-£90 per ha (£25-£36/acre).

These figures are highly variable, especially between parts of the country and levels of local demand. Good fencing, electricity supply, mains water etc. add a premium to grass keep as does the quality of grassland and any licensor fertiliser applications. Grazing may be offered to livestock keepers at very little or no charge where the need for maintenance of grassland is the driving factor (e.g. amenity value, requirement to cross comply or meet agri-environment scheme agreements, value of cattle and sheep to 'clean-up' pasture or to provide beneficial mixed grazing). The length of grazing period offered will also influence the premium of grass keep (e.g. grazing until 30th September or until 31st December) as will permission to take a grass crop from the land (hay, haylage, silage).

The Nitrate Vulnerable Zone (NVZ) rules in England mean that demand for grass keep is high in some areas, especially where dairy enterprises are commonplace. The additional acreage helps some producers to keep within their livestock manure loading limit.

Winter Keep (Cattle per head per week)

Grazing + 9 kg hay and some straw....................	£9.50
Full winter housing in yards	£9.50 - £12.50
Calf rearing for beef	£12.00 - £15.00

A typical rental for labour, buildings and maintenance diet would be £9.50 per head per week. These rates apply where feed to achieve maintenance plus some growth is supplied plus labour and buildings and bedding where applicable. A typical rental for labour, buildings and a maintenance diet would be £7.50 per head per week. In recent years the cost of bedding (usually straw) has influenced the final values of winter keeping cattle.

Heifer Rearing Charges

There have historically been two types of arrangement:

1. Farmer X sells calf to a Rearer at agreed price; the calf is then Rearer's responsibility and he pays for all expenses and bears any losses. Farmer X has first option on heifers, which he buys back two months before calving. Approximate price: £1,200 above cost of calf for Holstein Friesians. Rearer fetches calf; Farmer X supplies transport for heifer. *This system is now less common due to the increasing popularity and general transparency of option 2 below.*

2. Farmer X retains ownership of calf, but sends it to a specialist rearer. Approximate rearer charges range from £0.60 to £1.20 per head per day for winter rearing and £1.00 to £1.30 per head per day for summer rearing. Charges vary depending upon cattle, system and location. Newer agreements often include a fixed incentive payment to the Rearer if the cattle have met specification at the end of the rearing period. This is usually defined in terms of final liveweight and the level of in-calf heifers. A typical fixed fee incentive payment would be £50 per head.

   Usually the owner of the cattle is responsible for transport costs and the choice and cost of vaccine programmes. The cost of semen for artificial insemination of the heifers is also usually incurred by the owner and paid for over and above the standard rearing charge. The rearer is responsible for all standard rearing costs including for normal veterinary services and worming etc. and any animal losses over an agreed tolerance level. *Model agreements are available from industry associations and advisors.*

   Contract rearing on behalf of a third party may appeal to some producers who wish to reduce borrowing exposure and / or lower capital investment in a business. A well laid out contract rearing arrangement will also provide greater cost and income clarity to both the rearer and owner and therefore reduce the risk exposure to both businesses. It also enables each business to focus and specialise to achieve optimum performance without being distracted by other enterprises. Biosecurity issues are becoming increasingly paramount where an agreement is set up. In many cases the owner of heifers will require exclusive occupancy of a rearer's farm without cattle owned by the rearer or others being present. The Bovine TB movement rules must be considered by parties entering into heifer rearing agreements including the need for pre-movement TB testing between holdings.

RED DEER

A. *Breeding and Finishing*	Per 100 Hinds
Sales:	£
44 Stags (15-18 months) : 55kg dw @ £5.20/kg	12,584
34 Hinds (15-18 months) : 45kg dw @ £5.20/kg	7,956
8 Cull Hinds @ £200	1,600
1 Cull Stag @ £500	500
Less Replacements: 8 hinds @ £350 & 1 stag @ £1500	4,300
Output	**18,340**
Variable Costs:	
Concentrates @ 4.0 tonnes @ £225/tonne	900
Vet and Med	494
Miscellaneous	408
Total Variable Costs	**1,802**
Gross Margin before deducting Forage Costs	**16,538**
Forage Variable Costs (5.5 Hinds per hectare @ £201/ha)	3,661
Gross Margin per 100 Hinds	**12,877**
Gross Margin per Forage hectare (5.5 hinds/ha)	708
Gross Margin per Forage acre (2.2 hinds/ac)	287

Lowland systems assumed. Hind replacements home-reared in systems A and B.

Herd Life: hinds, 12 years; stags, 6 years; 33 hinds per stag. Calves reared per 100 hinds: 90. Purchase price of breeding stock (good quality): hinds £350 plus, yearling hinds £275 plus, stags £1500.

B. *Breeding and Selling Store Calves*	Per 100 Hinds
Sales:	£
45 Stag Calves @ £150/head (45 kg liveweight)	6,750
35 Hind Calves @ £150/head (40 kg liveweight)	5,250
8 Cull Hinds @ £200	1,600
1 Cull Stag @ £500	500
Less Replacements: 8 hinds @ £350 & 1 stag @ £1500	4,300
Output	**9,800**
Variable Costs:	
Concentrates @ 1.3 tonnes @ £225/tonne	293
Vet and Med	285
Miscellaneous	204
Total Variable Costs	**782**
Gross Margin before deducting Forage Costs	**9,019**
Forage Variable Costs (6.5 Hinds per hectare @ £147/ha)	2,268
Gross Margin per 100 Hinds	**6,750**
Gross Margin per Forage hectare (6.5 hinds/ha)	439
Gross Margin per Forage acre (2.6 hinds/ac)	178

C. Finishing Stag Calves

	Per 200 Stags
Sales:	£
195 Stags (15-18 months) : 55kg dw @ £5.20/kg	55,770
Less Purchases : 200 @ £150 per head	30,000
Output	**25,770**
Variable Costs:	
Concentrates @ 12.0 tonnes @ £225/tonne	2,700
Vet and Med	612
Miscellaneous	995
Total Variable Costs	**4,307**
Gross Margin before deducting Forage Costs	**21,463**
Forage Variable Costs (11.0 Stags per hectare @ £201/ha)	3,661
Gross Margin per 200 Stags	**17,802**
Gross Margin per Forage hectare (11 stags/ha)	979
Gross Margin per Forage acre (4.5 stags/ac)	396

The venison price reflects projected sales for 2016 to wholesale buyers and the higher prices being paid for farmed venison by supermarkets. Higher prices will be obtained for direct sales to consumers (e.g. farm shops and farmers' markets) and caterers, but extra costs will normally be incurred.

D. Deer Park

	Per 300 Hinds
Sales:	£
120 Stags (15-18 months) : 55kg dw @ £3.80/kg	25,080
110 Hinds (15-18 months) : 50kg dw @ £3.80/kg	20,900
25 Cull Hinds @ £200	5,000
5 Live Stag Sales @ £1,000	5,000
Less Replacements: 25 hinds @ £350 & 2 stag @ £1500	11,750
Output	**44,230**
Variable Costs:	
Concentrates @ 12.0 tonnes @ £225/tonne	2,700
Vet and Med	510
Miscellaneous	306
Total Variable Costs	**3,516**
Gross Margin before deducting Forage Costs	**40,714**
Forage Variable Costs (3.0 Hinds per hectare @ £82/ha)	8,227
Gross Margin per 300 Hinds	**32,487**
Gross Margin per Forage hectare (3 hinds/ha)	325
Gross Margin per Forage acre (1.2 hinds/ac)	131

Sales are based on skin-on carcases bought by a game dealer/butcher. Forage costs Refer to *Forage* on page 87.

Sources of further information: The British Deer Farmers Association, PO Box 7522, Matlock, DE4 9BR. Tel: 08456 344 758 www.bdfa.co.uk

Acknowledgement: Thanks to – John Fletcher BVMS, PhD, Hon FRCVS, FRAgS

HORSES: LIVERY

The horse industry is now reported to be the second biggest employer in the rural economy. Prior to the economic downturn it was also one of the fastest growing. Over the last 5 years the horse population has declined from its peak. Horse owners have tended to adopt spending reduction behaviours – looking for cheaper services such as DIY instead of part livery. Even so a premium segment of the market also persists, with owners of high disposable income seeking high quality services and facilities. Although there are other equine enterprises that farm businesses can operate, by far the most common is providing accommodation for horses; i.e. livery. There are many different forms of livery and the charges, therefore, vary widely also. This is apart from the effects of local supply and demand, which can lead to large price differences from one area to another. However, three fairly standard forms are offered on farms:

Grass Livery. Keep at grass, preferably with shelter, water supply and secure area to keep tack and store feed. Some grass livery will provide an exercise arena and off-road riding. Charges range from £30-£100 per week.

DIY Livery. The owner still has full care of the horse but has the facilities of a stable, grazing, and in some cases an all-weather exercise arena. The owner is responsible for mucking out, turning out, grooming, exercising and all vet./med. care and the cost of all feed and bedding. Charges range from £35-£110 per week.

Part Livery. As the above, except that the yard manager is responsible for certain tasks, such as turning out and feeding. Charges range from £50-£125.

In addition there is *Full Livery.* The yard supplies a complete service to the horse owner including tasks such as grooming and exercise. Services provided by the yard may be fitted to the needs of a horse/owner. Few farm-based liveries would offer such a high level of management unless there is equine expertise in the family. Full livery charges average £125 per week; with a range of £65-£185.

The above are only guidelines. There is a wide variation both within, and between regions.

Other Costs:

Grazing. Variable costs will average some £65 per horse per year. Average stocking rates are 0·8 ha (2 acres) for the first horse and 0·4 ha (1 acre) for each horse after.

Hay. Average price £4.00 per conventional bale (approximately 20kg) (range £2.5-£6.00), depending on the season. It has to be good quality. Average consumption is one to two bales per horse per week; less in the summer depending on the grass quality/quantity and the work of the horse. Some horses now have haylage; more expensive, dust free and higher fibre and energy/protein levels; less required per head (£6.50 - £8.50/bale)

Concentrate Feed. Can range from almost nil to 3.0-4.0kg per day depending, amongst other factors, on breed, size and intensity of work. Compound feed 35 to 65p per kg.

Bedding. Averages around £12 per stabled horse per week, with some horses stabled year round and others having significant turnout in the summer, which reduces bedding cost. Typical cost £300-£400 per year. Straw might cost only half as much; however, more expensive, but preferable, alternatives (such as wood shavings, shredded paper and hemp fibre) are now increasingly being used.

Vet. and Med. Averages approximately £200 per horse per year. Some yards include worming of the horse in the livery cost.

Rates. Livery is a non-agricultural use, and therefore any buildings being used for the enterprise are liable to business rates.

The supply of livery yards appears to be increasing, from both farms diversifying and other yards setting up. Filling a yard is, consequently, becoming more difficult. The level of service and facilities expected by customers has increased. There is a trend towards greater professionalism in the running and management of livery yards. Livery contracts should be exchanged showing clearly the responsibilities of each party. Comprehensive third party insurance is also important.

To be successful, a livery enterprise needs higher quality facilities than farm livestock. To the owner the horse can be anything from a highly trained athlete to a family pet. Horses are expensive: even modest quality horses cost between £1,500 and £3,000. Good customer relations and an effective security system (including burglar and fire alarms) are crucial to success, as is good market research and effective advertising. Ensuring prompt payment of livery fees is another issue, this can be helped by payment in advance or by direct debit.

A full livery yard will require stables, a secure room to store tack, a vermin-proof hard feed store, storage for hay and bedding, a muck heap, a riding arena and parking provision with room for horse boxes. Planning permission is required for the conversion of an existing building to stabling or the erection of new, purpose-built stables. Permission is also required for construction of an all-weather arena used for training horses and exercising them in bad weather. Hay and straw should be stored away from the stables and downwind of them to minimise the fire risk. A hard standing area with a water supply and good drainage should be provided for grooming and washing down the horses.

Good ventilation in the stables is crucial as horses are prone to respiratory diseases caused by spores and dust. Provision should be made for owners to soak hay in clean water before feeding it, to reduce respiratory problems.

Fences must be sound and free of protruding nails, wire etc. Ideally fields should be fenced using post and rail, but this is expensive. Barbed wire should be avoided wherever possible or should be 'protected' with an offset electrified fence. Fields should be divided into smaller paddocks to reduce the possibility of fighting between incompatible horses and to separate mares and geldings. Paddocks may be divided using two or more strands of electrified tape or rope but wire is not advisable as it is not easily visible to the horse.

Off-road riding opportunities on the farm are a real asset. The farmer may provide riding trails, a jumping paddock, or a cross country course. An all-weather ménage for exercising horses, possibly with floodlighting, is highly desirable, and some livery yards have horse walkers too. Good facilities can be rented out to individuals or organisations such as pony clubs. It is sometimes possible to link up with nearby farms to increase the length of riding tracks available.

Construction Costs. The cost of conversion of existing buildings will depend on their quality; prefabricated hardwood and steel internal stable partitions can be purchased from upwards of £1000 per stable, depending on size and specification. Free standing timber stables cost between £1,000 and £2,000 (plus base), depending on size and quality. As horses are fairly destructive animals (they both kick and chew) better quality stables will often prove more economic in the long run. All weather arenas (20 metres by 40 metres) cost between £20,000 and £50,000; construction is a specialist job as good drainage is essential; a badly constructed arena is worthless.

Contact*:* Further financial information on horse enterprises, including riding schools and equestrian centres, is available in the 'Equine Business Guide', 6th Edition, 2015, edited by Richard Bacon, Warwickshire College, in conjunction with Agro Buiness Consultants http://www.abcbooks.me/

WILD BOAR

Wild Boar is farmed in the UK on about 50 farms, with a population of roughly 1,750 sows. Wild Boar come under the Dangerous Wild Animals Act and farms must be licensed by the Local Authority. The cost of a licence varies greatly between authorities and ranges anywhere from £150 - £700 plus veterinary inspection fees. These have to be renewed annually following a farm inspection with renewal fees at a lower rate. Enclosures must be secure with strong fencing: a minimum height of at least 1.8 metres and most authorities require 30-80cm below ground plus an additional strand of electric fence inside the main fence. The estimated minimum cost of fencing using approved contractors is from £13.50 per metre erected plus the hire of a digger.

Wild Boar live outdoors in groups of up to 10 sows per boar. Large arcs are suitable for a group of gestating sows, or sows running with maturing boarlets. About a hectare would be needed for 5 sows and a boar. They forage but need feeding concentrate and root crops. Gilts mature at 18 months. Farmed sows can give two litters in most years. Young sows produce 2 to 3 boarlets and mature sows 6 to 9. A well-run enterprise should average 7 boarlets per sow per year raised to maturity. Wild boar can live from 12 to 15 years, but in a commercial herd the sows are usually culled at 7 to 8 years. Wild boar take 9 to 18 months to reach a slaughter weight of 75-85 kg. This produces a 45-50 kg carcase.

Capital Costs: Housing and fencing £4,200 per hectare (*£1,700 per acre*); pure-bred adult boar £500-£700; pure-bred in pig sow £350-£500. Labour requirements are low, owing to the 'hands off' nature of wild boar management. One person should manage a herd of 30-40 sows plus fatteners.

In spite of the demand for wild boar meat, there is no organised marketing system and producers develop their own outlets. There are some wholesale butchers and game dealers who will take whole carcases, but many producers organise their own processing and arrange their own retailing.

Finished Boarlets per Sow per Year	6	7	9
Finished Carcase Weight (over 15 months)	45	45	50
Price per kg deadweight	5.00	6.00	7.00
Sales:		£	
Meat sales per Sow per Year	1,350	1,890	3,150
Less Depreciation per Sow per Year	35	35	35
Output per Sow	**1,315**	**1,855**	**3,115**
Variable Costs:			
Concentrates sow		337	
fatteners (0.15kg each at £300/t)	324	315	405
Other Feed		180	
Bedding		40	
Vet, Med and Licence		100	
Miscellaneous (inc. Water and Electricity)		20	
Total Variable Costs per Sow	**1,001**	**992**	**1,082**
Gross Margin per Sow	**315**	**864**	**2,034**
Gross Margin per Hectare (5 Sows/Ha)	**1,574**	**4,319**	**10,169**

1. Cost of sow £350, cull value £200, active herd life 5 years, plus share of boar and 5% mortality
2. Including share of boar
3. Bought-in waste vegetables, these are necessary for wild boar.

GOAT DAIRYING

Performance Level	Low	Average	High
Milk Yield (litres) per Goat	600	800	1,000
Sales:	£	£	£
Milk Value	390.0	520.0	650.0
Value of Kids	2.8	3.6	3.6
Less Livestock Depreciation	36.8	36.8	36.8
Output per doe	**356.0**	**486.8**	**616.8**
Variable Costs:			
Concentrates	101.3	153.0	213.8
Miscellaneous (inc. Vet and Med)	75.0	75.0	75.0
Total Variable Costs	**176.3**	**228.0**	**288.8**
Gross Margin per Doe, before	**179.8**	**258.8**	**328.1**
deducting Forage Variable Costs			
Forage Variable Costs	10.4	13.8	17.3
Gross Margin per Doe	**169.4**	**245.0**	**310.8**
Stocking Rate (Goats per Forage Hectare			
(acre) - zero-grazed system)	10.0 (4.0)	12.0 (4.9)	15.0 (6.1)
Gross Margin per Forage Hectare	1,694	2,940	4,662
Gross Margin per Forage Acre	685	1,190	1,887

1. *Yield:* Per 300 day lactation, kidding each year. Autumn kidders tend to yield less.

2. *Price:* 65p per litre; 60p to 70p (+) with the higher prices being in the winter months (November to February) and the lower end of the range in the summer. 12.5% solids delivered.

3. *Kid(s):* Prolificacy relates to age, breed, seasonality and feed level. Assumptions: low 140%; average and high 180%. There is very little trade in kids for meat (£2 per kid assumed).

4. *Culls and Replacements:* Replacements at £200-240/head; culls £35 to £45, average productive life 4.5 – 5 years. Bucks: 1 per 40-50 does. Does normally mate in autumn; gestation 150 days; young goats can be mated from 6 months.

5. *Concentrates:* Average 0.85kg concentrate per litre (higher for 1,000 litre producers), at £225 per tonne.

6. *Forage:* Average 0.5 kg DM forage per litre at £105 per tonne DM (Refer to Forage Section page 87). Goats can be grazed but are normally storage fed to avoid problems with worms, fencing, milk taints and pneumonia. Farmers able to produce maize silage will have a better forage conversion ratio. 10% wastage has been included.

7. *Miscellaneous:* Bedding £30, vet and med. £25 (includes treatment for out-of-season breeding, vaccination against Johnes), sundries £20.

8. *Labour:* 1 full-time person per 150 to 200 goats, dependent on technology employed.

9. *Markets:* Herd sizes in the UK range from 50 to 3,000 milking does. Average herd size is growing as established producers expand. Successful businesses have been built on producer processing and retailing, as bulk purchasers of goats' milk are few and far between. Prolificacy and technical improvements allow higher annual growth than the market and there is a cycle in milk and stock prices.

SHEEP DAIRYING

Performance Level	Low	Average	High
Milk Yield (litres) per Ewe per Year	150	375	450
Sales:	£	£	£
Milk Value	173	431	518
Value of Lambs	64	64	64
Wool	2	2	2
Less Livestock Depreciation	27	27	27
Output per Ewe	**212**	**471**	**557**
Variable Costs:			
Concentrates		199	
Miscellaneous (inc. Vet and Med)		25	
Total Variable Costs (excluding forage)		**224**	
Gross Margin per Ewe, before deducting Forage Variable Costs	**-11**	**247**	**334**
Forage Variable Costs		18.3	
Gross Margin per Ewe	**-30**	**229**	**315**
Stocking Rate (Ewes with Lambs per forage Hectare (acre))		11 (4.5)	
Gross Margin per Hectare	-327	2,519	3,468

1. *Price*: 115p per litre at farm gate (range from 100p-120p per litre).

2. *Lambing %:* 175%. Assume a 300 Friesland ewe flock. Retain 60 ewe lambs for flock replacements. Sell 390 finished lambs reared from 2 days old (inc. 15% mortality) at £40. If meat-type terminal sires used then cross-bred lamb values increase to £65.

3. *Cull ewes:* Assumed 20% culled at £50 per head (average, including mortality).

4. *Concentrates:* Milking ewes: 200 days at 1.5 kg/head/day, 100 days at 0.5 kg/head/day; cost £200-£250/tonne. Ewe lamb replacements and artificially reared finished lambs at £75/head.

5. *Forage costs:* Quality silage: 1 tonne per milking ewe (or hay equivalent). Grazing: early grass in March/April; good grazing on leys or pasture; similar for dry stock and lambs. For details on *forage* refer to page 87.

   Fixed Costs per Ewe: Labour (paid) £90; Power and Machinery £33; Property Costs £17; Other £15; Total, excluding Finance and Rent, £155.

   Capital Costs of Equipment: Complete milking unit for 300 ewes (including yokes, bulk tank, dairy equipment, installation): £15,000-£30,000. A small 50 ewe unit can be put together for £10,000-£12,000. Any building works would be additional to the above costs.

Acknowledgements: thanks to - Anthony Hyde, FRICS, FBIAC, FRAgS and the British Dairying Association.

ANGORA GOATS

Angora goats produce mohair; angora rabbits produce angora; cashgora is produced by angora cross dairy goats; cashmere is produced by improved feral goats (valuable 'down' has to be separated from guard hairs; thus, with cashmere production, 'yield of down' must not be confused with 'weight of clip' as percentage down is low and can vary widely). Goat meat is sometimes called 'chevon'.

The UK angora goat population is thought to have reduced to about 1,000 animals which produce an estimated annual clip of 5 tonnes. The figures below are for a commercial enterprise. There is a strong demand for angora goats from small holders and smaller farmers which is making stock sales buoyant. Many UK angora flocks are kept on a semi-commercial or hobby basis, in which case different criteria may apply – does retained longer, mortality rates lower, doe/buck ratio different. There has been exceptional world demand for mohair for two years but the buoyant prices are adversely affected by the South African Rand:US dollar exchange rate. There is a world shortage of mohair. The figures used in the calculations are based on prices in 2015. Much of the UK clip is exported by the producers' co-operative, British Mohair Marketing, to South Africa where it is graded and sold through the Cape Mohair auctions. The rest of the UK annual clip is processed for other enterprises in UK and for hand spinning where higher prices can be achieved.

Performance:	Per Doe
Kids per Doe per Year	1.5
Fibre: Doe/Buck, 2 clips, 2.5 & 4kg/clip respectively	5.3 kg
Kids (1.5), first and second clips	5.0 kg
Wethers/Replacement Does (0.95), third clip	3.3 kg

	£
Fibre Sales per doe:	
Doe/Buck: 5.3kg @ £8.50/kg	45.2
Kids: 5.0kg @ £15.0/kg	74.3
Wethers/Replacements: 3.3kg @ £9.2/kg	30.6
Stock Sales:	
0.6 female kids sold for breeding @ £200 each	110.0
Wethers: 0.8 males sold for meat @ £50 each	37.5
Culls: 0.14 does @ £50 each	7.3
Skin Sales:	8.9
Less Replacements	30.9
Output per Doe	**282.9**
Variable Costs:	
Concentrates	60.4
Vet and Med	8.2
Miscellaneous	18.4
Total Variable Costs per Doe	**87.0**
Gross Margin per Doe before Forage Costs	**195.9**
Forage Variable Costs	30.7
Gross Margin per Doe	**165.2**
Gross Margin per Forage hectare	792.8
Gross Margin per Forage acre	321

Angora goats require more management than sheep. Fencing requirements are similar but housing costs rather higher. Margins are particularly sensitive to the value and number of breeding stock sold, yield and value of fibre, kidding percentage and meat values. There is a market for meat from older animals but no reliable market has yet been developed specifically for younger animals. Angoras are probably most successfully run as a subsidiary enterprise on a farm rather than a stand-alone operation.

1. 1.5 kids born alive per doe mated; 2% mortality to each clip. Of 0.7 surviving doe kids, the majority (0.5) are sold for breeding, the remainder (0.2) are retained for replacements. Culls (0.15) and casualties are equal to the number of replacements (unless the flock size is changing). Progeny are sold after 2 clips for breeding or after 3 clips for meat. Stock may be retained for further shearing. This has become more common, as the demand for breeding stock is small, fibre quality has improved and there is little market for meat.

2. The data for Breeding Does includes output and inputs for breeding bucks. Assumes 25 does to one buck.

3. Angora goats are usually clipped twice a year. Yield increases over first four clips, but quality decreases with age. Prices can be volatile, being dependent on fashion and on the world market dominated by South Africa and Texas. Demand and prices are highest for the high quality kid fibre <25 microns in diameter.

   The following yields and prices have been used:-

   Clip 1 = 1.2 kg at £15.00 per kg; clip 2 = 2.1 kg at £15.00 per kg; clip 3 = 3.5 kg at £9.20 per kg. Adult doe: 2.5 kg, adult buck 4.0 kg at £8.50 per kg.

   British Mohair Marketing arranges a collection once a year, currently in September. Since 2010, the entire collected clip has been containerised and shipped to South Africa where it has been sold by auction by Cape Mohair Ltd. The prices thus achieved were considerably better than those previously attained in the UK and easily covered the increased handling expenses. Membership of BMM costs £30 and there is a handling/marketing levy of £1.10/kg. (Some producers improve their return by processing and using the fibre themselves or selling to local spinners. Commercial processing costs are significant: combing about £3.50 per kg and spinning about £20 per kg).

4. *Stock sales.* Breeding stock in commercial flocks are culled after seven years on average. Subsequent shearing stock culled after a further 4 clips. Value of all cull stock: £50 each. Depending on quality, the skin can be worth £10 before curing or up to £120 after curing. Replacement costs: does, £200; bucks, £400. Shearing stock, £20 (as transfer from breeding enterprise). Show quality stock command a premium.

5. *Skin Sales:* From cull does and males sold for meat @ £10.00

6. *Concentrates.* Quantities: Kids - 50 kg to clip 2, 15 kg to clip 3; Adults - breeding adults 90 kg per year, shearlings 40 kg per year.

7. *Veterinary* costs can be high and include vaccinations, worming & foot trimming. Membership of disease control schemes (MV/CAE) or Scrapie monitoring will be extra.

8. *Miscellaneous* costs include £2.50 to £3.50 per shearing per head (it may be more) and bedding materials.

9. *Forage:* 4.8 does per hectare at £147 per hectare (grass), refer to *forage* on page 87.

Contact: *British Angora Goat Society*: www.britishangoragoats.org.uk British Mohair Marketing: www.mohairmarketing.org.uk

Acknowledgements: thanks to - Stephen Whitley, Corrymoor Angoras, Stockland, Honiton, Devon EX14 9DY socks@corrymoor.com www.corrymoor.com

OSTRICHES

Introduction

Ostrich production in the UK is 25 years old. Production is limited to a few small individual farms, selling most meat through farmers' markets and restaurants. There is minimal processing infrastructure in the UK. Slaughter is carried out under contract in dedicated ostrich plants and red meat slaughter plants with a ratite (flightless bird) license.

Ostriches are produced primarily for meat, with their skins (for leather), fat and feathers also providing revenue potential. Skins are generally sold in minimum numbers of 200 so it can require long-term storage to build up sufficient numbers.

Adult breeding stock are normally kept in trios of one male and two females, but pairs and colonies are not unusual. A trio requires about 0.2 ha (0.5 acre) well drained land and must be able to run. A stout hedge or smooth wire fence of 1.7 metres high should surround the enclosure. Adult birds need shelter from wind and rain, and a dry floor on which to sleep. Domesticated ostrich are generally docile and easily handled. There are two systems costed here, the production of chicks from trios, and fattening the chicks.

Production

Laying Bird Trios

Performance Level	Low	Medium	High
Eggs – *per hen per year*	45	60	70
Hatching - %	65%	75%	85%
Surviving Chicks - %	50%	70%	85%
Total Chicks per hen	15	32	51
Financial Data per Trio			
Sales:			
Chicks Per Year	29	63	101
Chick Income	461	992	1,593
Output per Trio	**461**	**992**	**1,593**
Variable Costs:			
Concentrates	564	784	907
Miscellaneious	35	35	35
Bird Depreciation	85	85	85
Total Variable Costs	**684**	**904**	**1,027**
Gross Margin per Trio	**-223**	**88**	**567**
Stocking Rate 5 Trios per hectare			
Gross Margin per Ha	**-1,114**	**441**	**2,833**

Notes:

1. *Chick Income:* Chicks sold out at £15.75 per head

2. *Concentrate feed:* £245/tonne. Low production birds eat 2.4 tonnes per trio, average = 3.2 and high production birds 3.7 tonnes/trio

3. *Miscellaneous:* includes vet & med., forage etc.

4. *Bird Depreciation costs:* replacement for a trio £1,485 over 15 year's productivity less £210 cull value

Meat is the highest value, especially if marketed into the restaurant sector. This clearly requires marketing expertise. Doubling meat yields and halving the time to reach slaughter transforms the economics as is shown below. Many systems involve a high cost building and fencing layout which should be taken into consideration with the economics of the gross margins shown here.

Slaughter Birds

Performance Level	Low	Average	High
Days to Slaughter	425	300	220
Sales:	£	£	£
Meat:	300	350	400
Value of Skin	53	53	53
Less Day Old Chick	16	16	16
Output per Bird	337	387	437
Variable Costs:			
Concentrates	192	174	101
Other Rearing Costs	110	91	60
Slaughter, Processing etc.	79	79	79
Marketing	6	6	6
Total Variable Costs	387	350	245
Gross Margin per Bird	-50	37	192
Gross Margin per year per bird	-43	45	318
Stocking Rate 5 birds per hectare			
Gross Margin per Ha	-213	227	1,592

Notes:

1. *Meat:* £10/kg, 30kg, 35kg and 40kg meat for low to high performance levels.
2. *£53 per hide,*
3. *Chicks* bought in at £15.75 each (see schedule above) but varies from £10 to £25
4. *Concentrates:* Price of feed rises as performance rises (£245, £320 and £360/t) but consumption per bird falls from 2kg/day to 1.12kg/day.
5. *Other Costs:* includes depreciation of site, vet. & med. and miscellaneous

Contact: British Domesticated Ostrich Association (BDOA), 33 Eden Grange, Little Corby, Carlisle, CA4 8QW. (Tel.: 01228 562 946); www.ostrich.org.uk

CAMELIDS

Llamas, alpacas, guanacos and vicunas are collectively known as South American Camelids. Originally they all came from Central America. They are all members of the same family and are related to camels. Camelids are herd animals and should not be kept in isolation but will live happily with other animals.

Llamas

The llama is the largest of the Camelids, weighing up to 180kg (400lbs) and standing 1.25m (4ft) at shoulder height. Llamas are strong animals traditionally used as pack animals and kept in the UK for trekking or pets. They have a life span of 15-20 years. They produce offspring for 10-15 years.

Llamas can be kept at stocking rates of 10-12/ha (4-5/acre). They are generally hardy animals but benefit from an open fronted shelter. They eat grass and hay, with occasional supplements. They can be bought from a few hundred pounds.

Alpacas

Alpacas are smaller with a shoulder height of 1m (3ft) and weigh around 70kg (155lb). They produce an outstanding quality fleece. Their fibres are very fine and exceptionally strong. An annual shearing will produce an average fleece of 0.7 to 5kg. The saddle or prime fleece part of the shearing will, when skirted (primary clean), sell to trade processors for;

- Baby Alpaca £8 per kg coloured, £12/kg white (21 micron or below)
- Fine Alpaca £5 per kg coloured, £8 per kg white (22-26 micron)
- Coarse Alpaca £0.40 - £1.00 per kg (27+ micron)
- Retail prices are substantially higher, typically £16-35 per kg

Alpacas require shearing annually with Huacaya (95% of UK alpacas) having a crimpy staple style suitable mostly for knitting yarms and Suri with longer curly locks like a Wensleydale sheep suitable for most woven cloth and some knitting.

Alpacas should be kept at 12–20 per hectare (5-8/acre). They are hardy animals well suited to the UK climate, but require shelter. They graze all year, with additional hay and a daily mineral supplement for breeding stock. Their feed and maintenance costs are similar to that of lowland sheep however they so no suffer from foot rot and are unlikely to be fly struck as they are clean under the tail and do not require tail trimming.

An alpaca can cost anything from £200 for non-breeding stock and £500 to £10,000 for female breeding stock. Fibre producing wethers typically cost £200 for coloured rising to £500 for white. Price will vary according to genetics, age, fertility, fibre quality and colour. The alpaca gestation period is 11-12 months.

The earning potential of an Alpaca is dictated by the quality of its fleece and through breeding. The UK alpaca meat market remains small and is generally associated with other on-farm meat products. Typical terminal prices are £60-£75 per live animal. Animals with low quality fleeces may have a value as pets, flock guards or tourist attractions. Alpaca fleece is a luxury fibre thus only the highest quality fleeces and stock command good prices.

Breeding and Fleece Production (per alpaca)

Performance Level	Average	High
	£	£
Fleece Weight (Kg)	2.00	3.00
Fleece Sales	14	27
Progeny Sales	371	421
Less Depreciation and Purchases	257	257
Output	**128**	**191**
Variable Costs:		
Feed Supplement Costs	30	30
Vet & Med	25	25
Shearing Costs	12	12
Miscellaneious Costs	15	15
Total Variable Costs (excl. forage)	**82**	**82**
Gross Margin per Alpaca, before		
deducting Forage Variable Costs	47	109
Forage Variable Costs	10	10
Purchased Hay	48	48
Gross Margin per Alpaca	**-11**	**51**
Alpcas per hectare	15 (6.1)	15 (6.1)
Gross Margin per Forage Hectare (Acre)	**-166** *(-67)*	**771** *(312)*

Notes:

1. *Fleece Sales:* Average performance fleece price £7.00/ kg. High performance fleece price £9.00/ kg.

2. *Progeny Sales:* Non breeding stock sold at £250/head, breeding geldings sold at £750/head, 25% breeding stock at average performance level, 35% at high performance level.

3. *Feed Costs:* 65g per day at £1.25 per kg.

4. *Bulk Feed:* 1 small hay bale per month

GRAZING LIVESTOCK UNITS (GLU)

Dairy cows	1.00	Lowland ewes	0.11
Beef cows (excl. calf)	0.75	Upland ewes	0.08
Heifers in calf (rearing)	0.80	Hill ewes	0.06
Bulls	0.65	Breeding ewe hoggets:	
		½ to 1 year	0.06
Other cattle (excl. intensive beef):		Other sheep, over 1 year	0.08
0-1 year old	0.34	Store lambs, under 1 year	0.04
1-2 years old	0.65	Rams	0.08
2 years old and over	0.80		
Breeding sows	0.44	Broilers	0.0017
Gilts in pig	0.20	Other table chicken	0.004
Maiden gilts	0.18	Turkeys	0.005
Boars	0.35	Ducks, geese, other poultry	0.003
Other pigs	0.17	Horses	0.80
Cocks, hens, pullets in lay	0.017	Milch goats	0.16
Pullets, 1 week to point of lay	0.003	Other goats	0.11

Source: as advised by DEFRA for the Farm Business Survey.

1. *Total livestock units on a farm* should be calculated by multiplying the above ratios by the monthly livestock numbers averaged over the whole year.

2. *The ratios are based on feed requirements.* Strictly speaking, when calculating stocking density, allowances should also be made for differences in output (e.g. milk yield per cow or liveweight gain per head), breed (e.g. Friesians v. Jerseys) and quantities of non-forage feed consumed.

FORAGE VARIABLE COSTS

Grassland	1-2 year Ley		Intensive 3-5 year Ley		Long Term Ley		Improved Permanent Pasture		Low Input Pasture	
Yield t/ha *(ac)*	50	*(20)*	47	*(19)*	42	*(17)*	35	*(14)*	25	*(10)*
Years Ley	2		4		7		-		-	
Kg/Ha *(units/acre)*										
N	250	*(199)*	200	*(159)*	150	*(120)*	100	*(80)*	50	*(40)*
P	35	*(28)*	33	*(26)*	29	*(23)*	25	*(20)*	18	*(14)*
K	120	*(96)*	113	*(90)*	101	*(80)*	84	*(67)*	60	*(48)*
Costs £/Ha *(£/ac)*										
Seed *per year*	70	*(28)*	35	*(14)*	22	*(9)*	16	*(6)*	3	*(1)*
Fertiliser	251	*(102)*	211	*(86)*	169	*(68)*	123	*(50)*	73	*(30)*
Sprays	18	*(7)*	13	*(5)*	10	*(4)*	8	*(3)*	6	*(2)*
Total £/Ha/Yr	338	*(137)*	260	*(105)*	201	*(82)*	147	*(60)*	82	*(33)*
cost £/t fresh weight	6.77		5.53		4.79		4.21		3.29	

Other Forages	Maize	Clover Ley	Kale	Swedes
Yield t/ha (t/acre)	40 (16)	40 (16)	45 (18)	70 (28)
Seed	175 (71)	29 (12)	58 (23)	172 (70)
Fertiliser	107 (43)	39 (16)	142 (57)	136 (55)
Sprays	50 (20)	18 (7)	50 (20)	54 (22)
Total	332 (134)	86 (35)	250 (101)	362 (147)
Cost £/t fresh weight	8.29	2.14	5.55	5.17

	Fodder Beet	Forage Rape	Maincrop Turnips	Stubble Turnips
Yield t/ha (t/acre)	70 (28)	35 (14)	65 (26)	35 (14)
Seed	133 (54)	28 (11)	56 (23)	19 (8)
Fertiliser	183 (74)	101 (41)	136 (55)	111 (45)
Sprays	162 (66)	26 (10)	53 (21)	28 (11)
Total	478 (194)	155 (63)	245 (99)	157 (64)
Cost £/t fresh weight	6.83	4.43	3.77	4.49

Forage Notes

1. *Seed costs:* vary according to the proportion of permanent pasture and length of leys.

2. *Fertiliser* is assumed to come partially from manure as well as bagged fertiliser. It is often less on permanent pasture, depending on management style which also affects stocking rates and productive levels per animal.

3. *Contract work* on maize, silage and cultivations: Refer to Page 196.

4. *Labour:* forage and conservation labour, pages 173

5. *Conservation machinery:* page 190.

6. *Standing maize* crops are typically sold for £750 to £920/ha (£300-370/acre) but can be over £1,000/ha (£400/acre), depending on the potential yield of the crop and local supply and demand which has become volatile with local demand from anaerobic digestion plants.

7. An appropriate combination of these forage gross margins is used to calculate the forage costs of all the grazing livestock margins throughout the book. In fact, for simplicity, only the grass (appropriate combination of all 5 types), maize and stubble turnips are used. Each livestock gross margin explains which forage crops are used.

8. *Plastic wrap* for bagged silage = £4.80/ round bale (120cm).

9. *Net wrap* for bales = £0.54/round bale.

Whole Crop (feed wheat). Variable costs are as for combined crop (page 5) plus contract harvesting and clamping at £168 per ha (£68/ac.). Fresh yield averages 27.5 tonnes per ha (11 t/ac.) harvested in late June at 35% dry matter. Urea treatment (for higher dry matter) for whole-crop alkalage: £7.80/treated tonne. For urea treated grain, add £16.00 per tonne. Standing wheat auctions for about £1,000 per hectare (£400/acre). This is based on 8.5t/ha at £135 which is the opportunity cost of harvesting as grain less harvesting (£87/Ha), carting (est. £20/ha) and storage costs.

TOTAL COSTS OF PRESERVED FORAGE

Cost of Preserved Forage	Clamped Grass Silage	Wrapped Grass Silage	Hay	Clamped Maize	Grazed Grass
Variable Costs £/Ha	260	260	260	332	260
Operational Costs					
Mowing		30	30		
Turning		16	32		
Raking		16	16		
Harvesting & Clamping	336	-	-	170	
Drilling	8	8	8	45	8
Land Preparation	29	29	29	116	29
Fertilising & Spraying	26	26	26	26	26
Land Rent	250	250	250	250	250
Land based Costs £/Ha	908	634	650	938	572
Less Basic payment	168	168	168	168	168
Total Costs £/fresh t	17.62	11.10	11.48	18.34	9.63
Fresh DM	18%	18%	18%	30%	18%
Preserved DM	25%	30%	85%	30%	18%
Sub-total £/t Preserved	24.48	18.50	54.22	18.34	9.63
Baling £/bale	0	3	3		
Wrap £/bale	0.0	4.7	0.0		
sheet £/t	1.00			1.2	
Bale Weight	1000	600	400		
Total Costs £/t Preserved	**25.48**	**31.40**	**61.72**	**19.54**	**9.63**
Total Costs £/t dry weight	**102**	**105**	**73**	**65**	**53**

Total Forage Cost Notes:

1. *Variable Costs*: Linked to previous schedule, grass silage using 'Intensive 3-5 year'.

2. *Operational Costs:* Taken from contractor's charges, page 196, land preparation and drilling divided by length of rotation.

3. *All costs* are charged to the forage, despite possible late season grazing.

4. Both *land rent and the Basic Payment Scheme* costs and incomes are included in this schedule. Depending on its use, will depend on whether you should include it in your costings. But if one is in, the other should be in most cases.

5. *Grass Silage costs:* Based on 2 cuts in the season and grass costs based on a 4-year ley.

Sale Value of hay and (far less common because of its bulk) silage vary widely according to the region and season (supply/demand situation), quality and time of year:

a.   *Hay* (pick-up baled) has an average ex-farm sale value of £50 to £120 per tonne, average £70. Seed hay £100 to £120 per tonne and £70-£90 per tonne for meadow hay; prices are higher in the west than the east and more after a dry summer (giving low yields of grass). Prices tend to be higher for horses as quality is higher. Big bale hay is £20 to £30/tonne cheaper.

b.   *Grass silage* is typically about £36 a tonne delivered (higher when forage is very short in an area and *vice versa*), maize silage approx. £32 a tonne.

Relative Costs of Grazing, Conserved Grass, etc.

	£/t Fresh Weight	Yield DM tonnes/ha (acre)		Cost per tonne DM (£)	MJ per kg DM	Pence per MJ of ME in DM
Grazed Grass	9.63	7.6	(3.1)	£53	12.8	0.42
Grass Silage	25.48	7.6	(3.1)	£102	10.9	0.93
Big Bale Silage	31.40	7.6	(3.1)	£105	10.8	0.97
Hay	61.72	7.6	(3.1)	£73	8.8	0.83
Kale (direct drilled)	16.66	6.8	(2.7)	£111	11	1.01
Forage Turnips (d.d.)	11.46	6.8	(2.8)	£109	10.2	1.07
Brewer's Grains	55	-		£229	11.7	1.96
Concentrates	220	-		£256	12.8	2.00

1. In interpreting the above figures for use in planning feed use on farm, it is important to remember that own land, labour and capital for equipment are included here for home-produced fodder but not for purchased feed, and much more storage is required.

2. The consumption of fodder is limited by its bulk although this very much depends upon its quality/digestibility.

3. The cost of forage will vary enormously depending on growing conditions, soil fertility and type, intensity of farming practice and management ability.

3. PIGS, POULTRY, TROUT, RABBIT

PIGS

Breeding and Rearing *(to 35kg liveweight)*

Performance Level	Average		High	
	per sow	per pig	per sow	per pig
	£	£	£	£
Weaners: (ave) 24.3 (1) @ £57	1388	57.00		
(high) 27.0 (2) @ £57			1539	57.00
Less Livestock Depreciation	70	2.80	82	2.95
Output	1318	54.20	1457	54.05
Variable Costs:				
Food	672	26.79	683	24.65
Miscellaneous	96	3.82	115	4.15
Total Variable Costs	768	30.61	798	28.80
Gross Margin (per year)	**550**	**23.60**	**659**	**25.26**

1. *Weaners per sow:* - average: 10.9 weaned per litter, 2.30 litters per year, 3% rearing losses = 24.3 weaners sold per sow per year. Productivity has improved markedly in the UK pig sector over the last few years.

2. *Weaners per sow:* - high: 11.8 weaned per litter, 2.35 litters per year, 2.5% rearing losses = 27.0 weaners sold per sow per year. For Outdoor Breeding performance figures see page 95.

3. *Price:* assumed pig cycle average. (See General Prices on page 93). Prices for 35kg weaners have varied from £15 to £60 during the past decade. Prices are currently relatively poor in line with finished pig prices. Values between £45 and £50 per head are forecast for the short to medium term.

4. *Average livestock depreciation* assumes an in-pig gilt purchase price of £200, a cull value per sow of £90 and a 52% replacement rate (i.e. approximately 4.5 litters per sow life). Sow mortality 4%. Boars (1 per 24 sows) purchased at £750 (40% a year replacement), sold at £85. 'High' compared with 'Average': higher gilt purchase prices, higher replacement rate and slightly fewer sows per boar assumed.

5. *Food:* total food per sow of 2.60 tonnes breaks down as:

	Tonnes	Value £/t	Total Cost
Sow	1.35	235	317
Boar	0.05	235	12
Weaner feed	1.20	285	343
Total	*2.60*	*258*	*672*

High performance: lower sow feed but extra piglet rearing feed for additional weaners. Piglets weaned at average 3.75 weeks, 7.5kg weight.

6. *Miscellaneous Average:* vet. and med. £33, transport £12, straw and bedding £18, miscellaneous £15, electricity and gas £11, and water £7.

7. *Direct Labour Cost* per sow: average £195, good £160; per weaner: average £7.90, good £5.70.   This figure does not include labour used for 'overhead' activities – repairs etc. For further fixed costs information see page 218.

8. *Building Costs:* see page 228.

Feeding (from 35 kg liveweight): per pig

Average Performance	Pork £	Cutter £	Bacon £
Sale Value..	92.00	106.60	120.10
Less Weaner Cost	57.00	57.00	57.00
Mortality Charge...............................	1.50	1.60	1.70
Output	33.50	48.00	61.40
Variable Costs:			
Food...	33.20	42.10	50.60
Miscellaneous..	7.00	7.50	8.00
Total Variable Costs	40.20	49.60	58.60
Gross Margin	**-6.70**	**-1.60**	**2.80**
Liveweight (kg)...	85	98	110
Deadweight (kg)..	63	73.5	84
Killing Out %..	74%	75%	76%
Price per Deadweight (p).............................	146	145	143
Price per Liveweight (p)...............................	108.2	108.8	109.2
Food Conversion Rate.................................	2.55	2.62	2.70
Food per Pig (kg)...	128	165	203
Average Cost of Food per tonne (£)	£260	£255	£250
Food Cost per Kg l/w Gain (p).....................	66.30	66.81	67.50
Liveweight Gain per Day (kg)......................	0.77	0.8	0.83
Feeding Period (weeks)...............................	9.3	11.3	12.9
Mortality (%)..	2.6	2.8	3.0
Direct Labour Costs per Pig (£)...................	4.10	5.00	5.70

High Performance (same pig price)

Food Conversion Rate.................................	2.25	2.32	2.4
Food per Pig (kg)...	113	146	180
Food Cost per Pig (£5/t less than ave.).........	28.69	36.54	44.10
Food Cost per Kg l/w Gain (p).....................	57.38	58.00	58.80
Gross Margin per Pig	**-2.30**	**4.10**	**9.80**
Direct Labour Costs per Pig........................	3.20	3.90	4.50

1. *Weaner cost* assumes on farm transfer. If purchased (i.e., feeding only) transport and purchasing costs have to be added: these are very variable but average about £2.00 per weaner.

2. *Average of home-mixed and purchased compounds:* There can be big variations in feed costs per tonne between farms, according to whether the food is purchased as compounds or home-mixed, bought in bulk or in bags, size of unit, etc.

3. *Labour:* see page 173.

4. *Building Costs:* see page 232.

5.   *Sensitivity Analysis.* The effect of changes in important variables are as follows:

Change in Gross Margin (£)	Porker	Cutter	Baconer
Price: 5p per kg dw difference	3.15	3.68	4.20
Food Cost per tonne: £10 difference	1.28	1.65	2.03
Food Conversion Rate: 0.1 difference	1.30	1.61	1.88

Combined Breeding, Rearing, and Feeding: per pig

	Pork £		Cutter £		Bacon £	
Performance Level*	Ave.	High	Ave.	High	Ave.	High
Sale Value	92.00	91.80	106.60	106.60	120.10	120.10
Sow and Boar Deprcn	2.80	2.95	2.80	2.95	2.80	2.95
Mortality Charge	1.50	1.40	1.60	1.50	1.70	1.60
Output	**87.70**	**87.45**	**102.20**	**102.15**	**115.60**	**115.55**
Food	59.99	53.35	68.89	61.15	77.39	68.75
Miscellaneous	10.82	11.15	11.32	11.65	11.82	12.15
Total Variable Costs	**70.81**	**64.50**	**80.21**	**72.80**	**89.21**	**80.90**
Gross Margin per Pig	**16.90**	**22.96**	**22.00**	**29.36**	**26.40**	**34.66**
Gross Margin per Sow	**424**	**636**	**552**	**813**	**663**	**960**
Labour Costs per Pig	11.99	8.92	12.89	9.62	13.59	10.22
Labour Costs per Sow	301	247	324	266	341	283

*   Performance levels refer to breeding and rearing differences as on the previous 2 pages and, for feeding, differences in food conversion rate, food costs and labour cost only.

Prices - General

Pig prices are notoriously difficult to predict. Over the last four years the GB average pig price (DAPP Eurospec) has ranged from 100p per kg deadweight to almost 170ppkg. The vast majority of UK pigs are taken to baconer weight. The level shown in the finisher margins for baconers above, of 143p, is an estimated average for late 2015 through 2016. In practice there is likely to be considerable variation around this level. The price shown is somewhat above the prevailing price at the time of writing (summer 2015). UK values have been pressured by the strength of Sterling and plentiful pigmeat supplies (both in the UK and EU). These factors are likely to persist through the budgeting period, although the worst effects are predicted to decline slightly as time goes on.

Further Performance Data

Source: AHDB Performance Data – 12 months to March 2015

All Breeding	Performance Level		
	Average	Top Third*	Top 10%*
Replacement rate (%)	52.2	54.4	57.3
Sow and gilt mortality (%)	5.0	5.0	3.2
Litters per sow per year	2.28	2.37	2.40
Pigs reared per litter	11.2	11.9	12.4
Pigs reared per sow per year	25.5	28.1	29.8
Weight of pigs produced (kg)	7.1	7.2	7.3
Average weaning age (days)	26.5	26.7	26.8
Sow feed per sow per year (tonnes)	1.34	1.38	1.44
Feed per pig reared (kg)	52	49	48
Average number in herd	573	618	491

* selected on basis of pigs reared per sow per year.

Rearing	Average	Top Third*	Top 10%*
Weight of pigs at start (kg)	7.5	7.3	7.3
Weight of pigs produced (kg)	37.3	35.6	27.3
Mortality (%)	2.6	2.3	2.1
Feed conversion ratio	1.75	1.55	1.34
Daily Gain (g)	494	504	443
Feeding period (days)	61	55	44

Feeding	Average	Top Third*	Top 10%*
Weight of pigs at start (kg)	36.8	32.2	23.0
Weight of pigs produced (kg)	108.3	108.2	104.4
Killing-out %	82.2	82.1	79.4
Carcass weight of pigs produced (kg)	76%	76%	76%
Mortality (%)	2.9	2.9	3.0
Feed conversion ratio	2.65	2.36	2.15
Daily Gain (g)	838	825	821
Feeding period (days)	88	94	101

* selected on basis of feed cost per kg liveweight gain.

Feed conversion ratio for rearing and feeding combined, from 7.5kg to 105kg liveweight is approximately 2.40.

Outdoor v Indoor Performance

Breeding	Outdoor	Indoor
Replacement rate (%)	48.0	52.2
Sow and gilt mortality (%)	3.3	5.0
Litters per sow per year	2.21	2.28
Pigs reared per litter	9.7	11.2
Pigs reared per sow per year	21.4	25.5
Weight of pigs produced (kg)	6.9	7.1
Average weaning age (days)	26.3	26.5
Sow feed per sow per year (tonnes)	1.61	1.34
Feed per pig reared (kg)	75.4	52.5
Average number in herd	851	573

1. *Stocking Rate for outdoor pigs* is mainly between 12 and 25 per hectare (5 and 10 per acre), 20 (8) being the most common. Good drainage is essential. A low rainfall and mild climate are also highly desirable. In 2003, MLC's Agrosoft put the cost of establishing a sow herd on a green-field site at £1,800 per sow place for an indoor unit and about £600 per sow place for an outdoor unit.

2. *Data on the split* of indoor and outdoor herds is hard to come by. However, it is thought that about 40% of the UK breeding sow herd is now kept outdoors. A somewhat smaller proportion (probably <10%) of pigs are finished outdoors.

Further costing information can be found in 'Pig Production in England 2013-14' produced by Askham Bryan College, York on behalf of Rural Business Research. See www.ruralbusinessresearch.co.uk

Acknowledgement: The main data source for the margins within the Pigs section is the AHDB Pork performance data, but the pig and feed prices are the author's responsibility.

EGG PRODUCTION

Brown egg layers; 55 week laying period, 2 week changeover period. This reflects current commercial practice

Level of Performance	Enriched Cages				Free Range	
	Average		High		Average	
	per bird	per doz eggs	per bird	per doz eggs	per bird	per doz eggs
	£	p	£	p	£	p
Egg Returns	20.15	78.0	21.45	78.0	27.00	108.0
Less Livestock Deprcn	3.56	13.8	3.57	13.0	3.66	14.6
Output	**16.59**	**64.2**	**17.88**	**65.0**	**23.34**	**93.4**
Variable Costs:						
Food	10.35	40.1	10.35	37.6	11.50	46.0
Miscellaneous	0.41	1.6	0.41	1.5	0.82	3.3
Total Variable Costs	**10.76**	**41.7**	**10.76**	**39.1**	**12.32**	**49.3**
Gross Margin	**5.83**	**22.6**	**7.12**	**25.9**	**11.02**	**44.1**

1. *Hen-housed data* are used throughout, i.e. the total costs and returns are divided by the number of birds housed at the commencement of the laying period. IPPC permit charges have not been included. *Large variations* in input costs and returns occur.

Cage Production

2. *Yields assumed* per bird per year are:

   Average................ 312 (26 dozen)
   High................. 330 (27.50 dozen)

3. *The price* used, 78p per dozen, includes all quantity and quality bonuses. If sold direct (to local shop, add 38p/doz., if sold to consumers (farm-gate) add 68p/doz.

4. *Livestock Depreciation* - average point of lay pullet is priced at £3.56 (16/17 weeks).

5. *Feed* is 45kg per bird at £250 per tonne. Feed cost is dependent on breed, housing and environmental conditions, quantity purchased and type of ration.

6. *Miscellaneous Costs:* refers to variable costs: water, medication and veterinary, electricity and bird insurance.

7. *Other Costs:* include repairs and maintenance, vehicle costs, administration, general insurance and clean-down between batches. These come to around 67p per bird in total. In addition, there are labour costs and housing costs (see below).

8. *Direct Labour Costs:* average £1.67 per bird. See page 187.

9. *Housing Costs:* see page 233. Deadstock depreciation averages about £3.00 per caged bird. Deadstock depreciation is calculated over 57 weeks (55 week laying period plus 2 weeks clean out).

10. *Stocking density:* 750cm^2/bird (13.3 birds/m^2) in enriched cage systems.

Free Range Production

11. *Egg yields:* 300 (25 dozen) and average price: 108.0p per dozen (9p each).

12. *Quantity of feed used* = 50 kg. Price £250 per tonne.

13. *Livestock Depreciation* - the average point a lay pullet is priced at £3.66 (16/17 weeks).

14. *Miscellaneous Costs:* see 'Cage Production' notes above for details. Other Costs in this case are likely to be around £1.00 per hen.

15. *Direct Labour Costs:* average £3.10 per bird, dependent on degree of automation.

16. *Stocking density in house:* 1,111 cm^2 /bird (9 birds per m^2) up from 855cm^2/bird (11.7 birds/m^2) since Jan 2012, stocking in multi-tier systems can be higher, if appropriate use is made of the height of the building. *Stocking density outside the house*; regulations allow 2,500 birds/ha (1,000/acre). Freedom Foods and the Lion Code allow 2,000 birds/ha (810/acre).

REARING PULLETS

Average per bird reared

	£
Value of 16/17 weeks old bird	4.20
Less Chicks @ 72p (inc. 3% mort. and levy)	0.72
Output	**3.48**
Variable Costs:	
Food: 6.35 kg @ £240 per tonne	1.52
Miscellaneous	0.95
Total Variable Costs	**2.47**
Gross Margin	**1.01**

1. *Chick Value:* Assumes 3 per cent mortality.
2. *Miscellaneous:* Excluding transport (28p), but including full vaccination costs.
3. *Labour (42p);* deadstock depreciation (42p).

TABLE POULTRY

A **Broilers** (per bird sold at 41 days)	p
Returns: 2.2 kg per bird @ 93.0p per kg lw	204.6
Less Cost of Chick	38.0
Output	**166.6**
Variable Costs:	
Food: 4 kg @ £295 per tonne	118.0
Miscellaneous	18.5
Total Variable Costs	**136.5**
Gross Margin	**30.10**

1. *Building depreciation* cost approximately 7.75p per bird sold. For capital costs of housing: see page 233.
2. *Labour*: 6.5p, excluding catching and cleaning out (5.2p) but includes management; see page 187.
3. *Stocking density*: 38kg/m^2, 263cm^2/kg
4. O.R. = Oven Ready

B All Year Round Turkey (per bird at 20 weeks, sexed stags)

	£
Returns: 14 kg per bird @ £2.80 per kg L.Wt.	39.2
Less Cost of Poult	2.1
Output	**37.1**
Variable Costs:	
Food: 50 kg @ £260 per tonne	13.0
Miscellaneous	5.5
Total Variable Costs	**18.5**
Gross Margin	**18.6**

1. 10% *mortality* allowed in cost of poult figures.
2. *Rearing turkeys* all the year round now tends to be just in the hands of a few large and vertically integrated companies. Imports have outcompeted many small operators.

C Christmas Turkey (Traditional Farm Fresh - indoor reared)

	Light	Medium	Heavy
	£	£	£
Returns per bird sold	43.89	49.84	71.30
Less Cost of Poult	5.15	5.15	4.25
Output	**38.74**	**44.69**	**67.05**
Variable Costs:			
Food	7.39	9.32	10.02
Miscellaneous	14.00	14.30	15.00
Total Variable Costs	**21.39**	**23.62**	**25.02**
Gross Margin	**17.35**	**21.08**	**42.03**
Killing Age (weeks)	18	22	22
Live Weight (kg)	6.6	8.0	12.4
Oven Ready Weight (kg)	5.4	6.6	10.2
Food Conversion	3.2	3.4	2.4
Food per Bird (kg)	20.8	27.0	29.5
Food Cost per tonne	£355	£345	£340

1. *Mortality*: 7, 8 and 10% mortality allowed for in cost of poult figures for light, medium and heavy weights respectively.
2. Performance Categories:
    a.   Light and medium = slow growing sexed hens.
    b.   Heavy = stags (as hatched).
3. *Liveweight Price per kilogram*: small £6.42p/kg, medium £6.02 p/kg, large £5.54p/kg
4. Miscellaneous costs include processing (inc. plucking and eviscerating) and marketing

Note: With both turkey enterprises, considerable variations will occur between individual strains and because of different production systems and feeding regimes. Free range systems for example will show higher costs and returns. The figures should therefore be used only as rough guidelines.

D Large roaster chickens (per bird sold at 12 weeks; Christmas - males only)

	£
Returns: 4.8 kg per bird @ £3.60 per kg O.R.	17.28
Less Cost of Chick	0.86
Output	**16.42**
Variable Costs:	
Food: 14.3 kg @ £300 per tonne	4.29
Miscellaneous	1.80
Total Variable Costs	**6.09**
Gross Margin	**10.33**

10% mortality allowed for in cost of chick figures.

E Ducks (Pekin type) (per bird sold at 7 weeks)

	£
Returns: 2.3 kg per bird @ £3.65 per kg O.R.	8.40
Less Cost of Duckling	0.65
Output	**7.75**
Variable Costs:	
Food: 11.3 kg @ £260 per tonne	2.94
Miscellaneous	2.45
Total Variable Costs	**5.39**
Gross Margin	**2.36**

Day-old costs allow for 10% mortality. There are very few indoor duck farmers left in the UK operating to this system, but they are large-scale.

F Geese (Traditional Farm Fresh - free range and dry plucked)

	£
Returns: 6.5 kg per bird @ £10.00 per kg O.R.	65.00
Less Cost of Gosling	6.75
Output	**58.25**
Variable Costs:	
Food: 56 kg @ £280.714285714286 per tonne	15.72
Miscellaneous	13.00
Total Variable Costs	**28.72**
Gross Margin	**29.53**

1. *Day-old costs:* allow for 6% mortality.

2. 16.5kg feed wheat at £145/t and 40kg goose concentrate at £335/t

3. Farm gate output values used

4. *Miscellaneous costs* include processing / marketing

Acknowledgement: The figures in the poultry section are supported by John Newton

RAINBOW TROUT (FRESHWATER)

	£ per tonne of fish
Returns: 1 tonne of fish @ £2.25 per kg	2,250
Less 4000 fingerlings @ 8.0p each	320
Output	**1,930**
Variable Costs:	
Food: 1 tonne @ £1350 per tonne	1,350
Vet and med	150
Miscellaneous	80
Total Variable Costs	**1,580**
Gross Margin	**350**

1. Fish growing to 350g from fingerlings at 4.5g.

2. Prices are estimated ex-farm to processor or wholesaler for portion sized (c.500g) freshwater rainbow trout. Higher prices of up to £4.20 per kg can be achieved by selling direct to retailers, caterers and consumers at, say farmers markets, but significant additional costs are associated with such sales.

3. Fingerlings price: varies according to quantity ordered and time of year.

4. Average feeding period, 10 months. Mortality, from fingerling to market size, 15%. Food conversion ratio 1.1:1, having a very low maintenance requirement. The price for fish food is for a pigmented high oil expanded pellet. It is a guide price as different diets and formulations will retail at different prices and at different economies of scale depending upon volume purchased.

5. Current capital costs for construction of earth pond unit approximately £90 per cubic metre, to include buildings, holding systems and installation of water supply and services, but excluding land.

6. Labour requirement: the basic norm has in the past been 1 man per 50 tonnes of fish produced per annum on a table fish farm, but to remain competitive farmers now need to produce at least 150 tonnes per annum of table fish per man.

The figures given are illustrative and don't reflect the complexities of trout farming. Trout farming varies in the UK from Cage Farming in Scottish lochs (freshwater and marine) to 'traditional' flow through earth/pond/concrete raceway river farming. Trout farming also encompasses both the table and restocking sectors, prices given above relate to the sale of fish for the table market. As such feed costs, conversion rates etc. do vary which obviously has an effect on the costings for the enterprise. Differences in water temperature will also impact significantly on food conversion ratios, growth rates etc.

Acknowledgement: thanks to - British Trout Association, The Rural Centre, West Mains, Ingliston, Edinburgh, EH28 8NZ. Tel: 0131 472 4080 www.britishtrout.co.uk

MEAT RABBITS

The UK consumption of rabbit meat is low. However, demand is increasing as rabbit meat has recently featured in a number of TV cookery programs. Restaurants and retail outlets are broadening their range of products. Consumption in many European countries is high. There are few specialist processors of meat rabbit in the UK, but that is due more to the shortage of rabbit breeders than the willingness of processors to take on the product. The demand for rabbit meat is seasonal. Producers allow a 20% surge in demand over winter months. Rabbit meat is sold for human consumption and also as fresh pet food. Fallen stock can be sold as reptile food. There is a strong demand for the pelts from European producers.

Meat rabbits in the UK have included the New Zealand Whites (NZ) and the Californian. These are popular for both meat and pelts. Other suitable breeds with a meat and pelt value are the Silver Foxes, the Satins and the Rex. A further seven breeds are considered suitable for the breeding for meat. Expect to pay £40 for a buck and £30 per breeding doe.

Meat rabbits require a lot of maintenance. Health, good hygiene and good stock-man ship are essential. At least one responsible stockman should be on hand 24 hours a day. With grass maintenance and record keeping taken into account a 200 doe unit is a full time job

A none-cage system is adopted which includes lightweight runs, which are moved frequently in order to allow for grazing. It gives a natural environment, and also minimises the cost of dry concentrates. Each doe has its own separate run. Each run is self-sufficient with nesting box, water supply and shelter. The weaners (fryers) are raised on a free range basis over allocated areas. The cost to set up a typical 200 doe unit is in the order of £29,000. No outbuildings are required. An outer fence is needed to keep out predators and the wild rabbit gene reservoir. Additionally an inner fence is adopted in order to contain the free range weaners. A stand-off of 15m is required between the outer fence and the inner fence, this reduces the risk of disease from the wild reservoir.

	£	£
	Per Doe	Per 200 Does
Finished Young per Doe per Year	46	9,200
Live Weight Each (at 12 weeks)	2.6	520
Price per kg to processor	2.25	450
Sales:	£	
Meat sales per Doe per Year	269	53,820
Sales of pelts	21	4,140
Less Depreciation per Doe (incl.Buck) per Year (2).......	12.0	2,401
Output	**278**	**55,559**
Variable Costs:		
Feed (doe & Progeny)	72	14,400
Bedding	2	440
Vet and Med	5	960
Miscellaneous	3	500
Total Variable Costs	**82**	**16,300**
Gross Margin	**196**	**39,259**

1. *Sales of Pelts:* A further income stream can be developed for pelts currently 90p (assume 50% sold) and fallen stock sold for reptile food.

2. *Depreciation* – Doe £10.14 (incl.15% mortality), Buck £0.78 per doe (incl. 15% mortality) Average 1 buck per 10 does. Does are kept for 2 years, bucks for 6 years. Does purchased at £30 each (15% mortality), culled at £15; buck purchased at £40 (15% mortality) negligible residual value.

3. *Feed conversion*: 4:1 includes doe, progeny and 10% of buck.

4. Young does are bought in at between 10 and 12 weeks old, mated at 20 weeks. A ratio of one buck to 6 to 10 does is recommended. Gestation is 31 days. Average litter size is 8 to 9 of which 6 to 7 should be successfully fattened. Re mating can be immediately post-partum or up to 6 weeks afterwards. A doe can have a useful life of 10 to 12 litters over 18 months. A mortality rate of 15% can be expected. Food conversion rate is around 4:1 making rabbit compatible with poultry

Acknowledgements: Thanks to – T & S Rabbits, part of T & S Nurseries and the Abbey Vineyard Group.

4. RENEWABLE ENERGY

GENERAL

Renewable energy enterprises are now commonplace across the majority of the UK. Returns have varied as with any enterprise, but most who undertook the research carefully have been pleased with the result. As with any diversification or capital investment, a full investment appraisal is necessary for renewable energy projects just with any other. Space is fundamental to the renewable energy sector (whether, wind turbines, solar panels or anaerobic digestion), it is capital intensive and requires an entrepreneurial approach to its implementation. Agriculture, which has all these resources is therefore a natural partner for the sector.

Renewable energy is fundamentally well understood. It includes the first forms of energy harnessed by man. Wind power and wood heating for examples clearly have long histories, as indeed has anaerobic digestion having been used by man for centuries. Even biofuels were available for the Second World War and second generation biofuels, whilst well understood are simply prohibitively expensive.

The Renewable Energy industry is developing in response to incentives to cut the emissions of climate changing greenhouse gases (GHGs) as a result of human activities. The main GHGs are:

- Carbon Dioxide (CO_2), which accounts for up to a quarter of the greenhouse gas effect

- Methane (CH_4) accounts for between 4% and 9% of the effect but is about 25 times more potent by volume than carbon dioxide

- Nitrous Oxide, which, whilst very low in concentration in the atmosphere, is about 300 times more potent than carbon dioxide

In 2014, human activity in the UK accounted (provisionally) for 520 million tonnes of GHG emissions (CO_2 equivalent), 8.5% down from 568.3mt in 2013. Agriculture accounted for 56.1mt CO_2 equivalent (2013), most of which comes from the enteric fermentation of ruminating animals (methane) and the use of (and manufacture) nitrogen fertilisers (nitrous oxides).

UK GHG Emissions 2013 (measured in million tonnes of CO_2 equivalence)

	GHG Total	Carbon Dioxide	Methane	Nitrous Oxide	Others
UK	568	467.5	56.2	27.6	14.7
UK percentage		82%	10.0%	4.9%	3.0%
UK Agriculture	56.1	7.2	27.1	30.3	0.0
Percentage	9.9%	1.5%	48%	79.0%	0%
GWP[1]		1	21	310	

1. GWP is the Global Warming Potential over 100 years relative to 1 tonne CO_2 Figures from DECC.

Agriculture, being a user of natural resources (such as land) will intrinsically have an unavoidable environmental footprint. Crops have generally been considered sequesters of carbon and animals releasers. The carbon-economics is not so simple though as accounting for the carbon costs of inputs often reduce the percentage carbon saving, even if raising the overall savings (through higher yield for example). Thus, different crops and technologies have differing GHG benefits and costs.

RENEWABLE ENERGY POLICY

Renewable Energy is a government led industry. It is only viable in its current model with subsidies and incentives. Policy is therefore more critical than other sectors less reliant on subsidies.

The EU's 2008 Climate Change Package became the 2009 Renewables Energy Directive (RED). It aimed to ensure the EU will achieve its self-set 2020 climate change targets by setting binding targets:

- a 20% reduction in greenhouse gas emissions
- a 20% improvement in energy efficiency, and
- a 20% share for renewables in the EU energy mix (the UK national target is 15%)
- of this target, biofuels and electricity should account for 10% of the EU's transport fuel consumption.

The UK 2008 Climate Change Act set legally binding targets for government, to steer it to achieve an 80% reduction of GHG emissions by 2050. It does this through additional targets; a 26% reduction of CO_2 emissions by 2020 against a 1990 baseline and capped emissions over 5 year periods, 3 budget periods set at a time, we're currently in the second (2013-2017). Published in July 2009 was the Renewable Energy Strategy which set out how the UK plans to meet its target of delivering 15% of UK energy by 2020.

In 2011, a coalition of agricultural industry partners launched the Greenhouse Gas Action Plan, to meet the climate change challenge without compromising production. In 2012, the same coalition demonstrated to Government (The Committee on Climate Change) the industry's voluntary actions to address its GHG emissions by 2018. This action needs to be robust to stave off policy intervention. Defra published a review of progress in reducing greenhouse gas emissions from English Agriculture in November 2012. The GHGAP updated its vision in 2014, redoubling its commitment to achieve its goals.

Energy use, the primary release of GHGs, is divided into three categories; electricity, heat and transport. The renewable generation of each is incentivised by government policy.

The Renewables Obligation (RO)

The primary mechanism for encouraging electricity supply from renewable sources in the UK is the Renewables Obligation (RO) which was introduced in 2002 in Great Britain, 2005 in Northern Ireland. Renewables Obligation Certificates (ROCs) are issued to registered electricity generators for producing electricity from renewable sources at between ¼ and 2 per megawatt hour (MWh) depending on the generation type. This so called 'ROC banding' was introduced in April 2009.

After 1st April 2016, the Government plans to stop issuing new agreements to onshore windfarms in Great Britain (beyond a few that have already achieved planning consent and started construction. This is in response to negative feedback from rural dwellers close to large-scale onshore wind farms. Most farm scale wind turbines are subsidised through the Feed-in Tariff (below). DECC will look to continue support for community-based projects.

Renewables Obligation Target, ROC Value and Non-Compliance Penalty

	Renewables Obligation Target (GB) (ROCs per 100MW)	*Non-compliance Penalty per MWh (buy-out price)*	*Average Value of ROCs*
2010/11	10.4	£36.99	*£48.10*
2011/12	11.4	£38.69	*£50.94*
2012/13	12.4	£40.71	*£45.19*
2013/14	13.4	£42.02	*£44.09*
2014/15	14.4	£43.30	*£42.08*
2015/16	15.4	£44.33	42.28
2016/17			*Market Price*

ROCs are required by registered electricity suppliers to offset their annual RO target (an annually rising target of ROCs per 100MW of use). If they do not have sufficient ROCs to meet their target, they are charged £30/MWh for the difference (index linked to 2002/03 making £44.33 in 2015/16). This money is re-circulated equally to all certificates after each year-end, meaning ROCs are worth more than their face value, especially if there is lots of non-compliance. Thus ROCs have a market value; their average price to the year July 2015 was £42.08/ROC. Electricity suppliers can fulfil their RO by purchasing ROCs from other generators. Farmers generating renewable electricity can sell the ROCs, having no obligation to keep them.

The introduction of 'ROC banding' meant some renewable electricity generation types 'earn' more ROCs per MWh than others as the next table illustrates. Micro generators (generating less than 50kw) are not eligible for ROCs.

Number of ROCS per MWh depending on Generation Type for England & Wales

Generation types	*ROCs per MWh*	
(non-exhaustive list)	*2015/6*	*2016/17*
Onshore wind (disbanding)	*0.9*	*0.9*
Hydro-electric	0.7	0.7
Energy from waste with CHP	1.0	1.0
Anaerobic digestion	1.9	1.8
Solar photovoltaic building mount	1.5	1.4
Solar photovoltaic ground mounted	1.3	1.2
Geothermal	1.9	1.8

Feed-in Tariffs (FIT)

Designed to facilitate the administration and subsidy receipts of small-scale electricity generators (farm-scale), Feed-in Tariffs encourage the production of renewable electricity at levels up to 5MW capacity. This is equivalent to a rather large offshore turbine or a very large anaerobic digestion plant. Almost all farm-scale renewable energy schemes would therefore fit within the FIT scheme. The Tariffs work as follows:

- A renewable electricity generator receives a fixed payment for each kWh electricity generated; the 'Generation Tariff'. This is set at different levels depending on technology type, installation size and start date (see below).

- The 'Export Tariff', a guaranteed market payment is available if required for its export to the wider market of 4.85 p/kWh (to 31 March 2016), less for existing installations.

- Generators can opt out of the Export Tariff by either selling electricity directly to an electricity consumer or making use of the electricity themselves (entirely or partially).

- The FIT payments are made by the registered Electricity Suppliers, the cost of which is redistributed among all suppliers in a pro-rata manner.

- Generators with capacity below 50kW (known as micro-generators) are eligible for FIT, whilst installations between 50kW and 5MW have the option to choose between FIT and the RO but cannot claim both.

This was implemented in April 2010. Generation Tariff rates for photo voltaic and wind technologies reduce most years for new claimants as technology becomes cheaper. Generation and Export Tariffs are index linked once commissioned. Tariffs are guaranteed for 20 years (25 for solar PV if installed before 1 August 2012).

Generation Tariffs for FITs for New Installations

Generation Technology	Scale	Generation Tariff p/kWh	
		To Oct 2015	After Oct 2015
Anaerobic Digestion	< 250kW	10.13	
	250 - 500kW	9.36	
	> 500kW	8.68	
Hydro	< 15kW	17.17	
	15-100kW	16.03	
	100kW – 500kW	12.67	
	500kW-2MW	9.90	
	2-5MW	2.70	
Photo Voltaic *	< 4kW	13.35/12.09	12.88/11.67
	4kW - 10kW	12.13/10.09	11.71/10.54
	10kW - 50kW	11.71/10.54	11.71/10.54
	50kW - 150kW	9.98/8.98	9.63/8.67
	150kW - 250kW	9.54/8.59	9.21/8.29
	250kW - 5MW	6.16	5.94
	<250kW Lower Rate	6.16	6.16
	Stand Alone **	6.16	4.44
Wind	< 100kW	14.45	
	100kW - 500kW	12.05	
	500kW - 1.5MW	6.54	
	> 1.5MW	2.77	
RO Migrated Installations		10.66	10.66
Export Tariff *of new installations*		4.85	4.85

*   *If electricity supplies a building with an Energy Performance Certificate of A to D, the first, higher rate is payable. If multiple installations and most achieve A to D rating, middle band, if neither of the above, lower band.*

**   *Stand Alone Systems are not attached to a building and not wired to provide electricity to an occupied building. Possibly an electric fence charger for example.*

The Renewable Heat Incentive (RHI)

Heat accounts for approaching half of all energy used in the UK. Government's target for 2020 is that 12% of this will come from renewable sources. The value of heat is low (possibly 1-2p/kWh thermal energy depending on local market) which rarely justifies the capital expenditure in the UK of harnessing heat or generating it from a renewable source. The RHI is designed to change this (in GB). The scheme is divided into domestic and non-domestic installations. Phase 1 was in July 2011, for non-domestic installations, the second is for domestic installations, launched in April 2014.

Domestic RHI

Payments shown in the table are irrespective of installation capacity and are available for new installations. The RHI is administered by OFGEM. The Domestic RHI will pay the following tariffs per unit of heat generated for seven years:

Levels of support for the Domestic Renewable Heat Incentive

Generation Technology	Domestic Tariff p/kWh Rates from July 2015
Air-source heat pumps	7.42
Ground and water-source heat pumps	19.1
Biomass boilers and stoves	7.14
Solar thermal	19.51

Non-Domestic RHI

Once a RHI rate is agreed, payments are index linked but not exposed to renegotiations of the policy for the 20-year term.

Levels of Support for RHI for Non Domestic Installations

Tariff name	Eligible technology	Eligible sizes	Tariff rate (p/kWh)*
Small biomass	Solid biomass; including waste	< 200 kWth	Tier 1: 4.4 Tier 2: 1.17
Medium biomass		200 - 1000 kWth	Tier 1: 5.18 Tier 2: 2.24
Large biomass		>= 1000 kWth	2.03
Large Biomass CHP			4.17
Air Source	Heat Pumps	all sizes	2.54
Deep Geothermal			5.08
Ground source	Ground and Water-source heat pumps;	Tier 1	8.84
		Tier 2	2.64
Solar thermal		< 200 kWth	10.16
Biomethane	Injection	1st 40,000 mWh	7.24
		next 40,000 mWh	4.25
		remaining mWh	3.28
Biogas	Biogas combustion	under 200 kWth	7.50
		200-600kWth	5.90
		Over 600kWth	2.20

* Tier Break is: installed capacity x 1,314 peak load hours (15% rating), i.e.: kWth x 1,314

The Renewable Transport Fuel Obligation (RTFO) and Fuel Excise Duty

The RTFO started in 2008. For every litre of biofuel that excise duty is paid on, a Renewable Transport Fuel Certificate (RTFC) is issued. Companies supplying at least 450,000 litres of any road fuel to the UK market annually (about 14 companies) must participate by incorporating a proportion of biofuel into their sales, buying RTFCs from another biofuel provider or paying a 'buy-out' penalty (fine) of 30p/l (index linked). As a compelling incentive, the 'buy-out fund' generated is redistributed equally to every RTFC issued by the year-end. This means that the further away the UK is from hitting the annual target, the greater the incentive to incorporate as RTFC values rise. These subsidies are essential to make the industry viable, without them there would be no biofuel industry. The required proportion of biofuels to incorporate is 5%.

Biofuels have the same duty payable as mineral fuels for most producers. A 100% duty exemption for small scale biofuel producers of up to 2,500l biofuel per year (notionally sufficient for home use) remains in place. The RTFO includes sustainability criteria of the Renewable Energy Directive (refer to page 104). The criteria include minimum carbon savings requirements. Greater rewards are now also available for fuel generated from waste materials.

Fuel Excise Duty:	to April 2016
Petrol, Diesel *ppl*	57.95
Bioethanol and biodiesel *ppl*	57.95
Rebated gas oil (red diesel) *ppl*	11.14
Biodiesel for non-road use *ppl*	11.14
Natural Gas (inc. biogas) *p/kg*	24.70
Liquefied Petroleum Gas *p/kg*	31.51

These figures are before VAT. Pump prices include VAT (20%)

BIOMASS FOR POWER

This section covers crops that are grown to be burnt directly to produce heat and/or electricity. The plant material is pelleted, chipped, or baled and is generally either used in boilers in dedicated biomass power stations, or mixed with coal for co-firing in conventional power stations. Biomass includes short rotation coppice, Miscanthus, straw, canary reed grass and switch grass as well as forest residues.

Previous Editions of this book have included estimates of planting including fencing, land preparation and plants themselves. It has come to £2,747 and £2,647 for Short Rotation Coppice and Miscanthus respectively before 50% planting grants. However the planting grant (Energy Crops Scheme) is no longer available and minimal panting will be taking place as a result. The new Rural Development Scheme does not currently include an Energy Crops Scheme, but if it is replaced for 2017, the new details will appear here in the next Edition.

Short Rotation Coppice

Short Rotation Coppice (SRC) is a fast growing willow (occasionally poplar) that when chipped and dried is used as a fuel for heat or power generation. SRC willow needs ample moisture but grows on any cultivated land. Planting is in the spring using un-rooted cuttings at a rate of 15,000/ha. Rabbit (or deer) fencing may be necessary. Crops are usually harvested on a 3 year cycle, 2 and 4-year cycles are practiced depending on conditions. Crops should last 20 years. Most growers apply some fertiliser post-harvest, 60 kg/ha N is sufficient. Sewage sludge is commonly used as are animal manures. SRC is stored as billets or chips, increasing density for transport efficiency. Pellets command a premium price over billets (6-8 inch lengths) and chips being more fluid.

Annual Net Returns: Output 25 odt/ha at £65 (delivered) every third year; £511/year (accounting for gradual yield increase). Harvesting £365/ha plus £50 fuel, transport and handling £12/tonne harvested. Planting costs (including fencing etc.) have been spread over the forecast period of the crop and include the 50% planting grant previously mentioned. Use the Amortisation Table in section VIII. Land is eligible for the Basic Payment.

SRC Gross Margin (gross margin per year, based on harvest every third)

Production level	Low	Average	High
Yield: tonnes per ha (tons per acre)	7 (2.8)	8 (3.2)	9 (3.6)
	£	£	£
Output	455 (184)	520 (211)	585 (237)
Variable Costs:			
Establishment		132 (54)	
Fertiliser/spray		21 (9)	
Harvest		122 (49)	
Cart, stack	44 (18)	50 (20)	56 (23)
Transport & Handling	84 (34)	96 (39)	108 (44)
Total Variable Costs		421 (171)	
Gross Margin per ha (acre)	**52** (21)	**99** (40)	**146** (59)

1. *Establishment costs* of £2,781/ha (£1,127/ac) including fencing (£1150/ha) spread over 21 years.

Miscanthus (Elephant Grass)
Miscanthus is a perennial grass crop lasting 20 years grown for energy and fibre. It is harvested annually with conventional farm machinery. After treatment, Miscanthus can be used as animal bedding, paper making biopolymer manufacture or to produce bio-degradable products, such as plant pots. Miscanthus is grown throughout the UK. It is usually propagated from rhizomes. A mature crop suppresses weeds. There are no significant pathogens or pests in the UK so agro-chemical use is minimal

Miscanthus Gross Margin

Production level	Low	Average	High
Yield: tonnes per ha (tons per acre)	10 (4.1)	12 (4.9)	14 (5.7)
	£	£	£
Output	550 (223)	660 (267)	770 (312)
Variable Costs:			
Establishment		127 (52)	
Fertiliser/spray		25 (10)	
Harvest		79 (32)	
Bale		164 (66)	
Cart, stack	42 (17)	50 (20)	58 (24)
Transport & Handling	120 (49)	144 (58)	168 (68)
Total Variable Costs	557 (226)	590 (239)	622 (252)
Gross Margin per ha (acre)	**-7** (50)	**70** (29)	**148** (140)

Yield accounts for average over 21 years

1. *Establishment costs:* of £2,675/ha (£1,083/ac) including fencing (£1150/ha) shared between 21 years.

2. *Fertiliser requirement:* is low. Whilst the harvest will remove P and K, the plant is deep rooted so accesses minerals from deeper than most crops. Sewage sludge is an ideal fertiliser. The Miscanthus gross margin below has a small cost for imported slurry, biosolids or other organic manure.

The crop shoots in April, and grows to 4 metres by September. Stems desiccate to 50% moisture during winter. The canes are harvested in February-March. Harvest method depends on end use. For energy, the crop is cut with a mower conditioner or modified forage harvester at 35% moisture and then baled 10 days later into Hesston bales at 16% moisture, the contractual benchmark moisture level. For other end uses a maize harvester is used.

The price for Miscanthus ranges from £45 to £75 with £60 fairly standard for energy crop contracts. Note most contracts now use fresh harvested weight (normally 16% moisture) rather than the former 'oven dried tonnes'.

In year 1, 50 to 60% of the mature yield is obtained. Recent precision planting machinery improvements facilitate evenly established crops, offering greater fresh weight yields of on light land 9 – 12t/ha and on medium to heavy land 12 – 18 t/ha.

Small on-farm boilers, to produce heat and energy, have been developed which offer potential for Miscanthus growers. This will be fuelled by the Renewable Heat Initiative (see page 107). Planting and establishment costs are in the region of £3,000 per hectare including fencing. Some agro-chemicals will probably be required in the first 2 years. In the UK there is a 50% establishment grant for all costs in the first 2 years.

ANAEROBIC DIGESTION

Anaerobic Digestion (AD) is the digestion of non-woody organic material in the absence of oxygen by micro-organisms to produce biogas (a mixture of *circa* 40% carbon dioxide CO_2 and *circa* 60% methane CH_4) and digestate (a soil conditioner). It works in the same way as a very large rumen. The biogas is collected and normally used in a combined heat and power (CHP) generator to produce heat and electricity for use or sale. The biogas can also be purified by removing the CO_2 and contaminant gasses (less than 1%) making biomethane and compressed for use as road fuel or in place of natural gas. AD is a natural process and is well understood by mankind having been harnessed for many years.

An extensive range of feedstock can be used. Livestock manure is cheap with high levels of micro-organisms but has a low biogas yield and not commercially viable as the sole feedstock. Energy crops such as maize silage offer high yields and are commonly used in AD business models. They are expensive feedstocks so add substantially to operating costs but are predictable and supply is easily managed. Non-farm waste streams from food processing companies or separated kitchen wastes offer a high return, with potential to earn revenue from gate fees. Regulatory controls and 'front-end' processing requirements are far greater when importing others' waste streams though, especially if animal by-products are likely to be included pushing up capital costs and changing the business model substantially. These tend to have unpredictable supply.

There are several types of AD plant, all suited to different situations and feedstocks. The rate of turnover of digestate is controlled by the rate at which feedstock enters the digester less the small (usually 3-10%) fall in volume from the production of biogas. Depending on feedstock and system used, digestion can take as little as a week up to 2 months in some circumstances.

Example On-Farm Feedstocks for Anaerobic Digestion

Feedstock	Biogas Yield m^3/t feedstock	Value of Biogas £/t feedstock*
Cattle/pig slurry	15 – 25	4.65 – 7.70
Poultry manure	30 – 100	9.30 – 31.00
Maize silage	190 – 220	58.80 – 68.00
Grass silage	150 – 200	46.50 – 62.00
Whole crop wheat	185	57.5
Maize grain	560	173
Rolled wheat grain	600	185
Crude glycerine	580 – 1,000	180 – 310
Rape meal	620	190
Fats	Up to 1,200	up to 370

* 9.36p/kWh Generation Tariff, 4.85p/kWh Export Tariff, 1p/kWh heat

Policy

When biogas is used to generate electricity, it can be sold with Feed in Tariffs or 2 ROCs can be claimed per MWhe (Mega Watt hour of electricity) as part of the Renewables Obligation. Biomethane for road transport is technically eligible for RTFCs (see Biofuels section above) or the RHI. AD also benefits indirectly from the Landfill Directive by diverting waste from landfill to uses such as AD. AD does not facilitate NVZ implementation regulations but has been a favoured renewable energy of the Government.

Economics

The two major costs associated with AD are usually the capital set up and feedstock (if home grown or purchased feed is used). Operating and maintenance costs such as insurance, labour and utilities are usually comparatively low. An average size plant (2,500m³ digester and 490kW CHP generator) would cost in the region of £1.8-2.25 million to build and commission. Depending on feedstock, temperature and other settings, this size plant could digest in the region of 20,000 tonnes of feedstock per year with a 45 day retention time (spent in the digester) or 30,000t with a 30 day retention period.

Revenue from this system digesting 20,000 tonnes using the assumptions from the table above, an average gas yield per tonne of feedstock of 100m³/tonne and an efficiency of 90% gas conversion would return income before costs and without gate fees of about £610,000 with FITs.

LIQUID BIOFUELS

Liquid biofuels are road transport fuels produced from organic materials, including farm crops. *Biodiesel* is produced from oilseeds such as oilseed rape, soybeans and palm and is a replacement for mineral diesel. *Bioethanol* is a petrol replacement, produced from starch/sugar-based crops including wheat, maize and sugar beet or cane. There are other fuels such as *biobutanol* that are not widely used in the UK.

Biofuels from cellulosic (woody) feedstock is possible referred to as 'second generation' biofuels. This would enable a higher energy return per hectare and the opportunity to process household, manufacturing and agricultural organic 'wastes'. Its production is not financially viable so may be some years from large-scale commercial production. It also requires substantially more energy in the processing to release the energy from cellulose.

Supply

About 40 million tonnes of road fuel is used in the UK (diesel exceeding petrol use by about 55:45). To meet the RTFO target, about 2m tonnes of biofuel are required (5%). The RTFO does not differentiate between biofuels so one may dominate the market. Splitting the market proportionately would require roughly 1.1 million tonnes of biodiesel and 900,000 tonnes bioethanol. This would need 2.6m tonnes OSR or equivalent feedstock (at 42% extraction) covering 800,000 hectares (at 3.25t/ha) and 3m tonnes of wheat (or equivalent feedstock) covering 353,000 hectares (at 8.5t/ha).

Farmers' options on whether to grow a crop to supply a biofuel facility are determined simply by price and contractual terms. As crops used in biofuel production are, in the most part, mainstream crops that could also be sold to other consumers, the processor that bids the farmer the best deal ought to win the contract. Clearly headline price is important, but also other contractual details including the risk of rejection or cost of claims, turnaround times etc. should be considered. There are therefore no farm-level gross margins for biofuel crops. Despite considerable investment, the biofuel industry has not managed to become fully operational in the UK, and is currently operating at about a third of capacity. It is uncertain what its future is.

SOLAR POWER

Solar Photovoltaic (PV)

Solar PV panels generate electricity through the direct conversion of daylight. Panels can either be roof mounted, free-standing or integrated as a form of building material though solar slates, tiles or glass laminates.

Capital and installation costs have fallen sharply in the last three years following the reduced FIT rates. Rates for anything above 20kW tend to be near or even slightly below £1,000 per kW. For example a 30kW roof mounted array with high specification panels would cost in the region of £32,000 to install, depending on connection fees, cabling, etc. a comparable 20kW system would currently cost nearer to £23,000 (£1,150/kW) to install. Smaller arrays are dearer per kW, at £1,200 to £1,400 per kW installed.

Little maintenance is required. There are companies that will 'rent' your barn roof for installation of solar PV if you did not wish to invest in equipment yourself. Terms vary but typically offer the electricity generated as rent whilst they keep the FITs.

Approximately 7-8m^2 of PV panels is required to generate 1kW of electricity. A typical panel weighs 13kg per m^2 so additional roof support may be required. Panels should last for 25 years although electricity inverters might need replacing after 5 -10 years.

For optimum results, modules should be south facing at an angle of 30-40 degrees and un-shadowed by trees or surrounding buildings. Productivity varies across the UK with levels between 1100 kWh per m^2 in the South West, to 800 kWh per m^2 in Scotland. Modules that face East or West will drop in efficiency to 85%.

In England and Scotland most private PV installations do not require planning permission, unless the building is of conservation status, is in a designated area or is a large free standing system. Wales and Northern Ireland will need to seek planning permission from their local planning authority.

Solar Thermal

Solar thermal systems use the sun's energy to warm water through using either evacuated tubes or flat plate collectors fitted to a roof. A conventional or immersion boiler is then used to heat the water further.

Costs of a typical water heating system are £3,000 to £7,000. Most systems come with a 5-10 year warranty and require little maintenance. Savings are modest; the average system can provide one third of water needs, reducing heating bills by approximately £90-£160 per year.

In England most systems will not require planning permission unless the building is listed or within a designated area. Wales, Scotland and Northern Ireland will need to contact their local planning authority.

HYDRO POWER

The UK has about 1,650MW hydro-electricity capacity, and generates 40% of renewable electricity in the UK. Most of this is from large (10-100 MW) schemes that have been built over the last 40 years. Viable sites vary from around 5kW to a few MW. Typically power output is more constant for hydro than wind or solar power but it is similarly unpredictable; electricity generation is not aligned with electricity requirement.

Hydro, like other renewable energy projects is capital loaded, expensive to install but cheap to operate and can have a very long life. Installation costs of around £3,000 to £6,000 per kWe for small hydroelectric systems are typical, but are very site dependant. Operational costs are low, generally 1-2% of capital setup. Capital cost and electrical capacity depend largely on the following:

- *The head (maximum vertical fall) of water:* The higher the head, the smaller the flow required to generate the same amount of electricity. Smaller flow means smaller pipe and turbine. High head is over 50 metres drop, medium head 10 to 50 metres and less than 10m is low head.

- *The flow rate of water* is determined by the catchment size, amount of rainfall and the proportion of flow abstracted. The latter is determined by the environmental sensitivity of the river. Flow for small schemes is measured in litres per second.

- *Project size:* The cost of construction per kW falls as capacity rises; smallest projects take longest to repay the investment. Access affects costs. Costs for obtaining planning permission, abstraction and impoundment licenses and detailed design and specification of the equipment are similar for a 5kW scheme or a 30kW scheme.

- *Construction management:* Projects can be contracted to a single turnkey contractor to undertake design, specification, procurement and construction work, requiring little input from the landowner but is dearer. Many landowners oversee the project management which with some specialist input, costs can be greatly reduced.

- *Grid connection:* The capacity of the grid can be a major limitation, with upgrade of grid connection lines being expensive, particularly so in more rural or remote areas.

- *Development companies* take on a complete project and pay a rent to the landowner, typically 5% to 20% of income. Schemes of interest to such companies are usually at least 100 kW. There is significant competition for larger schemes.

Typical costs of example projects:

- 5kW medium to low head scheme, by civil contractors with specialist hydro input. Annual generation 14 MWh. Cost around £80,000

- 15 kW very high head. Landowner undertook project management and most civils and pipe-laying works. Annual generation 45 MWh. Cost around £52,000

- 30 kW high head scheme. Managed by landowners using local contractors. Annual generation around 110 MWh. Cost around £77,000

- 100 kW scheme medium head, managed by the landowner with significant time input. Annual generation around 450 MWh. Cost around £410,000

- 300 kW scheme high head. Contractors led constructor with specialists. Annual generation around 1,200 MWh. Cost around £1,330,000

WIND TURBINES

There are currently 5,083 operational wind turbines spread across 914 wind farms throughout the UK (July 2015) (renewableuk.com). Small scale turbines can have capacities of as little as 100 watts (W) up to models of 3 megawatts (MW) and 6MW for offshore turbines. Wind farms are becoming larger; the average size a decade ago was 7MW and is now 20MW, albeit with considerable offshore wind farm growth. The average onshore turbine has 1.65MW capacity with the average wind farm over 10MW.

Wind turbines in good locations produce energy equivalent to their rated capacity for around 30% of the year. For example: for a turbine rated at 40kW this calculates as 40kW x 30% x 8760 (hours in a year) = 105,120 kWh per year (105.12MWh). If this electricity is sold at 19.30p/kWh (14.45p Generation Tariff + 4.85p Export Tariff) with FITs, then a return of £20,288 per year is achieved.

Typical costs for a range of turbine capacities are in the region of the following table. Good quality constructions should have an operational life of 20 years.

Guideline Figures for Capital and Revenue of Wind Turbines

Capacity kW	Capital Cost	Annual Output (kWh)	Revenue/yr using FIT*
5.0	23,000	13,100	£2,500
11	77,000	28,900	£5,500
75	225,000	197,000	£37,300
250	720,000	657,000	£108,700
800	1,250,000	2,100,000	£232,000

* Relevant FIT price as in FIT Table on page 106.

The land surrounding a wind turbine is usually un-affected, apart from access required up to the base of the tower. A minimum average wind speed of 5 meters per second (m/s) is required; they operate at their rated capacity at 11-15m/s. Many turbines have automatic shut-down mechanisms when wind speeds exceed about 25m/s to avoid damage. Selection of the correct turbine technology and size is important.

Planning permission is required and consultation with neighbours and stakeholders for all scale turbines. Wind farms (multiple large turbines) are built in association with developers as the costs and expertise required planning and preparing them is very high. Many schemes are operated by developers with land rented to them by the land owner for 20 years. In this situation, a rent will be payable to the landowner, usually at about 2-4% of income (£5,000 to £7,000 per mast per year is not uncommon plus similar construction access fees). Access to the turbines must be possible, but land between the turbines can be farmed normally. Other benefits like road improvements may also be included. An option to develop a site could be worth £1,000 to £5,000 per year. Beware the 'small-print' and make sure you understand it all before signing.

An 11kW turbine will have a hub (mast) height of 15 to 18 metres, blade diameter of 9 metres and a 63m³ swept area. Tip height will be up to 22.5m. A large (800kW) wind turbine has a standard hub height of 76m, a height at the maximum blade position of 102m, and a blade diameter of 53m. The area of wind captured by this size blade is 0.88ha.

5. OTHER ENTERPRISES

MUSHROOMS

The mushroom industry has shrunk considerably during the past few years. Several businesses of all sizes and locations have ceased production and few new growers have entered the business. Less than 75 firms remain in production. Those that remain are either highly efficient enterprises with strong links to supermarkets or small low cost family-run businesses selling largely to wholesalers. The reasons for this are static consumption levels and fierce competition from imports. There are a few organic mushroom producers who sell at a premium.

There have also been changes in production methods. Traditionally, most growers used Phase 1 compost, which was pasteurised and spawn-ran on the premises, to fill moveable trays or shelves in growing rooms. Now, the most prevalent system (70% of growers) use purchased Phase 2 compost (pasteurised, with spawn added). This is supplied in shrink-wrapped blocks, plastic bags or in bulk. Phase 3 compost (fully spawn-run) in blocks or bags is used by some growers. Organic Phase 2 and Phase 3 compost is also available.

Type of Compost Used	Phase 2	Phase 3
	per tonne compost	
Mushroom Yield/tonne compost	250 kg	300 kg
	£	£
Mushroom Price/kg	1.85	1.85
Spent Compost/tonne	2.10	2.10
Output	**464.6**	**557.1**
Variable Costs:		
Compost (incl. delivery)	96	136
Casing	16	16
Operations & growing labour at 6.6p/kg	17	20
Supervision & picking labour at 49p/kg	123	147
Packing materials at 22p/kg	55	66
Packing labour at 11p/kg	28	33
Energy costs at 11p/kg	28	33
Other costs at 15p/kg	38	45
Total Variable Costs	**398**	**495**
Margin / tonne compost	**67**	**62**
Variable Costs / kg mushrooms	1.59	1.65
Margin / kg mushrooms	0.27	0.21

Output: Growers using Phase 2 compost will fill on an 8-week cycle and produce 6.5 crops per year. Phase 3 compost can be filled on a 6-week cycle and allows 8.5 crops per year. Yields are expressed as kg per square metre of bed or kg per tonne of compost. Commercial yields are 25-35kg/m² of bed area per crop (250-350kg per tonne of compost) using Phase 2 or 3 compost, but only 18-20kg/ m² (180-200kg/tonne of compost) using Phase 1. Phase 1 compost costs £25/tonne, Phase 2 £85/tonne and Phase 3 £125/tonne plus delivery which can add £6-15/tonne, depending on distance and size of load.

Prices: Mushroom prices are in the range of £2.00/kg supplied to a supermarket to £1.00 or less sold on the wholesale market. Small growers marketing through a producer organisation would get around £1.60/kg delivered. At present 60% of the crop is sold by growers direct to supermarkets. Prices can be volatile and oversupply can lead to mushrooms being sold at a loss. Imports now account for 65% of all mushrooms sold in the UK, and 60% of the value of sales. Almost all imports are from the Netherlands and the Republic of Ireland.

Returns: The data suggest that ex-farm it costs £1.54 to produce 1kg of mushrooms using Phase 2 compost and £1.60 using Phase 3 compost. This does not take into account management or finance costs. The yield of the crop and the number of cycles each year are, of course, crucial.

Establishment Costs: A mushroom farm using Phase 2 compost on an 8-week cycle would require 8 rooms each with a 200sq m capacity. A farm using Phase 3 compost on a 6-week cycle would need 6 rooms of 200sq m capacity. In both cases one growing room would be filled each week using 20 tonnes of compost. To set up such a production system would require a capital investment of £200,000-£300,000 for the rooms, trays or shelves, heating and cooling systems, packing area, hard standings and equipment. If Phase 1 compost is used then buildings and equipment for composting, peak heating and spawning are also required.

Labour costs: All labour is included but labour for growing, if not picking and packing, could be regular. If Phase 2 or 3 compost is used, labour for growing amounts to around 10% of all labour costs while picking is 75% and packing 15%. Using Phase 1 compost labour cost for growing is significantly greater, perhaps 40p/kg or 40% of total labour, but the initial compost is cheaper.

TURF

The market for turf had shrunk as a result of the downturn in the home building industry, but is now improving again in line with the rest of the economy. Competition remains strong, particularly among the producers of general contract grade turf. The market is predominantly supplied with seed sown turf or cultivated lawn turf. Pasture turf is still available in some areas, but its importance is small and declining. Suitable pasture for turf lifting is scarce and it can be cheaper to grow cultivated turf than treat and prepare existing pasture. Special seed mixtures and cultivation techniques produce a range of types of turfgrass that can be matched to particular sites and uses. The Turfgrass Growers Association (TGA) has quality standards. It is estimated that there are around 16,000 ha (*40,000 acres*) of turfgrass grown in the UK. Although several turfgrass companies were originally set up by farmers, the production is now in the hands of specialist turf growers but there are also farmers who use turf as part of their agricultural rotation.

Selling existing pasture turf to a turf company

This is the traditional option but it now represents very little of the turf market. Minimum 5-6 year ley/pasture generally needed for spring or autumn lifting, 8-10 year grass is better for summer cutting.

Payment varies between £750-£1,500 per hectare (£300-£600 per acre), but mainly £900-£1,200 per ha (£360-£480 per acre). There is usually an initial payment plus further payments as turf is lifted. There may be a penalty clause if lifting delays prevent subsequent timely drilling. Lifting can take from two months to a year. It can be done at any time of year except when there is snow or frost on the ground. The turf company sprays against broadleaved weeds, fertilises and mows before lifting; the farmer may do these tasks, for payment. He may graze the land, for a rent, if lifting is delayed.

The effect on the land of cultivated turf production is not detrimental, the amount of topsoil removal is not much greater than other root crops; some say there are benefits (removal of accumulated pests, etc. in the top half inch of grass, roots and topsoil). Some local authorities require planning consent for turf harvesting. In some instances it has been refused on the grounds that pasture turf is not an agricultural crop. Cultivated turf, however, is deemed to be an agricultural crop. On tenanted land landlord's permission is necessary to cut pasture turf.

Farmer cutting, lifting and selling pasture turf himself

This is extremely uncommon. The turf must be treated, as in option 1. A small turf cutting machine can be hired for £65 a day. This slices off the turf which must then be cut into lengths and picked up by hand. It is slow going even in good conditions. Wastage is commonly 10-20% of the area. It is possible to hire a machine which cuts and picks up the turf but the charge will be considerably more.

Renting land to a turf company for production of cultivated turf

Turf companies rent land for turfgrass production. Typically the land is rented on a per crop basis and one or two crops grown. A turf crop usually takes 12 to 18 months from preparation to harvest but autumn sown crops may be harvested within 12 months. Rent levels depend on the quality of the land, the provision of irrigation and the profitability of competing agricultural enterprises. Currently rents are in the order of £700-£1,300 per hectare per crop (£280-£525 per acre) or £525-£780 per ha per year (£210-£315 per acre).

Cultivated turf production

Important features when choosing fields: good root structure, number and type of weeds, level, well-drained, stone-free land; good access. Turf has a short life once cut and stacked - a maximum 1 to 2 days in summer, 3 to 4 days in winter, depending on temperature. On their own land turf producers can grow turf continuously, taking a crop every 18 months to two years on average. On rented land (as in option 3), they take one or two crops and move on. Usually they produce a quick growing turf on rented land and cultivate more specialist and slower growing turf on their own. A high level of agronomic expertise and considerable investment in machinery are needed and labour requirements are heavy. A high degree of marketing expertise is essential. Whilst the bulk of the trade goes into general landscaping or garden centres there is an increase in the number of contracts where the quality and type of turf is specified. It is estimated that a turf farm would need to be 150-200 hectares (400-500 acres) or more in size to be viable – in order to justify the machinery and equipment necessary and to produce a succession of turf for the market. There are significant economies of scale. The cost of specialist machinery for turf production can be £350,000. A new one-man harvesting machine costs in the order of £120,000-£200,000 but significantly reduces labour costs.

Costs and Returns

Variable Costs plus Rent:	£/ha	(£/ac)
Seed	750-1,100	(300-445)
Fertiliser	350-700	(140-280)
Herbicide	90-150	(35-60)
Fungicide	100-210	(40-85)
Rent (for 15 months)	700-1,300	(385-525)
Total Costs	*1,990-3,510*	*(805-1,400)*

It may be necessary to irrigate and on occasions use netting to grow the grass for certain sites.

Labour: Special seed bed preparation (including subsoiling and stone burying), regular mowing (twice a week May/June), picking up clippings, harvesting (2 men on harvester plus one loading lorry) between 0.2-0.4 hectares per day (0.5-1.0 acre). The new one-man harvester can do 2 ha (5 acres) a day.

Total costs of the order of £5,000-£7,500 per ha (£2,000-£3,037 per acre), approximately 50-75p per square metre.

Value of Turf (on the field)

	per m²	per sq. yd.	per ha*	per acre*
Pasture turf	38-43p	32-36p	£3,420-£3,850	£1,380-£1,570
Hardwearing, domestic general contract	70-95p	58-79p	£6,300-£8,550	£2,550-£3,460
Football, hockey, prestige landscape	115-145p	95-120p	£10,260-£12,825	£4,150-£5,200
High quality/specialist**	190-475p	160-405p	£17,100-£42,750	£6,910-£17,290

*   assuming 90% recovery, but some producers work on 85%.

** for some contracts the price may be higher.

Delivery charges 45-55p per m² for a full lorry load. Higher for smaller deliveries.

Acknowledgements: Turfgrass Growers Association, PVGA House, Nottingham Road, Lincolnshire, LN11 0WB. Telephone: 01507 607722. www.turfgrass.co.uk. *Robert Laycock,* Littlegarth, Low Street, Lastingham, North Yorkshire, YO62 6TJ. Telephone: 01751 417191. www.robertlaycock.co.uk.

GOLF

The game of golf is slowly recovering and club closures appear to have stabilised. Most clubs continue to struggle but have been ingenious in trying to retain existing members and attract new.

The sale price of courses continues to be relatively depressed since bottom line profits have not really improved. Many clubs have been happy to survive with the number of new clubs still being in single figures. Clubs bought by overseas investors as 'bargains' have seen further falls in revenue which has scared off a number of potential new investors. The lack of buyers for real estate on golf resorts has seen many attractive opportunities for investors overseas. The diversion of this money has meant a relatively low number and size of sales in the UK.

The game still suffers from a 'staid' image that is at odds with the demand for high-adrenalin sports from the younger generation. Despite many attempts at different formats including 'Footgolf' and short courses the lack of interest from the younger generation continues to be an issue. The length of time required for a round of golf does not fit well with the commitments of modern life. The age bracket of those playing continues to rise and the spend per head at the clubs continues to fall in real terms although some clubs have capitalised on the wedding market and other functions

It looks as though golf will continue to struggle financially for years to come and we continue to see no sign of future significant growth in the game in the UK

The continued rise in agricultural land prices means that it is virtually impossible to generate a profit on a stand-alone golf site. Driving range development has also virtually stopped with a declining marketplace and less practice taking place. The lack of finance from banks and institutions has meant few sales and even fewer new projects. Anyone considering development is well advised to resolve their financing in principle before entering the design / development phase.

In many cases the planning system has failed to identify sites for new golf developments within the Local Plans. There are no known locations left where there is proven demand. In our experience, the old guidelines of 1 course per 18,000 people no longer apply and should be revised to a minimum of 1:30,000. For those who are interested in development the following guidelines may help but the best advice is to check that there really is a market before starting to even think about development

Type of Facility and Costs

- 18-hole 6,400 metre (7,000 yard) course: 70-80 ha (*170-195 acres*) including Clubhouse and Pro Shop (600 sq. metres), parking, proper access and maintenance buildings. *The course will take between 1 and 2 years to construct, and will cost £2.5m-£3.5m according to drainage, earthmoving and irrigation, but excluding green keepers building and machinery. A Clubhouse (600 sq. metres) will cost from £1,200,000 or £3.2m fitted out. A full inventory of new machinery for an 18-hole course will cost £580,000*

- 9-hole course: 35-40 ha (*84-95 acres*). Cost: *£900,000-£1.3m*

- 9-hole Par 3 course: 7 ha (*17 acres*). Cost: *£700,000-£950,000*

- 6-hole Par 3 or 4 course: 14 ha (*34 acres*). Cost: *£550,000-£850,000*

- Driving range: 4 ha (*10 acres*). Cost: *£350,000-£900,000, to include offices, storage, equipment, fencing and floodlighting*

- Pitch and putt course: 1.5 ha (*4 acres*). Depends on overall site area

Direct labour may reduce costs by around a third. Using own farm labour it is possible to reduce costs by up to 40% but it is very risky in terms of resultant course quality.

Anything involving plastics such as irrigation and drainage supplies has seen prices rise considerably in the past few years. Despite the fall in oil prices the cost of such items has not yet reduced.

It is crucial to obtain professional advice at the outset for investment appraisal, feasibility study and a business plan. Before starting design work, it would be wise to commission a Feasibility Study which needs only cost £10-15,000 to check that there really is a demonstrable business case on which finance can be raised.

Type of business organisation

To sell land with planning permission: The cost of development of an average new course will be significantly more than the value of the facility when it is complete. There is currently no premium over agricultural value unless the situation or planning consent offers something exceptional. The cost of obtaining permission can vary enormously depending on the sensitivity of the site but it would seldom cost less than £250,000 including design, environment impact study and Local Authority fees.

To let land to a developer/operator: Assuming the latter pays for constructing the course, a long lease will be required. Rental levels will depend on the expected profitability of the facility but currently, in our experience, leases remain around £40-£80,000 for an 18-hole course. *To form a joint company with a developer/operator*: This obviously means the farmer shares in the success or failure. The land would be all or part of the farmer's equity. There are no known active developers in this market at present

To develop and operate the course himself: The farmer would need good knowledge of golf and exceptional management ability besides access to substantial capital.

Returns

It will cost considerably more to build and fit out a course than it will be worth for resale. Returns on capital are therefore negative unless the course has spin off benefits such as increasing an associated hotel occupancy or room rates.

Bankable rates of return on new courses are extremely rare. Associated residential or other development could make developments profitable, but planning permission for such developments is very difficult.

Acknowledgement: *International Design Group* Studio 5.17, The Paintworks, Bath Road, Bristol BS4 3EH. Telephone: 0117 316 0592. www.idgplanet.com

CHRISTMAS TREES

About 7 million real Christmas trees are sold a year in the UK; this figure has reduced as the quality of artificial trees has improved. Most real trees sold are UK-produced, with the balance from imports, chiefly from Scandinavia. A decade ago 80% were Norway Spruce, but this is now down to around 15%, with Nordman Fir, which retains its needles longer, at around 75%. Other firs and spruces such as Fraser Fir, Noble Fir and Blue Spruce make up the remainder. The most popular sizes are between 5 to 7 feet.

There are 400 British growers across all parts of the country, with plantations ranging from less than one hectare to 300 ha. It is estimated that there are in excess of 50 million trees being grown, covering up to 9,000 ha. The majority of sales are through big garden centres, which require a uniform tree, netted and palletised, but there are successful 'choose and cut' operations and the enterprise works well on a farm with a farm shop. Internet sales are growing.

The enterprise is slow to make a return. Nordman Firs are typically harvested in years 7 to 9. The quicker-growing Norway Spruce is harvested in years 5 to 7. This makes the enterprise vulnerable to changing market conditions. About 20% of the crop is harvested in the first harvesting year, 50% in the second, 30% in the third. All species need a well-drained site free from late frosts, with good access. As with any crop, the better the land, the better the crop. The budget below if for an eight-year rotation.

	Nordman Fir	
	£/ha	(£/ac)
5000 5 to 7 foot trees per ha @ price of . .	£3.50 - 4.00 / ft	
Output (average)	112,500	(45,528)
Variable Costs:		
Plants	4,025	(1,629)
Planting	1,035	(419)
Fertiliser	600	(243)
Weed control	450	(182)
Plant protection	900	(364)
Pruning and shaping	5,005	(2,025)
Harvesting	4,675	(1,892)
Marketing	11,250	(4,553)
Total Variable Costs	27,940	(11,307)
Gross Margin (whole period)	84,560	(34,221)
Gross Margin per year over 8 years	**10,570**	**(4,278)**

1. *Output:* Sale number of 5,000 trees per ha is based on approx. 90% saleable from a population of 5,500 per ha (see below). Price shown is for sales to local garden centres and shops. Prices will be 20-30% lower if selling to wholesalers, national garden chains or DIY stores. Prices can be raised by 50% for retail sales direct to the public

2. *Establishment:* Rabbit fencing (£4-£5 per m) is necessary and possibly deer fencing (£6-£8 per m). Spacing is possible from 60cm x 60cm to 1.8m x 1.8m, but 1.2m x 1.2m gives 5,500 plants per ha allowing for 20% land loss for headlands, access, etc. Losses of up to 5% in the first year means around 250 replacements are needed in second year. Norway Spruce transplants 25p-40p each, Nordman Fir 50-90p (*70p used in margin*). Planting, by hand or machine, 15-20p/per plant (*18p used in margin*).

3. *Variable Inputs:*

   Fertiliser is typically a split 70:30 top dressing of 350 kg/ha in late March and mid-September.

Weed control through residual herbicide in March at £70/ha and glyphosate at £10/ha in October/November plus spot weeding of perennial weeds until the canopy closes over.

Insect control will require aphicide at £10-£50/ha and spider mite control £5-£100/ha commencing in the year of planting and subsequently in January for spruce and April for Firs.

In years 5 - 7 Nordmann Fir will require leader control. Approximately 50% of the trees treated twice annually with cutters or growth regulators over three years at a cost of 10p/tree = £300/ha in total.

Fraser Fir and Noble Fir will also require 4 - 6 week applications to suppress phytophthora at £30-£50/ha/application.

4. *Pruning and Shaping*: This is essential to produce the shape of tree the market demands. Nordman Fir: basal pruning in year 3 or 4 at 20p per tree plus shaping in the same year at 16p per tree and bud-rubbing every year except harvest at 5-10p per tree per year. Norway Spruce: shaping 17p per tree per year from year 3 or 4.

5. *Harvesting:* Done over 3 to 6 weeks, for dispatch Nov 20th to Dec 12th. A full-time person is needed per 3,000 trees sold, or one person per week per 400-500 trees. Cost: Norway Spruce 70-90p per tree, Nordman Fir 75-100p. Marketing costs around 10% of output.

6. *Machinery:* Inter-row plantation tractors £15,000-£65,000; stump clearing machines £7,000-£25,000; palletiser £13,000-£14,000; mist blowers £8,000-£10,000; hydraulic netting funnel £8,000-£10,000; manual netting funnel £175.

7. *Labour:* Planting and pruning can be done in January/February and tagging for height and quality from August to November. Thus it fits in well with combinable cropping. Casual help is likely to be required for harvest and sales.

The gross margins given are high, but these will only be achieved by a high level of expertise and commitment and the long period before any return is obtained must also be stressed, together with the risk this entails.

Acknowledgement: Thanks to - British Christmas Tree Growers Association, Fynn Valley Farm, Main Road, Tuddenham St Martin, Ipswich, Suffolk, IP6 9BZ. Tel: 01473 785100 www.bctga.co.uk. Colin Palmer, Woodview Cottage, Raycomb Lane, Coddington, Herefordshire, HR8 1JH. Tel: 01531 633500 www.ruralservices.info

COARSE FISHING

In excess of 1.5 million people regularly coarse fish in the UK and numbers are rising. It is a freshwater method of line fishing usually from the banks of a watercourse. Coarse fish species include Rudd, Roach, Bream, Barbel, Tench, Chub, Perch, Pike, Carp, exclude sea species and 'game' fish like salmon and trout (usually caught by 'fly fishing'). Coarse fish are returned to the water after catching and weighing. Facilities can be rivers, streams, canals, lakes, ponds and even drains. The close season for coarse fishing is 15th March to 15th June although most canals and still waters are exempt from the close season. Anyone fishing must have a rod licence (available from the Environment Agency).

Fishing permit prices vary depending on the location, quality of the fishing, species etc. They will be higher if the water is actively managed to attract more or certain fish species. Maintenance and landscaping of the water banks will add a premium to a facility as will secure car parking and easy access to fishing pegs (platforms). Typically permits cost:

- Half-Day Ticket (per rod)   £4.00 to £7.00
- Full-Day Ticket (per rod)   £5.00 to £13.00
- Season Ticket (per rod)   £50.00 to £180

Typical Net Margin for Coarse Fishing Lake, Labour excluded

1 Hectare (2.4 acre) Lake	per peg	per Lake
	£	£
Fishing Permits	1,300	13,000
Fish Sales	80	800
Output	1,380	13,800
Costs		
Peg Capital	48	475
Peg Maintenance	11	110
Fish Restocking	21	210
Feed Feed	150	1,500
Plants and Ground Maint.	40	400
Total Variable Costs	270	2,695
Gross Margin per ha (acre)	1,031	10,305

Ponds and lakes can be initially stocked costing around £5,000 for a 1 hectare lake. Pegs should be spaced at no less than 25m apart (dictating income potential). Ponds and lakes can be initially stocked or routinely restocked. A 2 acre carp lake would cost around £5,000 to stock with annual feeding costs of £1,500. Plants and other costs would total around £3,000 initially and will then need maintaining.

The larger the fish the higher the price that can be charged therefore the smaller fish can be routinely removed and sold. The total income from a two acre managed lake would be in the region of £10-15,000. Further diversifying into accommodation (log cabins) on a two acre lake stocked with 30lb carp could demand up to £1,000 per week for 4 anglers. Labour could become significant to manage the permits, stock and landscape. Generating this return might take some building up of regular fishers, managing the layout and facilities and so on and requires an existing suitable lake.

BED AND BREAKFAST

The person running bed and breakfast should enjoy meeting people, have good social skills and be prepared to work unusual hours. In a crowded market, and with rising customer expectations, the standard of the product and service is critical. Farms must provide a standard of accommodation equal to that found in hotels. This will involve some refurbishment; both before starting the enterprise, to upgrade existing B&B to rising standards and ongoing repair of wear and tear.

It is vital to know the planning, legislative and financial requirements involved in B&B. Details are available from VisitBritain in the *'The Pink Booklet' - a practical guide to legislation for accommodation providers'*. This is available online at www.accommodationknowhow.co.uk/. Advice is also provided by National Tourist Boards of England, Scotland and Wales and Regional Tourist Boards.

Marketing is important. Some establishments produce a brochure or card giving details of the B&B, its location, facilities, and quality standards rating. New routes to customers have been opened up recently by of 'peer-to-peer' renting websites such as Airbnb. To join a marketing organisation the B&B should have a Quality Assurance Standard rating. These are awarded either by the official National Tourist Board inspectorate (which in England is Quality in Tourism), or the AA. The rating is at one of five levels, expressed as stars.

As there is considerable competition it is useful for the enterprise to offer something special or different such as accommodation for visitors' horses, a welcome for pets, or access to view the working farm. Establishments that can accommodate bigger parties are gaining in popularity. The number of B&Bs offering an evening meal has declined in recent years, but providing locally grown produce can be a draw.

Prices that can be charged reflect the quality of accommodation and location but cannot be far out of line with other local B&Bs and hotels. Prices can also vary depending on length of stay and time of year. The price range for one person per night ranges from £30 to over £150 on the basis of two adults sharing a room. A higher rate per person usually applies for single occupancy. There are regional differences with higher prices generally being charged in the south and east.

The range of B&B facilities has become enormous in the last decade. Decide the marketplace that suits you by identifying your selling point. Is it low cost, luxury, access to a working farm, family comfort etc.? Prepare the B&B enterprise, target your marketing and price the rooms accordingly to meet that marketplace.

Receipts from the enterprise can be calculated as follows: If the B&B is open for 40 weeks of the year at £40 per person per night, given a 60% occupancy rate the gross return per bed place will be around £6,720. Most farmhouse B&Bs have 4-6 bed spaces, which would generate a gross return of between £27,000 to £40,000 p.a.

Costs vary considerably: As every farmhouse B&B is different and some costs are difficult to apportion between guests and family, the following provides some pointers. Variable costs are food, electricity, heating, laundry, cleaning materials and additional help. There will also be regular redecoration costs, repairs, and replacement and renewal of glassware, china, cutlery, towels and bed linen. Variable costs if no non-family labour is used average about 20% of the nightly charge. If casual labour has to be included variable costs rise to 30-35% of the nightly charge.

Fixed costs include insurance, business rates (if they apply), membership of marketing organisations, regular advertising, repayments on loans taken out for building and equipment and regular labour; they are likely to average 30-35% of charges.

Contact: Farm Stay UK, Tel: 02476 696 909. www.farmstay.co.uk, *VisitBritain,* Tel: 020 8846 9000. www.visitbritain.org. *Quality in Tourism*, Tel: 0845 300 6996. www.qualityintourism.com.

CAMPING AND CARAVAN SITES

To some, camp sites and caravan parks appear to be an easy way to increase farm turnover and therefore profit. Their revenue potential is divorced from the vagaries of the agricultural markets and, largely unaffected by economic depressions. However, to run a successful site requires capital investment and dedicated management time. The range of camping and caravanning experiences offered is from a well-drained stone-less field with access to a toilet and shower, to a fully developed 'park' with set pitches with electrical hook ups, entertainment, and other amenities.

The key requirement is the correct location. Ideally a tourist area, quiet from busy roads, a good view, a well-drained field (at least a half hectare), relatively stone-less (for camping) space with fairly flat areas is necessary. Water and electricity are required. The site needs to be licenced by the local authority (not Scotland). Exemptions apply for some camping and caravanning organisations. They also require planning permission.

Capital
Infrastructure to consider includes; toilets and showers (with hot water) with disabled access, refuse collection, electrical hook-ups for caravans, compressed gas storage and landscaping which could include creation of recreational space, road and footpath improvements, land levelling (at least at the pitches), and screening (hedges and fences). Capital spending will vary according to what is already in location. However, minimal capital costs for a new, well sited 1 hectare field with water and electricity already available could start at £15,000:

- Planning and licencing £1,000
- Small toilet and shower block £10,000
- Landscaping (hedges, fencing destoning, flattening pitches, grassing) £2,000
- Good mower £1,500
- Website and other business development £500

Costs
This would give an annual depreciation cost of £3,000 at 20%. Ground maintenance costs of another £1,000 and utility fees of £1,000 coupled with the time required to manage the field and grass need including. Farm insurance policies will not include the site.

Some locations have access to existing toilet and shower facilities which would reduce the cost considerably. Ongoing management would also be necessary; managing booking enquiries, promotion of the site (e.g. website) collecting payments, maintaining the grounds, cutting the grass, site management, and so on. Allow at least 2 hours per day for a small site in and ahead of the season (minimum £3,000). Full time staff will be required for larger parks in the camping season.

Receipts
Depending on location and facilities, family tents in high-season can be charged £20 per night, £40 per caravan. However these prices fall substantially out of season or in less attractive locations. Connecting to other local attractions is useful such as nearby pubs, pony trekking stables or open farms. This can help extend the camping season for many locations. Clearly, this is a very seasonal enterprise, often busiest during peak farming workloads so is not always the best use of 'underutilised' farm resources.

Assuming minimal annual costs of £8,000 (as detailed above), and an average pitch price of £20 per night, 400 tent/caravan nights will be required. This could be 15 pitches per night in August or fewer for a longer camping period. The longer the season, the more the overall management costs. The key criteria is the number of pitches booked per night – making both good profits and high losses possible.

LOG CABINS AND GLAMPING

A renewed interest in British short breaks and holidays has led to a popularity surge of 'alternative' accommodation as well as the more traditional cottage rentals or caravan and camping. There are many examples where log cabin rentals for tourism and leisure purposes have been extremely successful as farm diversification projects. As with any tourism and leisure based enterprise, location is everything and can determine the success (or failure) of the proposal. It will also determine the rental income and occupancy that can be achieved. There may also be potential for using log cabins as a substitute for 'permanent', traditional buildings for office, storage facilities etc.

Log cabins vary in size and quality from glorified cladded caravans on bricks to opulent, luxurious and spacious living spaces. Some even have hot tubs, access to pools and sports facilities.

Full planning permission will be required before the construction of any log cabin. It is recommended that professional support is sought in this respect prior to any expenditure on equipment / groundwork.

Build Costs

Prices for cabins vary considerably, primarily linked to the size and finish (quality) of the final build and the cost of routing any mains services. The figures below are a guide to log cabin purchase and build costs, but excluding fixtures and fittings which may add £85.00 to £125.00 of additional cost per m². Costs in routing mains services to the cabins will depend on remoteness, topography, environmental restrictions etc. and the extent of supplies required (bottled gas and septic tanks can be used in place of mains gas and sewage):

'Fishing' Log Cabin   30m² floor space plus sleeping 'loft'   £10,000 - £42,000

'Holiday let' Log Cabin   60m² floor space with 2 bedrooms   £20,500 - £55,500

For cabins larger than the examples above, add £250.00 to £300.00 per m² for every m² over and above the sizes stated

Rental Potential

Good occupancy rates of the cabins will be paramount to the viability of any investment. Annual occupancy rates will vary depending on location, seasonality of local attractions and level of discount given in the 'off' season. Rental incomes again vary considerably, but typically range from £250 to £1,100 per week, with the higher incomes being achieved where the cabins are located in more desirable locations i.e. near to areas popular for fly and course fishing, mountain biking, walking, coastal activities, tourist attractions etc. Single night stays and short breaks often command a higher income pro rata than weekly lets but more work as well.

Other Accommodation

Yurts, tipis and other 'high specification' camping can also be lucrative if the resources are in place and high occupancy achieved, although these may not have a long a life as the cabins. Weekly rents of £200 to £600 per week can be achieved with the right locations and glamping specification. Capital cost for a furnished yurt can be £4,000 to £10,000 depending on size and specification. Ground and site maintenance as well as yurt preparation and booking administration should also be accounted for.

GAME SHOOTING

Game shooting is an increasingly popular activity. It refers to the shooting of game species which include both feathered and fur animals. The most common birds shot in the UK include pheasant, partridge, duck, woodcock, snipe and grouse. Most feathered game are reared in captivity and then released but wild populations can be enhanced by different management techniques. There are strict and differing shooting seasons for different species, both game and pests.

'Driven' game shooting is the most popular method of game shooting in the UK whereby game birds are 'flighted' towards a standing line of guns. The quality and type of driven shoot varies according to landscape and management factors as well as the number of birds present. These variances also have a major impact on the cost of partaking in a shoot.

	per bird	per Gun	per Shoot Day	per Season
		22 birds	8 guns	8 shoots
	£	£	£	£
Charge for Gun	35.00	770	6,160	49,280
Other charges				1,500
Output	35	770	6,160	50,780
Costs				
Bird Placing	12.00	264	2,112	16,896
Bird Feed	2.30	51	405	3,238
Hospitality		75	600	4,800
Beaters & Pickers		80	640	5,120
Ground Maint. Costs			*1,063*	8,500
Capital depreciation			*500*	4,000
Gamekeeper			*1,000*	8,000
Attributable Costs	14.30	470	6,319	50,554
Net Margin	0.16	4	28	226

1. *Bird Placings:* at £4/head. Many more are placed than shot, this example is 3-fold.
2. *Beaters and Pickers:* 15 beaters per shoot and pickers
3. *Capital Deptreciation:* Bird pens, feeders, water, etc.
4. *Gamekeeper:* Half time wage included here. May include imputed costs.

As a rough guide, a 200 bird day driven shoot will cost in the range of £800 per gun (participant), at £32 per bird. A driven shoot normally has 7 to 9 guns with up to 8 'drives' in a day.

The expensive nature of most driven game shoots is required by the amount of work and cost involved in running a shoot (buying birds, feeding, structural equipment costs, game plot establishment, game keeper and beater's costs, shoot day hospitality etc.) and so margins may be small given the investment required.

Further information: British Association for Shooting and Conservation – www.basc.org.uk

OTHER DIVERSIFICATION

Well calculated diversification is to be encouraged. Non-agricultural enterprises managed in conjunction with the farming operation can offer several benefits to the business. These include:

- Spreading risks of returns; if the economics of agricultural production declines, revenue from non-commodity based enterprises may boost business income.

- Resource efficiency; most farm systems have quieter and busier periods for staff and management which may be switched into other roles for examples.

- Increased profit.

Any new enterprise will have its own risks associated with it. These must be clearly and objectively calculated (this will be a requirement if borrowed money is necessary). Each resource employed will have its own opportunity cost (what could it be earning if it was not being used for this new venture?). Cash (return on capital) is the obvious one, what could it earn elsewhere? Labour is less straight forward. For example, a B&B might require minimal new capital under some circumstances, but tie somebody to the house at key times of the day, restricting other employment opportunities.

Before a major investment or change in business structure to incorporate new diversifications, business plans and market research to assess the income potential are needed. Most new enterprises require new skills (such as different production systems, new marketing and sales techniques). These take time and dedication to acquire. Developing new ideas and expanding a novel business venture can be exciting and time consuming; maintaining sufficient management time on the existing farm business is a common problem.

Nevertheless, many ventures exist where entrepreneurial skills have achieved notable success. Conversion of surplus farm buildings, for offices, workshops, retail and storage, has been the primary farm diversification activity up to date. Well over half of all farms have some kind of diversification, but if letting farm buildings is stripped out the percentage of diversified farms falls to between a quarter and a third. Arable farms tend to be more diversified than livestock and farms in the South East are more diversified than elsewhere in the UK. Diversified enterprises might have a different VAT and taxation treatment. Check in advance with your accountant.

Some 'diversification' enterprises have been included above. There are many others, such as;

Novel Crops/Livestock
- Herbs
- Carp and Crayfish
- Quails
- Snails & Worms
- Maggots

Barn Conversions
- Business Lets
- Dwelling Let

Sporting
- Fisheries
- Stalking
- Clay Pigeon Shooting

Horses
- Riding School
- Trekking

Tourism
- Holiday Cottages

Vertical integration
- Yoghurt / Ice cream
- Farm Shop
- Meat sales

Adventure Games
- Motor Sports
- Go-carting

Many of these have been taken to new levels in recent years, for example the farm shop has moved on substantially from where it was 10 years ago and is now a vibrant and growing industry for high-end shoppers in market towns and motorway service stations. Other services as well as sale of fresh produce are being provided. Camping has given rise to Glamping, again focussing at the more affluent end of the market keen on luxury and service, one that is covered in the book now.

6. FORESTRY

ESTABLISHMENT COSTS (BEFORE GRANT)

Unit Cost of Operations

Year/s	Operation	Cost (£)
1.	Trees for planting (1)	
	(i) Bare rooted:	
	Conifers	220-350 per 1,000
	Broadleaves	250-400 per 1,000
	(ii) Cell grown:	
	Conifers	270-355 per 1,000
	Broadleaves	330-430 per 1,000
1.	Tree Protection	
	(i) Fencing (materials and erection)	
	Rabbit	4.20-6.00 per metre
	Stock..	4.15-5.15 per metre
	Deer	6.50-8.50 per metre
	Deer and Rabbit............................	8.00-10.50 per metre
	Split post and rail	5.50-8.50 per metre
	(ii) Tree guards/shelters	
	Spiral and canes (750mm)	28-32 per 100
	Plastic tubes (1,200mm).................	100-135 per 100
	Stakes..	50-70 per 100
1.	Spot spraying	80-100 per 1,000 trees
1.	Hand planting	
	Conifers	350-600 per 1,000 trees
	Broadleaves (2).............................	350-600 per 1,000 trees
	Machine planting (loams and sand based on 2,250 plants per ha)	225-450 per ha
2-3.	Replacing dead trees (3)	
	Operation......................................	110-200 per ha
	Plant supply	90-150 per ha
1-4.	Weeding per operation	
	Herbicide (4)................................	70-130 per ha weeded
2.	Inter-row mowing..	70-200 per ha

Costs specific to location		Upland	Lowland
1.	Ground Preparation: ploughing	132-209 per ha	66- 99 per ha
	mounding	275-385 per ha	275-385 per ha
1.	Drainage	88-110 per ha	—
1.	Fertilising	132-297 per ha	—

1. Price dependent on size and species

2. Includes cost of erecting guards/shelters.

3. Replacing dead trees (beating up) may be necessary, once in the second year and again in the third year. Costs depend on number of trees.

4. Up to 2 weeding operations may be necessary in each of the first 4 years in extreme situations. Costs are inclusive of materials.

Access roads may need to be constructed and can typically cost between £13,500 and £33,000 per kilometre run (£21,700 to £53,000 per mile) depending on availability of road stone and the number of culverts and bridges required.

Total Establishment Costs up to Year 3

1. *Conifer—Lowland Sites:* On a fairly typical lowland site, requiring little or no clearing or draining, the approximate cost before grant of establishing a conifer plantation would be in the range of £3,500-£6,000 per hectare. Up to 8 separate weeding operations may be required.

2. *Conifer—Upland Sites:* Establishing a similar conifer plantation on an upland site could cost £3,000 to £5,500 per hectare. Normally some form of site preparation and drainage is required but only one weeding operation may be necessary. Overall costs tend to be £500 per hectare less than on lowland sites.

3. *Hardwoods:* Costs of establishing hardwood plantations are highly dependent on the fencing and/or tree protection required. If tubes are needed the overall costs will be influenced by the number of trees per hectare. Costs could be in the range of £4,000-£8,000 per hectare. Site conditions normally mean that hardwoods being grown for timber production are restricted to lowland sites.

4. *Farm Woodlands:* Establishment costs for farm woodlands may be lower than those indicated for hardwoods in (3) above if lower planting densities are used; costs of about £6,800 per ha for woods under 3 ha and £5,500 per ha for woods of 3 to 10 ha would be typical. However it should be noted planting at lower densities may increase maintenance cost and will lead to production of lower quality material.

5. *Size Factor:* Savings in fencing and other economies of scale may reduce average costs per ha by 10 to 20% where large plantations are being established.

6. *Method of Establishment:* A range of organisations and individuals undertake forestry contracting work and competitive tendering can help to control costs.

The costs of establishment given above, and those for maintenance given below, are estimates for England. Costs in Scotland tend to be lower.

Re-Stocking Costs

Once trees on a site have been felled, the Forestry Commission usually requires the site to be restocked as a condition of awarding a felling licence. This can be done by replanting or through natural regeneration, leaving a proportion of the trees standing and using seed from these trees to re-stock. Site preparation is usually required for natural regeneration through scarification and ongoing maintenance will be required to encourage a viable crop. Re-stocking a clear felled area would incur similar costs to those above.

MAINTENANCE COSTS

Once trees have been established they normally require some maintenance and management work each year. For trees being grown primarily for timber production on a large scale, operations required may include ride and fence maintenance, pest control, fire protection, management fee and insurance premiums. Costs are normally £60-£90 per ha per annum depending on the size of the plantation and the complexity of management. In upland areas, fertiliser is occasionally applied once or more times in the first 20 years of the tree's life depending on the quality of the site. Estimated cost of £110-£275 per ha, depending on elements applied. For trees being grown for sporting and amenity purposes, annual maintenance costs are likely to be less and may range up to about £30 per ha.

Brashing is no longer practised on large-scale conifer plantations as a result of mechanical harvesting techniques.

PRODUCTION

Production is usually measured in terms of cubic metres (m³) of marketable timber per hectare and will vary according to the quality of the site, species planted and thinning policy. Sites in lowland Britain planted to conifers typically produce an average of 12 to 18 m³ of timber per ha per year over the rotation as a whole and would accordingly be assessed as falling in yield classes 12 to 18. Under traditional management systems, thinning begins 18 to 25 years after planting and is repeated at intervals of approximately 5-7 years until a conifer wood is clear-felled at between 40 and 60 years, or a broadleaf wood at 80-120 years. Approximately 40-45% of total production will be from thinnings. Broadleaves typically produce an average of between 4 and 8 m³ of timber per hectare per year and fall in yield classes 4 to 8.

Prior to a thinning sale, the trees normally have to be marked and measured at an estimated cost of 75p - £1 per m³. For a clear-felling sale the cost can range from £300 to £400 per ha, or about £1.50 per m³ where a full tariff applies. These costs associated with mensuration and marking can vary significantly and will correlate to the value of the crop to be harvested.

Felling permission is required when more than 5m³ is to be removed in any one calendar quarter. This requires an application to the Forestry Commission for a Felling Licence which will vary in complexity depending on the size and variety of the woodland. A felling licence must be obtained from the Forestry Commission before any felling takes place, unless a Forest Management Plan has already been approved by them. Grants are available for preparing a Woodland Management Plan under the Countryside Stewardship Scheme in England. Similar provisions operate in other parts of the UK.

TIMBER PRICES

Prices for standing timber are extremely variable, depending on species, tree size and quality; ease of extraction from site; geographical location (nearness to end user); quantity being sold; world market prices and effectiveness of marketing method used. The use of wood for energy generation continues to provide a market for poorer quality hardwood, conifer logs and forest residues.

Conifers/Softwood

Coniferous Standing Sales Price for Great Britain from the Forestry Enterprise Estate

Year to:	Average Price (per m³ overbark)	
	Nominal terms	Real terms (2011 prices)
31ˢᵗ March 2006	7.25	8.39
31ˢᵗ March 2007..	7.97	8.97
31ˢᵗ March 2008..	12.48	13.71
31ˢᵗ March 2009..	9.15	9.77
31ˢᵗ March 2010..	9.61	9.99
31ˢᵗ March 2011..	13.70	13.88
31ˢᵗ March 2012..	14.10	13.96
31ˢᵗ March 2013..	13.29	13.01
31ˢᵗ March 2014..	15.62	15.03
31ˢᵗ March 2015..	18.48	17.39

Source: Forestry Commission: Timber Price Indices. March 2015.

Hardwoods

The hardwood trade is very complex. Merchants normally assess and value all but the smallest trees on a stem by stem basis. Actual prices fetched can show considerable variation depending on species, size, form, quality and marketing expertise of the seller. Felling usually takes place in the winter months.

Some indicative prices for hardwoods are given below, but it is important to note that actual prices fetched can vary quite widely. Wood quality is particularly important in determining prices.

Product	Price (standing)
Ash logs	£3-£7 per hoppus foot (1)
Oak logs – milling timber	£3-£8 per hoppus foot (1)
Firewood	Average £20-£24 per tonne
Softwood sawlogs	Between £25-£27 per tonne
Cricket bat willow	Between £200-£250 per tree
Ash hurley stick butts - roadside	£180-£200 per

1.   A hoppus foot is an imperial measurement that is still used in the hardwood trade (but not for softwood). It estimates what volume of a round log would be usable timber after processing (allowing for wastage). Because of the wastage factor a hoppus foot is larger than a cubic foot. $1m^3 = 27.736074$ hoppus feet

TIMBER MARKETING

In-house marketing by the owner or agent can be cost effective but only if they have detailed, up-to-date knowledge of timber buyers in the market place. The alternative is marketing through a forestry manager or management company.

Sales can take place of either standing timber or felled timber at roadside. Standing sales place felling and extraction costs on to the purchaser who will usually pay for the timber on an outturn basis, whether by weight (tonne) or volume (m^3). These types of sales suit thinning and lower quality material. Roadside sales require the owner to pay for trees to be felled and extracted to a collection point where they can be accurately measured and inspected by potential purchasers. These types of sales are generally suitable for higher value timber.

Nationwide electronic sales of timber by auction and tender are now available for all types and quantities of timber.

MARKET VALUE OF ESTABLISHED PLANTATIONS AND WOODS

The value of woods depends on many factors, such as location, access, species, age and soil type. The table below gives an indication of the range of current (2015) market values of commercial woodlands of different ages, based on recent sales. From years 20 to 25 onwards, prices of commercial woods will also be increasingly influenced by the quantity of merchantable timber they contain. Depending on the time of clear-felling, the timber may be worth between £900 to £6,000 per hectare (£360 to £2,500 per acre).

Relatively small woods or those with high amenity or Ancient Woodland status often command a premium over prices for commercial woodlands as can those that are freehold with minerals or sporting rights; this is particularly in southern England. Conversely conservation designation can restrict value due to a perception of preventing economic forest management; however this need not be the case. Recent sales of predominately broadleaved woodlands of amenity type range from £10,000/ha to £20,000/ha with exceptional woodlands exceeding this by over 20%. The value of woods containing mature hardwoods will depend on the quality and value of the timber they contain and the quality of access.

Market Value of Commercial Conifer Woodlands

Age of Commercial Woods and Plantations	Price Range for crop and land	
	£/ha	£/acre
0-10 years	4,200-4,600	(1,700-1,860)
11-20 years	6,500-7,000	(2,630-2,830)
21-30 years	6,800-7,200	(2,750-2,900)
31-40 years	6,900-7,300	(2,800-2,950)
40+ years	5,200-6,300	(2,100-2,550)

WOODLAND GRANTS

Each part of the UK has its own woodland grant scheme funded via the Rural Development Programme (RDP) and administered by the Forestry Commission. Details of all the schemes are on the Forestry Commission's website (www.forestry.gov.uk) or www.gov.uk.

Countryside Stewardship Scheme - England

The main priority of Countryside Stewardship Scheme (CSS) is to protect and enhance the natural environment, in particular the diversity of wildlife (biodiversity). Water quality is another important priority as are flood management, the historic environment, landscape, genetic conservation and educational access.

The scheme is jointly run by Natural England (NE), Forestry Commission England (FC) and the Rural Payments Agency on behalf of Defra. Applications are competitively scored. Applications need to demonstrate that the meet the specific scheme priorities/statement of priorities.

To enter into any of the Countryside Stewardship schemes, applicants need to have all the following in place:

- Single Business Identifier (SBI)/Business Name;

- Land registered on the Rural Land Register (RLR);

- Registered on the Rural Payments Service and hold a Customer Reference Number.

The CSS provides both capital grants and funding for ongoing management. Capital grants are available for;

- Woodland Creation

- Tree Health measures

- The creation of a Woodland Management Plan

A Management Plan must be in place for any woodland that is to be entered into a ongoing management agreement under the Woodland Improvement Scheme.

1. *Woodland Creation:* The first round of Capital Grants closed at the end of April 2015 but will open again in early 2016 for Woodland Creation schemes.

- Woodland creation £1.28/unit + various supplements for enhanced protection measures – maximum £6,800 per hectare;

- Maintenance £200 per hectare per year for 10 years.

2. *Woodland Tree Health:* Grants are available for restoration and improvement but only available for trees infected by *Chalara* or *Phytopthora ramorum.* Official confirmation of infection is required to be eligible for this grant.

3. *Woodland Management Plans:* Capital grants for the production of a Woodland Management Plan are available on a rolling basis i.e. there is no application window. Management plans can secure 10 years' felling permission by the creation of a Plan of Operations.

  - Minimum grant is £1,000 for three hectares and over of woodland;

  - First 100 hectares is paid at £20 per hectare; £10 per hectare thereafter with no further limit.

4. *Woodland Improvement Grant (WIG):* This is a multi-year scheme (5 years +) offering annual payments to undertake practices that will benefit the environment. It falls under the 'higher tier' of the CSS. Infrastructure grants and Capital grants to support the management objectives are also available under this scheme.

   Some example woodland options under the WIG are as follows:

Option	Funding
Woodland improvement (WD2)	£100 per Ha per year
Woodland Edges on Arable Land (WD3)*	£323 per Ha per year
Management of Wood Pasture and Parkland	£46 per Ha per year
Restoration of Wood Pasture and Parkland	£244 per Ha per year
Creation of Wood Pasture	£409 per Ha per year
Deer Management / Protection Measures	various unit costs
Woodland Infrastructure	40% of actual costs
Scrub Control and Felling Diseased Trees	£260-£1,680 per Ha
Rhododendron Control	£2,800-£4,400 per Ha
Supplement for Use of Individual Tree Shelters	£1.60 per unit

* the only woodland option available under the mid-tier

CARBON FUNDING

The Forestry Commission will not fund applications for new woodland creation that include carbon co-funding if there is any link between the proposals and use of the term 'offsetting'. It will, however, allow co-funding provided certain criteria are met and appropriate language is used. This has been formalised with the Forestry Commission's Woodland Carbon Code which new plantations can be registered with to verify their CO_2 sequestration and allow it to be marketed as a potentially valuable asset to be sold or reported in the short or longer term. Carbon is currently being valued at around £5-10 per tonne however the Department of Energy and Climate Change predict values to reach £10 per tonne minimum by 2015 even on the lowest scenario. A typical broadleaved planting on a no-thin option may sequester over 500 tonnes of carbon per hectare over 60 years (http://www.forestry.gov.uk/carboncode).

WOODLAND TAXATION

Income from commercial woodlands is not subject to income tax, and tax relief cannot be claimed for the cost of establishing new woodlands. In general, grants are tax free but annual Farm Woodland Payments are regarded as compensation for agricultural income forgone and are liable to income tax. The sale of timber does not attract capital gains tax, although the disposal of the underlying land may give rise to an assessment.

Woodlands which are managed commercially or which are ancillary to a farming business may be eligible for business property relief or agricultural property relief respectively, for inheritance tax purposes, if owned for more than two years.

Acknowledgement: The above estimates are based on information supplied by Justin Mumford FICFor CEnv of Lockhart Garratt Ltd (Tel: 01536 408 840).

7.   ORGANIC FARMING

The Organic Sector:

The total organic land area fell in the UK in 2014 by 8½% and has fallen by over a quarter of its 2010 area. Whilst sheep, pigs and poultry numbers fell, there was a sharp rise in organic cattle (7%). The total number of registered organic producers and processors fell 1% in 2014 to 6,000, having been at 7,287 in 2010.

Throughout 2014, 3.2% of UK agricultural land (excluding common grazing) was in organic production. In 2014 the area (in thousand hectares) devoted to organic production was as follows:

Area in '000 Hectares	Fully Organic	In conversion	Total	% of Agric. Area	of UK Organic Area	% of UK Organic Producers
England	296	13	308	3.4	56.0	74
Wales	92	4	96	5.9	17.4	13
Scotland	133	3	136	2.4	24.7	10
N. Ireland	9	0	9	0.9	1.6	3
Area in hectares						
2014	548,600	19,700	529,000	3.2		
2013	550,999	24,350	575,349	3.3		
2012	573,406	32,223	605,629	3.6		
2011	619,073	36,914	655,987	3.8		
2010	667,551	50,794	718,345	4.0		
2009	619,268	119,441	738,709	3.7		
2008	594,413	149,103	743,516	3.6		

The 6-year decline in organic food consumption in the UK has been led by a sharp fall in production of organic goods in the UK. Organic food and drink sales have fallen by 33% since their peak in 2008 despite sales of all 'ethical produce' having risen annually since 2007, despite the downturn (Food Statistics Pocketbook 2014). The premium for organic is dearer than most others. However, some evidence suggests an upturn for organic goods in 2015/2016 with the Soil Association reporting an increase in organic consumption. This is thought to be particularly of high value top-end products rather than 'commodity' foods.

Organic Prices

The table below gives an indication of prices comparing organic with conventional. Note it is not possible to simply change the prices or even gross margins in a farm system, the overhead structure would also change, probably considerably.

Farm Gate Prices (estimate for 2015)

	Organic	Conventional	Difference	
Feed Wheat	£200	£135	£65	48%
Milling Wheat	£220	£151	£69	46%
Feed Barley	£190	£125	£65	52%
Milling Oats	£190	£125	£65	52%
Beans	£280	£180	£100	55%
Finished Beef (R4L Steer)	£3.85/kg dw	£3.50	35p/kg	10%
Stores (lowland Suckler)	£1.95	£1.85	10p/kg	5%

Finished Lamb	£3.60/kg dw	£4.05	45p/kg	11%
Finished Pig	2.80	1.80	£1.00	60%
Milk	34.5p/l	24.5p/l	10ppl	41%
Free Range Eggs (med.)	£1.75/doz	£1.08	£0.67/doz	62%

The allocation of resources in organic farming is more expensive per unit of output than conventional farming systems; for example yields per hectare or per unit of labour tend to be lower meaning land and labour costs per unit of product are increased. Higher sale prices (or greater subsidisation) are therefore necessary to make organic farming as financially viable.

Many hill livestock have converted to organic production to receive the higher prices and support. With inputs already low, management changes need only be small. Two thirds of all organic land is permanent pasture and rough grazing. Similar factors have meant that a sizeable number of extensive lowland beef and sheep producers have also embraced organic production. This highlights an important fact that there is a large grey area of farming systems between 'totally organic' to 'totally un-organic'. Below are the land use statistics of producers of organic and in conversion crop areas and livestock numbers for the applicable years:

Organic Land Use according to Crop Type (UK)						year on year
'000 ha	2010	2011	2012	2013	2014	% change
Cereals	56.9	52.5	47.8	43.7	42.2	-3.5
Other arable crops	10.8	9.3	8.3	7.5	7.3	-3.7
Fruit & Nut	2.3	2.1	2.1	2.1	2.1	+3.3
Vegetables & Pots	17.9	15.7	12.2	11.3	9.4	17.1
Herbs & Ornam's	6.2	6.1	5.8	6.8	0.3	-96
Temporary pasture	124	116	106	98.9	93.7	-5.2
Permanent pasture	497	435	406	387	370	-4.5
Woodland	8.1	8.3	7.4	7.6	15.3	+101
Unused Land	12.4	10.9	10.2	10.4	8.7	-16
Total area ha	718	656	605	575	549	-4.6

Organic Livestock Numbers (UK)						year on year
'000 head	2010	2011	2012	2013	2014	% change
Cattle	350.2	334.8	290.2	283	304	+7.4
Sheep	981.2	1,162	1,152	999	959	-4.0
Pigs	47.4	52.6	34.6	30	28	-6.1
Poultry	3,870	2,838	2,458	2,488	2399	-3.6
Other Livestock	4.5	5.0	4.1	4.0	5.7	+38.5

Economics of Organic Farming

It has been no easier to make profits out of commodity farming in the organic sector than in the conventional systems in most areas of farming in the last year. Sales of organic farm goods have retained a premium over conventional commodities but they have reduced as the base price has also fallen. Mostly, only those adding value to the output, making a product from the farm commodity are making better margins, thereby the added-value enterprise is capturing the value rather than the farming *per se*.

When market volume declines, it changes at varying rates, meaning, the demand for some products will be out of balance with others. Indeed, with livestock (several cuts of varying cost), it is currently a challenge to capture the organic premium for the entire beast and much fifth and fore-quarter (lower value) meats are not finding organic homes. Indeed, by definition, the organic market being added value trade means this is not uncommon.

Organic livestock farming is usually slightly easier in the summer when forage is easily available, but costs of keeping stock rise in winter and this is exaggerated in the organic sector with high cost feeds. If output prices do not pick up by then, we could see further fallout of the sector.

Aid for Organic Farmers:

In England, support for organic farmers has been through the Organic Entry Level Stewardship (OELS) (see Section III). Existing OELS schemes will be continued but there will be no new ones. Organic farming will receive support under the Countryside Stewardship Scheme from 2016 onwards, which will grant an agreement to all those organic farmers who apply (i.e. it will not be competitive). This provides support for the two-year conversion period of £50-450/ha/year depending on land use. Rates then drop to a 'management' level thereafter at £20-300/ha. Organic farming in Wales will be supported under Glastir Organic whilst in Scotland support will be provided under Agri-environment Climate Scheme.

Further Information:

No gross margin data for organic enterprises are included in this section because a specialist publication is available on the subject: the '2014 Organic Farm Management Handbook', (10th Edition) by Nic Lampkin, Mark Measures and Susanne Padel, Organic Research Centre, Elm Farm, Newbury. Tel: 01488 658 298.

8.   SUMMARY OF GROSS MARGINS

This page summarises the key figures of the gross margins over the previous pages. There are well in excess of 100 gross margins in the Pocketbook and additional data for other enterprises too. They cannot all be directly compared on a like for like basis, as different resources are required in order to produce each one and some offer whole farm benefits beyond the gross margin. Some, for example require different resources such as higher quality land, more overheads in terms of machinery, labour, buildings or working capital than others. Management requirement varies from one enterprise to another. Others are subject to having a supply contract with the processor.

Summary of Arable Crop Gross Margins

Crop (£/Ha)	Price £/t	Yield t/Ha	Output £/Ha	Variable Costs £/Ha	Gross Margin £/Ha	Gross Margin £/t
Winter Feed Wheat	£135	8.50	£1,148	£491	£656	£77
Winter Milling Wheat	£151	7.80	£1,178	£541	£637	£82
Spring Milling Wheat	£150	5.75	£863	£364	£498	£87
Red Spring Wheat	£210	5.00	£1,050	£479	£571	£114
First Feed Wheat	£135	8.93	£1,206	£482	£724	£81
Second Feed Wheat	£135	8.22	£1,110	£543	£567	£69
Winter Feed Barley	£125	6.90	£863	£392	£471	£68
Winter Malting Barley	£141	6.00	£846	£359	£487	£81
Spring Malting Barley	£151	5.45	£823	£301	£522	£96
Winter Oats	£125	6.30	£788	£297	£490	£78
Spring Oats	£125	5.50	£688	£244	£443	£81
Winter Rape	£280	3.40	£952	£449	£503	£148
Spring Rape	£280	2.00	£560	£275	£285	£143
Spring Linseed	£302	1.75	£529	£235	£294	£168
Winter Linseed	£302	2.30	£695	£311	£384	£167
Winter Beans	£180	4.00	£720	£255	£465	£116
Spring Beans	£185	3.70	£685	£255	£429	£116
Blue Peas	£190	3.75	£713	£274	£439	£117
Marofats	£250	3.40	£850	£399	£451	£133
Vining Peas	£230	4.75	£1,093	£453	£640	£135
Maincrop Potatoes	£132	45	£5,940	£3,279	£2,661	£59
Early Potatoes	£230	23	£5,290	£2,178	£3,112	£135
Sugarbeet	£26	70	£1,818	£1,268	£549	£8

Summary of Arable Crop Gross Margins (Continued)

Crop (£/Ha)	Price £/t	Yield t/Ha	Output £/Ha	Variable Costs £/Ha	Gross Margin £/Ha	Gross Margin £/t
Lupins	£220	3.00	£660	£272	£388	£129
Rye	£145	6.20	£899	£353	£546	£88
Triticale	£130	5.00	£650	£270	£380	£76
Naked Oats	£183	5.50	£1,007	£282	£724	£132
Durum Wheat	£185	6.20	£1,147	£350	£797	£129
Borage	£3,400	0.40	£1,360	£324	£1,036	£2,590
Crambe	£180	2.50	£450	£300	£150	£60
Hemp	£160	7.50	£1,200	£438	£762	£102
Grain Maize	£150	7.50	£1,125	£332	£793	£106
Millet	£235	3.00	£705	£266	£439	£146
Poppies	£600	2.00	£1,200	£333	£867	£434
Soya	£370	2.50	£925	£277	£648	£259
Sunflower	£325	2.00	£650	£306	£344	£172
Itallian Ryegrass	£1,000	1.40	£1,400	£714	£686	£490
Early Per. Ryegrass	£1,100	1.30	£1,430	£694	£736	£566
Int. Perennial	£1,200	1.30	£1,560	£694	£866	£666
Late Perennial	£1,300	1.10	£1,430	£664	£766	£696
Hybrid Ryegrass	£1,200	1.30	£1,560	£687	£873	£671
Dry Bulb Onions	£145	41.00	£5,945	£1,768	£4,177	£102
Cauliflower	£375	12.00	£4,500	£3,476	£1,024	£85
Calabrese	£384	10.00	£3,840	£3,318	£522	£52
Dessert Apples	£725	35.00	29,175	£20,300	£8,876	£254
Culinary Apples	£403	37.50	16,750	£15,224	£1,527	£41
Pears	£593	22.50	14,138	£10,932	£3,206	£142
Raised Bed Strawb.s	£3,010	20.50	62,793	£54,435	£8,358	£408
Everbearer Strawb.s	£3,010	36.00	111,840	£93,688	£18,153	£504
Raspberries	£6,308	11.50	75,818	£60,316	£15,502	£1,348
Blackcurrants	£650	6.50	£4,225	£1,430	£2,795	£430
Hops (£/kg)	£6.56	1500	£9,840	£5,985	£3,855	£3
SRC /year	£65	8.0	£520	£421	£99	£12
Miscanthus	£55	12.0	£660	£590	£70	£6
Mushrooms *	£1.85	250	£465	£398	£67	
Christmas Trees	£3.75/ft		£14,063	£3,493	£10,570	

* = £/Tonne compost

Summary of Livestock Gross Margins

Livestock		Output	Variable Costs	Gross Margin /Head	Gross margin £/Ha
Dairy					
Spring Calving Friesians	per Cow	£1,174	£457	£717	£1,720
Autumn Calving Friesian/Holsteins	per Cow	£1,552	£743	£808	£1,778
All-Year-Round Calving Holsteins	per Cow	£1,726	£933	£793	£1,744
Channel Island	per Cow	£1,733	£703	£1,031	£2,577
Friesian Followers	per Head	£912	£518	£394	£540
Channel Followers	per Head	£778	£454	£325	£560
Beef Cattle					
Bucket Reared Calf 3 month	per Calf	£120	£105	£14	
Bucket Reared Calf 6 month	per Calf	£205	£175	£29	
Spring calving lowland sucklers	per Cow	£298	£253	£45	£81
Autumn calving lowland sucklers	per Cow	£428	£311	£118	£194
Spring calving upland suckler	per Cow	£446	£241	£205	£328
Autumn calving upland sucklers	per Cow	£595	£312	£283	£354
Store Cattle Keeping Summer	per Head	£283	£60	£223	£1,281
Store Cattle Keeping Winter	per Head	£275	£208	£67	
Summer Store Finishers	per Head	£344	£176	£168	£503
Winter Store Finishers	per Head	£349	£353	-£4	
Summer finished sucklers	per Head	£632	£284	£348	£1,044
Winter finished sucklers	per Head	£356	£332	£24	
Maize Finishing (dairy)	per Head	£716	£328	£387	
Maize Finishing (suckler)	per Head	£669	£292	£377	
Cereal Bull Beef (continental)	per Head	£690	£550	£140	
Cereal Bull Beef (dairy)	per Head	£809	£550	£259	
Sheep					
Lowland Spring Lamb	per Ewe	£83	£53	£30	£298
Upland Spring Lamb	per Ewe	£64	£48	£16	£133
Gimmering Ewe Lambs	per Ewe	£62	£22	£40	£495
Finishing Store Lambs	per Ewe	£20	£16	£4	£106

Summary of Livestock Gross Margins (Continued)

Livestock		Output	Variable Costs	Gross Margin /Head	Gross margin £/Ha
Pigs					
Weaners	per Sow	£1,318	£768	£550	
Pork	per Pig	£34	£40	-£6.70	
Cutter	per Pig	£48	£50	-£1.60	
Bacon	per Pig	£61	£59	£2.80	
Combined Pork	per Pig	£88	£71	£16.90	
Combined Cutter	per Pig	£102	£80	£22.00	
Combined Bacon	per Pig	£116	£89	£26.40	
Poultry					
Enriched Caged Eggs	per Bird	£16.59	£10.76	£5.83	
Free Range Eggs	per Bird	£23.34	£12.32	£11.02	
Pullets	/Bird Reared	£3.48	£2.47	£1.01	
Broilers	p/Bird	167p	137p	30p	
All year turkey	£/Bird	£37.10	£18.50	£18.60	
Christmas Turkey	£/Bird	£44.69	£23.62	£21.08	
Large Roaster Chickens	£/Bird	£16.42	£6.09	£10.33	
Ducks	£/Bird	£7.75	£5.39	£2.36	
Geese	£/Bird	£58.25	£28.72	£29.53	
Other Livestock					
Breeding & Finishing Deer	/100 Hinds	£18,340	£5,463	£12,877	£708
Deer Calves	/100 Hinds	£9,800	£3,050	£6,750	£439
Finishing Stag Calves	/200 Hinds	£25,770	£7,968	£17,802	£979
Deer Park	/300 Hinds	£44,230	£11,743	£32,487	£325
Alpacas	Per head	£191	£139	£51	£771
Ostriches ~ Laying Trios	per Trio	£992	£88	£904	£441
Ostriches ~ Fatteners	per bird	£387	£350	£37	£227
Wild Boar	per Sow	£1,855	£992	£864	£4,319
Dairy Sheep	per Ewe	£471	£242	£229	£2,519
Dairy Goats	per Doe	£487	£242	£245	£2,940
Angora Goats	per Doe	£283	£118	£165	£793
Trout	/tonne Fish	£1,930	£1,580	£350	

III.   GOVERNMENT SUPPORT

1.   INTRODUCTION

Agricultural support to farmers and the rural economy is largely provided through the European Union's Common Agricultural Policy (CAP), and delivered in the UK by the devolved Governments of England, Wales, Scotland and Northern Ireland. The World Trade Organisation (WTO) provides a global tier in the hierarchy of agricultural (trade) policy.

The CAP has two main budgets (or Pillars). Pillar 1 includes the Basic Payment Scheme (BPS) (previously the Single Payment Scheme), which provides direct aid to farm businesses and also market support for agricultural produce – the latter once being the mainstay of CAP support, but now much reduced in importance. Pillar 2 is support through Rural Development and provides direct support to farmers and also to rural communities. In 2014, Pillar 1 amounted to approximately 74 per cent of support paid to English Farmers and 26 per cent for Pillar 2. Market support (which is not paid direct to farmers) is not included.

The Basic Payment Scheme (BPS) replaced the Single Payment Scheme (SPS) from January 1st 2015. The BPS builds on the use of 'entitlements', a concept introduced for the SPS in 2005, so we have given a summary of the SPS on page 152. In individual situations businesses should always check with the latest legislation and their devolved administrations' publications.

2.   THE BASIC PAYMENT SCHEME

A political deal on the main elements of reform to the Common Agricultural Policy (CAP) was concluded on 26th June 2013. This will shape Europe's farm policy from 1 January 2015 to December 2019 and possibly beyond then if agreement on the next round has not been completed as happened last time. Many decisions were left to member states to decide. In the UK, England, Scotland, Wales and Northern Ireland have each made their own decisions following consultations, where these are different it is shown separately in the text that follows.

ENTITLEMENTS AND REDISTRIBUTION

In many ways the Basic Payment Scheme is similar to the Single Payment Scheme, (see page 152 for details) with entitlements having to be matched against eligible land which then generates a yearly payment as long as certain land management rules are followed (cross-compliance). But unlike the SPS the BPS forms the 'foundations' of the new support arrangements, with a system of top-up payments that is available from the Pillar 1 budget. The mechanism of the scheme and the additional top-ups are discussed in detail below. Regardless how many to-ups are used in each member state, the total funds for Pillar 1 (the National Ceiling) in any region remains unchanged, they simply allocate the funds differently:

- **_Entitlement Roll-over._** Countries already operating the regional payment system (as in England) were able to roll-over existing entitlements into the new system. Defra made use of this, which means there was no re-grant of entitlements in England – entitlements farmers held at the end of 2014 were converted into BPS ones for 2015. However, if a claimant held excess entitlements in 2015 (i.e. more entitlements than they had eligible hectares), the excess entitlements were confiscated.

- **_Entitlement Grant._** Countries operating the historic system (including Wales and Scotland) were required to issue new BPS entitlements. These were allocated on the basis of land occupied in 2015. However, entitlements were only granted to those that received a payment (of any size) under the SPS in 2013. There are mechanisms for cases where this did not happen: There is a 'national reserve', comprising up to 3% of funds, to deal with hardship claims. Farmers growing certain crops in 2013 (fruit, vegetables, potatoes, ornamentals and vineyards) were eligible to establish entitlements even if they did not claim the SPS in 2013. There were rules to deal with 'mergers and scissions' of holdings between 2013 and 2015 and there was also the Private Contract Clause. This applies where all or part of a holding was sold or leased between 2013 and 15th May 2015.

- **Internal Convergence**. This is the term for the move to a flat rate regional payment in countries currently operating the historic system (e.g. Wales and Scotland).

    Scotland and Wales have decided to phase in the flat rate system fully by 2019. This will be done in equal steps of 20% per year i.e. in 2015 a farmer's entitlement value will be made up of 80% of the historic value and 20% of the flat regional payment (see below). This will mean farmer's entitlement values will change each year until 2019. England went through this process between 2005 and 2012. Scotland and Wales will go through this process over a shorter time frame. There will be winners (extensive producers) and losers (intensive producers). Examples of estimated payment rates are given at the end of this section.

- **Regions.** The flat rate regional payment depends on the region the land falls into. Member states are able to divide their countries into sub-regions so the regional payment rates reflect the intensity of farming possible on each hectare. This can make the transition from historic to flat rate less pronounced as the less productive land can be given a lower rate and the better, more productive land, a higher flat rate payment.

    In **England** when the SPS was introduced in 2005, Defra split the country into three regions; Lowland, Severely Disadvantaged Areas (SDA) and Moorland. Defra has kept these regions for the BPS. Entitlements are not tradable across these regions, but in order to 'move money up the hills', from 2015, the payment rate in the Lowland and the SDA region will be the same. The Lowland rate will be reduced slightly and the SDA rate will increase to match the Lowland value. The Moorland rate will see an increase from 2014 levels.

    Scotland has created three regions. Better land (arable and grassland) is classed as a single payment region (approx.1.8m ha) – Region 1. Rough grazing has been split to avoid any over compensation for the least productive land. This has been done using the Less Favoured Area Support Scheme (LFASS) classification (see Rural Development Section). Rough grazing in the non-LFA and in LFASS grazing categories B, C and D, are in one payment region (approx. 1m ha) – Region 2. The least productive rough grazing land in LFASS grazing category A forms the third region covering approximately 2m ha. In this region coupled support for beef and sheep enterprises is available - see Top-Up Schemes later.

    Wales initially decided to create three regions. But following a legal challenge a decision has been made to introduce a flat rate payment system across all of Wales by 2019 in five equal steps. A Redistributive Payment will apply to the first 54 hectares (133 acres) of any claim. However at the time of writing it looks likely that a (further) Judicial Review maybe launched into this new proposed system.

GREENING

Greening is the biggest change for farmers under the BPS. It is about requiring farmers to provide environmental benefits in return for their direct payments. It is seen as a way of making farm support more acceptable to tax payers and voters. Greening payments are set at 30% of the total BPS. Therefore it will change as a result of the 'internal convergence' mechanism set out above.

Under the Rules of 'Equivalence' if a member state can demonstrate to the EU Commission that existing or proposed schemes (national environmental certification schemes) provide equivalent environmental benefit to greening, then this can replace the basic greening requirement. None of the UK administrations have taken up this measure. They have all taken up the three basic EU measures of crop diversification, permanent pasture retention, and Ecological Focus Areas (EFAs) although Scotland is interested in devising an equivalence scheme for 2016.

Under the rules of equivalence, claimants are exempt from greening on organic land although the greening payment will still be made.

- *Land Definitions*. Under greening there are three key types of land, all three categories added together are known as the claimant's eligible area;

  ➢ Permanent Pasture – land that has been in grass for five years or longer. The sixth time it is entered as grass on the subsidy claim form it becomes permanent pasture. It doesn't matter if it has been reseeded, it is the length of time the land has been out of the arable rotation. If a catch crop (e.g. stubble turnips) has been planted, this could break the sequence but it would have to be demonstrated.

  ➢ Permanent Crops – land in crops that are in place for five years or more without replanting and that yield repeated harvests e.g. vines, orchards, short rotation coppice, Miscanthus, nurseries.

  ➢ Arable Land – any eligible land that is not permanent pasture or permanent crops, including fallow land and temporary grass.

- *Crop Diversification*. Where a claimant's arable land area (as defined above) is between 10-30 hectares a minimum of two crops are required. Three crops will be needed when the arable land area is above 30 hectares. No crop should cover more than 75% of the farm area. Where three crops are required, the two main crops together should not exceed 95% of the area. The crop rotation requirement does not apply where;
  ➢ more than 75% of the arable land is used for temporary grass or left fallow (as long as the remaining arable land area is below 30 hectares)
  ➢ more than 75% of the entire holding is permanent or temporary grass (again, subject to a 30 hectare limit on the remaining arable land area).

A crop is defined by its *genus* and *species*. Wheat, barley, oats, oilseed rape, linseed, potatoes, sugar beet etc. are all classed as separate crops. Spring and winter crops are also treated as separate crops. Fallow is a 'crop type', as is temporary grass. There are some oddities though so refer to scheme guidance.

- *Permanent Pasture*. Under the existing cross-compliance rules there is a requirement for permanent pasture to be maintained. This is enforced at member state level. It was proposed that this protection of grassland would move to a farm-level basis. However, it is optional for member states to retain the implementation at a regional or national level. England, Scotland and Wales have all decided to continue with the national-level enforcement. Under the new rules the overall percentage of permanent grassland in each country compared to the total agricultural area must not fall by more than 5%.

- *Ecological Focus Areas (EFAs)*. EFAs are set at 5% of a farm's eligible *arable* land area. This could rise to 7% after 2017 depending on EU commission research. Countries choose from a list of possible features to offer to farmers as eligible EFA features. This includes landscape features (hedges and trees), buffer strips, fallow land, protein-fixing crops, agro-forestry and short-rotation coppice. A matrix system converts linear features (e.g. hedges) into EFA area equivalents and gives some features extra value. E.g. in England a 1m stretch of hedge can be worth $10m^2$. EFAs are not required on farms where more than 75% of the land is grassland (temporary or permanent) as long as the remaining arable area is less than 30 hectares. Farms with less than 15 hectares of arable land are also exempt from the EFA requirement. Farmers need to re-calculate their EFA requirement annually and different EFA's can be used each year. The table below shows the features each devolved region has chosen.

The EFA requirement, apart from woodland (& coppice) options, must be sited on or adjacent to arable land i.e. hedges between permanent pasture fields are not eligible.

Other Points Regarding Greening

- ➤ *Double funding and Agri-environment schemes*. This is where farmers could potentially be paid twice for the same action. This is not allowed under EU rules. Some Agri-Environment Scheme options are similar to EFA options and so are seen as double funding, in which case a reduction will have to be made on some Agri-Environment Payments.

- ➤ *Penalties*. Penalties for not complying with greening will be based on the shortfall in requirement and will range from 0 to 15% for each of the Crop Diversification and EFA rules separately on arable land only i.e. up to a maximum of 30% (100% of the greening payment). From 2017 further administrative penalties for non-compliance will be introduced increasing the penalty to 120% of the greening payment, from 2018 this rises to 125%.

Feature	Notes	EFA m² per m² or M Feature		
		England	Scotland	Wales
Fallow land	The 'default' EFA option. No production is allowed during the fallow period. Each devolved region has its own fallow period.	1.0	1.0	1.0
Hedges	Refer to scheme literature for management rules	Both sides 10 One side 5	n/a	Both sides 10 One side 5
Traditional Stone Walls	Min height 1m, Max. width 4m. No cement allowed	n/a	n/a	1.0
Buffer strips	Must be next to a watercourse or parallel with and on a slope leading to a watercourse (Eng.) The same buffer strip can be used for Greening and Cross Compliance rules.	9.0	1.5	n/a
Field Margins	Can include hedges and ditches. Min. width 1m, max. 20m	n/a	1.5	n/a
Catch crops & green cover	England and Scotland only but different management rules	0.3	0.3	n/a
Nitrogen fixing crops	Includes beans, peas, lupins, clover (plus soya, sainfoin and lucerne in Eng. & Wales plus alfalpha and trefoil in Scot.). From 2016 Scotland will require a mixture of at least two of these crops	0.7	0.7	0.7
Short Rotation Coppice	Includes Alder, Silver Birch, European Ash, Sweet Chestnut, Willow, Poplar, Hazel, Lime and Sycamore.	n/a	n/a	1.0
Forested Areas	Areas used to claim the SPS in 2008 and are now afforested under the WGS, FWPS, Better Woodlands for Wales, Improved Land Premium or Glastir	n/a	n/a	1.0

Note: *This table only shows a very brief summary of the features available in each region. Each feature has detailed management rules which can be different depending on which country the land is in, claimants should consult scheme literature for further guidance.*

TOP-UP SCHEMES

The Basic Payment Scheme and Greening form the 'foundations' of the new support arrangements, but there is a system of top-up payments that are available from the Pillar 1 budget.

- *Young Farmers Scheme.* This is compulsory for member states to implement under Pillar 1. It is funded by a minimum of 2% of the total BPS budget and provides a 25% top-up to the value of entitlements for 5 years to those under 40 years old. In Wales and Scotland, the top-up is equivalent to 25% of the final (2019) payment rate. There is a limit on how many hectares qualify – the average farm size in the region, but with a minimum and maximum area of 25 and 90 hectares. In England and Scotland it is the maximum hectares. In Wales it is the minimum. At 90 hectares the extra payment would be worth around £3,500 per year.

- *Coupled Support.* There are no coupled payments in England or Wales. Scotland has coupled support for beef and sheep enterprises. Cattle with 75% beef genetics receive an annual payment, dependant on the number of animals claimed each year but is estimated to be €100 per calf. Additionally there is a coupled top-up for beef producers on the islands in the region of €160 per calf. There is coupled support for sheep producers who farm in Scotland's rough grazing areas (80% of BPS area in region 3 and less than 200ha in region 1). Payment rates will vary annually depending on the number of animals claimed but will be around €100 per eligible yearling ewe.

- *Redistributive payment.* This is a new payment which provides a 'top-up' on the first few entitlements held by each claimant. It is optional for member states and is limited to the initial 30 hectares, or the average national farm size if larger (54 hectares in the UK). The top-up is capped at 65% of the regional average payment rate, and total funding limited to 30% of the BPS fund. At the time of writing it looks like Wales will make use of this – see Regions earlier.

- *Small Farmers Scheme.* This is optional for member states. Participants would face less stringent cross-compliance regime and not be subject to greening in return for a fixed annual payment. No UK administrations have taken this up.

- *Hill Support.* It is possible for member states to pay additional support to hill areas from the Pillar 1 (BPS) budget. This is limited to 5% of total funds and is in the form of a top-up to entitlement values. None of the GB regions are making use of this.

ELIGIBILITY AND RESTRICTIONS ON AID

- *Active Farmer.* To be eligible for the BPS a claimant must be an 'active farmer'. This rule comes in two parts. There is a simple 'negative list' of entities not eligible by default for the Basic Payment; operators of airports, water companies, railways, sports grounds and real estate services. Member states can add to this list with the permission of the EU Commission (GB devolved regions have not). If claimants are operating one of the above negative list entities they may still be eligible for the BPS:

  ➢ If the claimant received less than €5,000 direct payments in the previous year

  ➢ In England if the claimant has more than 36 hectares of eligible land they are automatically an 'active farmer', in Wales the area is 21 hectares. Scotland does not have an area readmission route.

Or by the income routes:

> If the amount of direct payments is at least 5% of the receipts obtained from non-agricultural activities in the most recent fiscal year, or

> If the total receipts from agricultural activities represents at least 40% (33% in Scotland) of the total receipts of the business in the most recent fiscal year for which evidence is available

> If agricultural activity is a principle business objective i.e. is in the founding documents (Scotland Only)

Secondly, if more than 50% of a claimant's land is in 'areas naturally kept in a state suitable for grazing or cultivation' and they do not comply with the minimum activity rule (see below) the claimant is deemed not to be an 'active farmer'.

- *Minimum Agricultural Activity.* Member states are required to set out minimum activity levels on 'areas naturally kept in a state suitable for grazing or cultivation'. *England* has no land in this classification and therefore this is not an issue. In *Wales* saltmarsh and coastal dunes have been identified as such. If such land covers more than half of the agricultural holding, to be an active farmer, claimants must have either a minimum stocking density of 0.01 to 0.05 European Livestock Units per hectare or maintain stock proof fencing and provide water, or control injurious invasive plants. In *Scotland* payment Regions two and three (see earlier) have been designated as 'land naturally kept in a state suitable for grazing'. If more than half of the agricultural holding is located in these regions to be classed as an active farmer a minimum activity must take place. There must either be an average stocking level of 0.05 Livestock Units per hectare for 183 days in each scheme year or an Annual Environmental Assessment must be carried out.

- *Minimum Claim size.* The EU's minimum claim size is 1 hectare or €100. Member states can set higher levels if they wish. The minimum BPS claim size in each of the GB regions is

> England – 5 hectares (up from 1ha)

> Scotland – 3 hectares (remaining the same)

> Wales – 5 hectares (up from 1ha)

- *Degressivity.* The concept of 'degressivity' is new. It is mandatory for all member states. It is a 5% reduction in aid rates above €150,000. The greening element is not affected. Member states can raise levels of degressivity up to 100 per cent and reductions can be 'banded'. England and Scotland levies the minimum EU degressivity requirement of 5% reduction on aid above €150,000.

Wales has a banded policy:

> an absolute cap on payments above €300,000 (excluding greening payments);

> 55% on payments between €250,000 and €300,000,

> 30% on payments between €200,000 - €250,000 and

> 15% on payments between €150,000 and €200,000.

- *Pillar Transfer.* This replaces modulation. A transfer of funds between the two CAP Pillars is allowed either way, to a maximum of 15% of funds. The rates can be different for each year. Any money switched between Pillars has had to be match-funded in the past. This is not required in the BPS. Each of the devolved regions has taken this option at different rates:

> *England* – 12% with the option to rise to 15% for 2018 and 2019

> *Scotland* – 9.5%

> ➤ *Wales* – 15%
> ➤ *Northern Ireland* – 0%

- *Financial Discipline.* This is the mechanism by which direct payments are kept within the EU Budget. The threshold for financial discipline will be set at €2,000 (previously it has been €5,000). Payments under this threshold are exempt.

- *External Convergence.* This is the term for all member countries getting a fairer share of Pillar 1 funding.

Other Issues

- *Sugar* - Sugar quotas will end on 30th September 2017.

- *Milk Market* - Despite strong pressure from the European Parliament, moves to put some new market management mechanisms in place after the end of milk quotas in March 2015 have been rejected.

- *Conversion Rate* - For countries outside the euro i.e. the UK, the conversion of Pillar 1 aid is calculated on the average of exchange rates throughout the month of September. This is instead of simply using the official 30th September exchange rate as previously and should help reduce the effect of currency fluctuations.

ESTIMATED BPS PAYMENT RATES

The rates below are estimated by The Andersons Centre for illustrative purposes. In Wales and Scotland every claimant has a different entitlement value based on their history which will converge by 2019. In these two countries, different initial entitlement values have been used to show how there are 'winners and losers' as businesses move from the Historic method to a Regional Average Payment. The exchange rate is €1=£0.7773 for 2014 and estimated at €1=£0.715 (£1 = €1.40) thereafter.

England

Estimated Flat Rate Area Payments in England

	2014	2015	2016	2017	2018	2019
Lowland £/ha (acre)	193 (78)	169 (68)	168 (68)	167 (68)	160 (65)	159 (64)
Non-Moorland SDA £/ha (acre)	154 (62)	169 (68)	168 (68)	167 (68)	160 (65)	159 (64)
Moorland SDA £/ha (acre)	27 (11)	48 (19)	48 (19)	47 (19)	46 (18)	46 (18)

Wales

The table below uses a gross entitlement value of €500, €250 and €60 per entitlement in 2014.

Estimated Payments for Wales

Gross Entitlement in 2014 €/ha (acre)	2014	2015	2016	2017	2018	2019
			£/Ha (acre)			
€500/ha	389	274	237	199	163	127
(€202)	(157)	(111)	(96)	(81)	(66)	(51)
€250/ha	194	168	158	147	137	127
(€101)	(79)	(68)	(64)	(59)	(55)	(51)
€60	47	87	97	107	117	127
(€24)	(19)	(35)	(39)	(43)	(47)	(51)

Based on 100ha farm including redistributive payments on the first 54ha

Scotland

The first table below illustrates how payments will change using an example gross entitlement value of €500, €100 and €30 per entitlement in 2014 for the three regions; Arable & Grassland (Region 1), Rough Grazing (Region 2) and Poor Rough Grazing (Region 3) respectively. Note: there is coupled support of around €100 per yearling ewe in Region 3.

Example Payments for regions in Scotland

	2014	2015	2016	2017	2018	2019
Region 1	384	315	273	232	192	152
£/ha (acre)	(155)	(127)	(110)	(94)	(78)	(61)
Region 2	77	62	52	43	34	25
£/ha (acre)	(31)	(25)	(21)	(17)	(14)	(10)
Region 3	23	19	16	13	10	7
£/ha (acre)	(9)	(8)	(6)	(5)	(4)	(3)

The example farms below illustrate how claimant's payments may change over the next five years. They are for illustrative purposes only. *Note: They show the average rate per hectare. In practice where a farm's eligible land crosses payment regions, entitlements will have different rates depending on which region they were established in.*

Example A - is a 150ha intensive beef finisher or dairy farm. In 2014 the gross entitlement value was €400/entitlement. In 2015 all the land is in Region 1.

Example B – is a 150ha mixed beef and sheep farm with some arable land. In 2014 the gross entitlement value was €200/entitlement. In 2015 70ha is in Region 1; 50ha in region 2; with 30ha within region 3.

Example C – the final example is an extensive sheep farm, comprising 300ha which is within Region 3 in 2015. In 2014 the gross entitlement value was €50/entitlement.

Estimated Payments for example farms in Scotland

	2014	2015	2016	2017	2018	2019
Example A	307	258	231	204	178	152
£/ha (acre)	(124)	(104)	(93)	(83)	(72)	(62)
Example B	154	130	117	105	93	81
£/ha (acre)	(62)	(53)	(47)	(42)	(38)	(33)
Example C	38	30	24	18	13	7
£/ha (acre)	(15)	(12)	(8)	(7)	(5)	(3)

Does not include any coupled beef and sheep payments

3.   MARKET SUPPORT

Market support measures are the other part of Pillar 1 funding, including intervention buying, export subsidies, quotas and tariff barriers. The main measures are tariffs which are unlikely to change much in the short term following the lack of WTO trade deal. Milk quotas in the EU ended on the 31st March 2015.

Sugar prices are supported within the EU. Following the 2006 reforms, 'institutional' sugar prices have been cut to reach a minimum EU beet price of €26.4 per tonne in 2009 to 2012. Although in Britain, actual prices paid are determined through the Inter-Professional Agreement between British Sugar and the NFU (refer to page 33).

4.   SINGLE PAYMENT SCHEME

The SPS ended in 2014 but as its replacement builds on some of the principles introduced under this scheme an overview is given here.   Previous editions of the Pocketbook give a more comprehensive summary.

SINGLE PAYMENT SCHEME HISTORY

Major reforms of Pillar 1 of the CAP were implemented for the most part, in January 2005, this saw the introduction of the Single Payment Scheme. In November 2005 a reform of the Sugar Regime was agreed including price cuts and compensation to farmers starting with the 2006 sugar beet crop. In 2007 a reform of the Fruit and Vegetable regime was agreed. These subsequent reforms have been incorporated into the SPS legislation and there have been some significant simplifications. The latest changes were in 2008 when the 'Health Check' of the CAP was agreed. This was not a radical reform. The SPS ended on 31st December 2014.

SINGLE PAYMENT SCHEME BASICS

The major, essential change of the 2005 reforms was *decoupling*. This means that farm support is not linked to what is being produced on the farm, i.e. the crops being grown or the livestock kept. In most member states (including Wales, Scotland and NI), the 'Single Payment' (SP) (also referred to as the 'Single Farm Payment') was made according to the support received by each claimant during the three years 2000-2002 (the reference period). This is known as the 'historic system' of SP allocation. England opted for a system which moved the payment to being calculated on a 'flat-rate' Regional Average Payment (RAP) per hectare with a transition period from 2005 to 2012, starting mainly historic and changing annually to become entirely a flat rate regional average. The regional payments in England differ according to topography, with three types; lowland (or non-SDA), non-moorland severely disadvantaged areas (SDAs) and moorland SDA.

In order to receive SPS payment, recipients had to be farming 'eligible' land which was at their disposal on 15th May and be a 'farmer' – exercising an agricultural activity, this included keeping land in good agricultural and environmental condition (see below). They were also required to satisfy 'cross-compliance' rules, which are in two parts: 'Statutory Management Requirements' (SMRs; EU directives, largely already in force, on public and plant health, animal welfare and the environment) and keeping the land in 'Good Agricultural and Environmental Condition' (GAEC). They applied to the entire holding.

Also to receive payments farmers required 'entitlements'. These were a new concept introduced for the SPS and can be considered as a 'right to receive aid'. Initial entitlements were awarded to the IACS claimant of agricultural land in 2005.   They were transferable/tradable and could be sold with or without land, or leased only with an equivalent area of land. They were not attached to the land, they belonged to the business/ sole trader. SPS entitlements changed into Basic Payment Scheme entitlements in England on 1st January 2015 – see next section.

SPS PAYMENTS

Claims for payment were made annually, with 15th May being the deadline. As payments are calculated in euros the pound:euro exchange rate is important. The rate used was that prevailing on 30th September each year. The tables below shows the rates used (€1 = £) in each of the years

	2005	2006	2007	2008	2009
€1= £	0.68195	0.6777	0.6968	0.7903	0.9093
	2010	2011	2012	2013	2014
€1= £	0.85995	0.86665	0.79805	0.83605	0.7773

Payments were also subjected to deductions. 'Modulation' saw a percentage of the Single Payment taken off and given to the Rural Development Fund (Pillar 2) see Section 5. In England 19% was taken off from 2009 to 2014. 'Financial Discipline' was also a mechanism by which EU Farm Ministers could reduce payments to keep spending within stipulated budget thresholds. Financial Discipline was 2.45% and 1.3% in 2013 and 2014 respectively.

Every farm had a different payment per hectare each year up to 2011 because their historic payments were unique. In Wales and Scotland these differences will persist until they change from the wholly historic system in 2015 under the new BPS (see Section 4) until 2019. In England the payment rates in each region (lowland, SDA and moorland) are now the same. Previous editions of the Pocketbook showed examples of how three different English farms' (arable, beef and sheep) payments changed from 2005 to 2012. Welsh and Scottish farmers will go through this process, but over a shorter time frame. There will be winners and losers similar to when English farmers undertook the change.

The following are actual rates of the area payments in 2014 in the three areas (or sub-regions) of England. 'Lowland' covers all non-SDA (Severely Disadvantaged Area) land, which is more than 84% of farmed land.

2014 Flat Rate Area Payments in England

	Lowland £/ha (acre)	Non-Moorland SDA £/ha (acre)	Moorland SDA £/ha (acre)
Payments before deductions	251.39 (102)	201.32 (81)	35.26 (14)
Payments after deductions	192.87 (78)	154.45 (63)	27.05 (11)

SDA = Severely Disadvantaged Area   Converted at €1=£0.7773
Deductions at 20.3% (modulation at 19% and FD at 1.3%)

5.   RURAL DEVELOPMENT

Rural Development, or Pillar 2, supports environmental protection and improvement of the countryside, and encourages sustainable enterprises and thriving rural communities. The Rural Development regulation sets the legislative framework across the EU, providing a menu of schemes and aid from which member states can choose from. A new set of national Rural Development Programmes has been drawn up by each of the devolved regions, England, Scotland, Wales and Northern Ireland for the period 2014 to 2020. But due to the delay in EU budget negotiations and CAP reform, most new schemes were not open until 2015.   Under this round of EU Rural Development legislation the previous 'axes' have been replaced by 6 'priorities' (LEADER has also be retained);

1.   fostering knowledge transfer in agriculture and forestry

2.   enhancing agricultural competitiveness and enhancing farm viability

3.   promoting food chain organisation and risk management in agriculture

4.   restoring, preserving and enhancing ecosystems dependent on agriculture

5.   promoting resource efficiency and supporting a shift towards a low-carbon and climate-resilient agriculture

6.   promoting social inclusion, poverty reduction and economic development in rural areas

The priorities will contribute to achieving the following objectives:

- The competitiveness of agriculture,

- The sustainable management of natural resources, and climate action,

- A balanced territorial development of rural areas

As many of the previous scheme contracts are for more than one year and will carry on for many years until the agreements are brought to an end brief details of these schemes are also included in the sections below.

ENGLAND 2014 - 2020

In England the new Rural Development Programme started on 1st January 2015. Over the next seven years £3.5 billion will be invested in a range of schemes to improve the environment and grow the rural economy. The schemes centre around three themes:

- The environment (87% of funding)
- Increasing productivity (4%)
- Rural economic growth including LEADER (9%)

The Environment – **The Countryside Stewardship Scheme (CSS)**

The majority of funding will continue to be available for Agri-environmental schemes (£3.1bn).   The existing Environmental Stewardship Scheme (ESS), England Woodland Grant Scheme (EWGS) and capital grants from the Catchment Sensitive Farming (CSF) programme have been replaced by the new Countryside Stewardship Scheme (CSS).   The aim of the scheme is to support measures to 'restore, preserve and enhance the natural environment'. The scheme is open to farmers, foresters and land managers. It is being run jointly by Natural England, Forestry Commission England and the Rural Payments Agency (RPA); it provides three tiers of funding:

- *Higher Tier* - Multi-year agreements for environmentally significant sites, commons and woodlands where complex management requires one-to-one advice and support from Natural England or the Forestry Commission to help build an application. Applicants can select from the full range of the 244 scheme options and capital grants available. Similar to the previous HLS, most agreements will be by invitation.

- **Mid-Tier** - Multi-year agreements for environmental improvements in the wider countryside. Applicants can choose from 120 management options and capital items. The minimum annual value of a Mid-Tier agreement must exceed £1,000 per year. 'Priorities' for different areas have been identified. Agreements will be scored against these and only those offering the best outcomes will be given an agreement. Collaboration is not a pre-requisite;

- **Capital Grants** - Funding up to a maximum of £5,000 will be available for 1 to 2 year grants for hedgerows and boundaries, improving water quality, developing implementation plans, feasibility studies, woodland management plans, woodland creation (establishment), woodland improvement and tree health. This will be open to all, not just those with an agreement.

Higher & Mid-Tier agreements will normally run for five years, although ten year agreements may be offered if benefits will take longer to achieve. There is a menu of management options and capital items to choose from depending on the agreement. There is an on-line Countryside Stewardship Grants Tool to help applicants select the right combination of options. It includes the value, eligibility requirements and a brief description of each option and can be found at https://www.gov.uk/countryside-stewardship-grants   Only one agreement per holding will be allowed, with no 'underpinning' and no separate 'strands' for uplands or organics, although there are specific options for these types of land (see below).

- **Organic** - The scheme provides 11 options that are only available to organic farmers and land managers. These include options for conversion and maintenance. The organic conversion and management options can be used alone by applying through the Mid-Tier process or in combination with other options within the Mid or Higher Tier as long as they are compatible with organic status. Conversion payments will be paid for 2 years, except for permanent crops where a 3 year conversion period applies. For the duration of the agreement applicants must be registered with an Organic Control Body and the land parcels must be in their first year of conversion at the start of the agreement.

- **Uplands** – There are 12 uplands grants available. These include management of enclosed rough grazing, managing grazing for birds, management of moorland and supplements for moorland re-wetting and introducing or reintroducing shepherding. There are also capital payments for Historic Building Restoration.

- **Facilitation Funds** – Funding is available to deliver the CSS on a landscape scale. It is competitive and only available to those organisations/people who have environmental land management skills and who can also help groups of land managers work together. The 'group' must manage at least 2,000 hectares (unless there is a smaller more obvious environmental boundary) and be spread across at least four neighbouring holdings.

- **Scoring** – Unlike the previous agri-environment scheme, applications for Countryside Stewardship are competitive, which means that applications will be scored against criteria, and that not everyone who applies will be successful. Applicants should use the 'Statements of Priorities' and supporting maps for their area to identify the priority features and issues being targeted to help choose which options to include as part of an application. This will mean the application will score more highly. To further enhance their chances of an offer, applicants can choose options from the '*wild pollinator and farm wildlife package* (WPFWP). These options are designed to benefit wild pollinators, farmland birds and other farm wildlife. Applications which select these options and meet the minimum area thresholds; 3% for Mid-tier and 5% for Higher-Tier, will enhance their score. *Note: applications for organic conversion* *and management options are not competitive. All eligible applications will be accepted subject to the availability of budget.*

- *Application window* – There are different application windows depending on which element of CSS is being applied for;

  The Mid-Tier and Higher Tier application window is open from July to 30th September in 2015. With agreements starting on 1st January 2016. A similar application window is expected in 2016/17. Applications for the Boundaries and Hedgerows grant is planned to open between February and April 2016. Applications for Woodland Management Plans and Tree Health can be made all year round, Woodland Creation is between February and April each year. Applications for grants for feasibility studies and implementation plans can be made all year round from early 2016.

Increasing Productivity – The Countryside Productivity Scheme

About £140 million will be available over the life of the current RDPE through the Countryside Productivity Scheme to improve the competitiveness of farming and forestry businesses. Applicants will have to bid for funds for projects which are innovative, use new technology and the latest research and which will improve skills & training in the business. Co-operation and collaboration with other farmers, foresters and others in the land-based sectors together with projects which benefit the environment in a number of ways i.e. tackle environmental problems whilst increasing productivity will be able to bid for a share of the funds. Grants will cover up to 40% of total eligible costs. The scheme will be open in a series of rounds. The first round ended on 30th June 2015. Funds were available in the following areas in the first round, it is possible that these may change in future rounds;

- *Animal Productivity, Health and Welfare* – automated dairy cow lameness detection, rumination monitoring, on-farm analysis of foodstuffs, calving detectors, oestrus detectors, monitoring of pig production, static handling and weighing systems

- *Arable and Horticultural Productivity* – LED lighting, controlled atmosphere storage, remote crop sensors, crop robotics

- *Forestry Productivity* – woodland harvesting, extraction and small scale processing

- *Resource Management* – slurry application systems, air scrubbers & heat exchangers, livestock LED lighting, water management, poultry litter drying systems.

  There are two types of grants

- *Small Grants* – funding between £2,500 and £35,000. One application can include more than one small grant item.

- *Large Grants* – funding between £35,000 and £1,000,000. Can include more than one large grant item.

EIP-Agri grants (European Innovative Partnership for Agricultural Productivity & Sustainability) are also a part of the Countryside Productivity Scheme. These are aimed at collaborative groups of farmers, foresters, researchers involved in agriculture or food, agricultural or agri-food businesses and non-governmental organisations. Funds of between £5,000 and £150,000 will be available. This will cover the costs of running an innovative project for up to three years which will seek new ways of solving a recognised industry problem. The scheme is expected to open in summer 2015.

Rural Economic Growth

Funding for Rural Growth is available through Local Enterprise Partnerships (LEPs) or LEADER Local Action Groups (LAGs). LEPs will have £177 million to spend. Each LEP is drawing up its own strategy depending on local priorities around the following themes;

- Knowledge and skills

- Support for small or micro-businesses
- Broadband and renewable energy
- Promotion of rural tourism.

  Information on the different LEPs plans is available on GOV.UK

A new LEADER scheme (worth £138 million) commenced on 1st January 2015 it has a wider remit than under the previous Programme. This funds programmes run by local community partnerships called Local Action Groups (LAGs) and funds projects which improve the rural economy and create jobs. More information can be found at www.rdpenetwork.defra.gov.uk.

ENGLAND 2007 - 2013

This section outlines the schemes recently operating in England under the Rural Development Regulation from 2007-2013. The schemes are now closed to new applicants but as many are multi annual agreements and will continue until their contract ends a brief description has been included. Refer to previous editions of the Pocketbook for more detail.

Axis 2 Schemes

Administered by Natural England (NE) and the Forestry Commission and received approximately 80% of funding, the available schemes were:

- Environmental Stewardship Scheme (ESS)
- English Woodland Grant Scheme (EWGS)
- Energy Crops Scheme (ECS)

Environmental Stewardship Scheme (ESS)

The Environmental Stewardship Scheme started in 2005. The scheme is now closed to new applications. It comprises four elements:

- Entry Level Stewardship (ELS)
- Organic Entry Level Stewardship (OELS)
- Higher Level Stewardship (HLS)
- Uplands Entry Level Scheme (UELS)

ELS: was designed to encourage a large number of farmers across a wide area to adopt simple environmental management practices such as hedgerow management, stone wall maintenance, low input grassland, buffer strips and arable options. The scheme was non-competitive and open to all as long as scheme requirements were met. Points were awarded for each management option adopted. There was a large range of management options including; hedgerow; 2m, 4m, 6m buffer strips; overwintered stubbles; beetle banks etc.

Applicants had to achieve 30 points per hectare to be accepted into ELS. An annual payment of £30 per hectare is made half yearly in arrears. ELS agreements last for five years. Above the moorland line in the LFAs the payment is £8 per hectare for parcels of land over 15ha.

OELS: was open to all farmers with land registered as organic or in conversion and not receiving aid under the Organic Farming Scheme (closed). OELS had similar options to those under ELS and participants receive annual payments of £30 per hectare for carrying out options on the organic land plus an additional £30 per hectare (organic land only) for farming the land organically. There was also an option to apply for organic conversion with a payment of £600 per hectare per year (for 3 years) for top fruit orchards and £175 per hectare per year (for 2 years) for improved land. OELS agreements last for five years.

HLS: was targeted towards achieving significant environmental benefits in high priority areas with the objectives being wildlife conservation, protecting historic environments, maintaining and enhancing landscape quality, encouraging public access and resource protection. It was a competitive application. Payment depends on the management options adopted, and can include a mix of capital items and per hectare payments. HLS agreements were normally for ten years with a break clause for either party after five years.

UELS: Upland ELS replaced the Hill Farm Allowance (HFA) scheme in 2010. The scheme was open to those who farmed within the Severely Disadvantaged Areas (SDAs). Farmers were able to have an ELS agreement over all of their land and enter all their SDA land into the UELS. There were different points' targets depending on the classification of the land. Producers have to achieve the combined total.

Similar to the ELS, applicants had to achieve the points target by selecting from a menu of 'options'. Once achieved the points equate to the level of payment. SDA Moorland parcels 15ha and above receive £23/ha; all other SDA land receives £62/ha.

The scheme was not available to farmers who had other agri-environmental scheme agreements still running e.g. CSS and ESA schemes. In order that these farmers did not lose out now the HFA has finished, from 2011 there was an Uplands Transitional Payment (UTP). Payments were made to farmers who had an on-going old Countryside Stewardship Scheme (CSS) or Environmentally Sensitive Areas (ESA) agreement and who extensively grazed eligible land with sheep breeding flocks and suckler cows but not dairy farming or other enterprises such as deer farming.

The 2014 UTP payment (received in March 2014) was £16.62/ha for Moorland and Common Land, Severely Disadvantaged Land (SDA) received £43.88/ha. The full rate is paid on the first 350ha, half rate on the next 350ha. No payment is made on land in excess of 700ha. The 2014 payment was the last year, the UTP is no longer available.

English Woodland Grant Scheme (EWGS)

The previous Woodland Grant Scheme (WGS) and the Farm Woodland Premium Scheme (FWPS) were replaced by the English Woodland Grant Scheme (EWGS), administered by Natural England and the Forestry Commission. Under the new Rural Development Regulation for England (RDPE) woodland grant options will be within the new Countryside Stewardship Scheme (CSS).

Energy Crops Scheme (ECS)

The Energy Crops Scheme provided aid for the planting of Short Rotation Coppice (SRC) and Miscanthus (elephant grass). There was a minimum application size of 3 hectares. Agreements were normally for five years.

Axes 1, 3 and 4 Schemes

The delivery of the socio-economic elements of the RDPE 2007-2013 was managed through the Defra RDPE Delivery Team. More recently key priorities have been improving the competitiveness of farming, skills & knowledge transfer and development of the rural economy. This has been centred on the following schemes:

- Farming and Forestry Improvement Scheme (FFIS)

- Rural Economy Grant (REG)

- Skills and Knowledge Transfer

- Rural Community Broadband Fund
- Paths for Communities
- Dairy Fund

In addition Local Action Groups (LAGs) have been able to support local projects, communities and businesses. These schemes are now closed.

Farming and Forestry Improvement Scheme (FFIS)

The Farming and Forestry Improvement Scheme aimed to make businesses more profitable and resilient whilst reducing the impact of farming on the environment. Grant rates of between 15% and 50% were for projects which met one or more of the above objectives. The application process was in rounds.

Rural Economy Grant (REG)

The Rural Economy Grant provided grants for large scale projects which would result in a significant change in performance – 'game-changing' for farming, forestry, agri-food businesses and micro businesses in rural areas of England. Funding up to 40% of eligible costs was available. The minimum grant was £25,000 up to about £1 million

WALES 2014 - 2020

Over the next seven years £953m will be available through the Welsh Rural Development Programme to be invested in a range of schemes to;

- Increase the productivity, diversity and efficiency of farming and forestry businesses. Improving their competitiveness and resilience and helping them move from the 'historic' system of payments to the flat rate system and reducing their reliance on subsidies.
- Improve the environment by encouraging sustainable land management practices and the sustainable management of our natural resources and climate change
- Promote strong, sustainable rural economic growth and encourage community-led local development.

The Welsh Rural Development programme was given approval by the European Commission in May 2015. At the time of writing not all scheme details had been released. Funds will be split between five key elements;

- Area-based measures (60% of funds)
- Investment measures (15%)
- Human and Social Capital measures (11%)
- LEADER and local development (10%)
- Technical Assistance (4%)

Area-based Measures

The majority of funding will be available for the Area-based schemes and this will be through a continuation of the current Glastir Programme together with some new measures which have been approved by the European Commission along with the wider Welsh Rural Development plan. These include:

- Farmers will not be required to participate in Glastir Entry to be eligible to enter other Glastir Schemes

- Online applications will be rolled out in 2015 and will become compulsory in 2016

- The success of the Commons Development Officers will be built upon to encourage collaborative agreements within Glastir Advanced and Glastir Habitat Network

- The Glastir Efficiency Grant will be replaced by a Sustainable Production Grant (see Investment Measures) which will be available to improve economic and environmental performance through capital investment across three themes; nutrient, energy and water efficiency

- The introduction of a small woodland planting scheme, to fund plantings for schemes that are smaller than those eligible under Glastir Woodland Creation

- The introduction of a new Organic Farming Scheme (see below for details) within Glastir.

Glastir

Under the Rural Development Programme 2014-2020 Glastir will continue to be the main scheme through which funding for area based measures will be channelled.

Glastir has six elements;

- Glastir Entry (GE)

- Glastir Advanced (GA)

- Glastir Commons (GC)

- Glastir Woodlands (GW)

- Glastir Organic (GO) (New in 2015)

- Glastir Small Grant Scheme (new in 2015)

Note the Glastir Efficiency Grants (GEGs) will not be available under the WRDP 2014-2020.

Glastir Entry is open to all farmers in Wales. The first agreements under the new scheme commenced in 2012. Glastir Entry is a whole farm entry level management scheme. Contracts are for five years and applicants must enter all the eligible land they will have full management control of for the full five years. Applicants have to obtain a points threshold for their farm which is either 34 (standard entry level threshold) x total hectarage or 17 (reduced entry level threshold) x total hectarage. To reach the threshold applicants choose from a number of management options. Each option is allocated a set number of points. Occupants can also opt to choose from a list of options in the Regional Package. These are considered to offer the greatest environmental value for their area. If the regional options are chosen the applicant will receive 10% more points per option. Dairy farmers can increase their points by 10% if they choose management options within the 'Dairy Package'. Under Glastir 2014-2020 a number of options have been removed and others changed. Refer to the most up to date scheme details.

Application windows have been abolished and applications are accepted throughout the year, with a yearly cut-off date. Applications received by 30th September in the year should have a 1st January start date of the following year. Payment for Glastir Entry is £34 per hectare for all land in the scheme or £17 per hectare for reaching the Reduced threshold. There are no different payments for land within the LFA. Claim for payment is made annually on the SAF.

To be eligible for the scheme, producers also need to comply with the Whole Farm Code; 13 standards of environmental practice. This attracts an additional payment of:

0 – 20 hectares   £15/ha

21 – 50 hectares	£8/ha
51 - 100 hectares	£2.75/ha

Glastir Advanced addresses concerns over soil carbon management, water quality, water quantity management, biodiversity, the historic environment and improving access. Land is assessed against target maps. At this level management is of a prescribed nature, payments consist of both capital and non-capital items. Farmers are not now required to enter GE before they apply to the GA. Those with a reduced entry level threshold are not eligible.

Glastir Commons is available for those who hold rights on Common Land and who have joined together to establish a Grazing Association.

Glasir Woodlands provides funds for woodlands under the Glastir Woodland Creation Grant (WCG) and the Glastir Woodland Management (GWM) scheme. Under the WCG there are three grants; Establishment grants (£500 - £3500/ha, 1st yr), fencing grants (£3.15/m) and Woodland Creation Premium (£300/ha per year for 15 years for farmers). The Expression of Interest window for WCG on 15th June and closed on 17th July 2015, similar application window is expected next year, refer to Gwlad for dates. Under the GWM scheme payments are available for managing existing woodlands over 0.5ha. Payments range from £54 to £120/ha. A grant for small woodland planting will be available through the Glastir Small Grant Scheme (see later)

Glastir Organic brings support for organic farming in Wales under the Glastir 'umbrella'. The Glastir Organic Scheme is a stand-alone scheme and farmers joining the organic scheme will remain eligible for other parts of Glastir. Conversion and maintenance contracts are for five years and applicants must be an 'Active Farmer'. Support for ongoing training and skills development is available and applicants will need to show they have a business plan in place. The maximum area supported per holding is 400 Ha. The Glastir Organic 2016 Expression of Interest window opened on 20th July 2015 and closed on 2nd September 2015. A similar window is expected next year. Applications can only be made via RPW Online.

Unlike the previous organic scheme there isn't any specific payment for arable crops, but other elements of Glastir have arable cropping options which organic farmers can make use of. The table below summarises the payment rates;

Glastir Organic Payment Rates

	Conversion £/Ha		Maintenance £/Ha	Certification* £/ha
	Years 1-2	Years 3-5	Years 1-5	
Horticultural	600	400	400	80
Enclosed Land	130	65	65	10
Rough Grazing	15	15	15	3

* Certification costs will be capped at £500 per contract

Land with more than 40% down to horticultural crops in a temporary grassland rotation, as well as top fruit producers will qualify for the highest payments (Horticultural). The Enclosed Land category includes all enclosed lowland. Rough Grazing includes enclosed upland, sole grazed commons, grazed woodland, as well as lowland bogs and heaths

Glastir Small Grant Scheme is a stand-alone scheme. At the time of writing limited details are available, but it is expected to fund small scale environmental capital works outside of the wider farm agreements i.e. small areas of tree planting, dry stone walling etc.

Investment Measures

Schemes under this element will include:

Young Entrants Support Scheme (YESS) – At the time of writing The Welsh Government is working on a new young entrants' scheme and will release details later in 2015 on the Welsh Government website and the online Gwlad magazine these can be found at http://gwlad.gov.wales/?lang=en . The rules are expected to be broadly similar to those of the previous scheme, see later

The Sustainable Production Grant will replace the Glastir Efficiency Grants which were available to fund capital works to improve the resource efficiency of farms under the 2007-2013 RDP. Funds of up to 40% of eligible expenditure will be available; minimum of £16,000 up to a maximum of £400,000; to improve farm profitability and environmental outcomes. Projects must address either; soil and crop management, handling and housing, animal or plant health welfare or crop storage issues. The window for the initial round of Expressions of Interest is open from 27th July to 30th September 2015. Further rounds are expected to open regularly throughout the life of the Programme.

The Food Business Investment Scheme (FBIS) is designed to help primary producers of agricultural products in Wales to add value to their outputs by providing support to those businesses that do first and/or second stage processing activities. It is also designed to improve the performance and competitiveness of their businesses; to respond to consumer demand; to encourage diversification and to identify, exploit and service new emerging and existing markets. FBIS covers capital investments in processing equipment along with some associated costs. Priority will be given to Micro, Small or Medium Enterprises (SME's). Applicants must demonstrate that a viable market has been identified for their product(s) and that the project would not proceed without the grant. The scheme is discretionary. The scheme is open to all businesses involved in primary and/or secondary processing of agricultural products. The grant rates range from 20% of the total investment up to 40% depending on size, location and whether both the input and output are agricultural products. The maximum grant threshold per project is £5,000,000 and the minimum is £2,400. The initial round of Expressions of Interest opened on 20th July 2015 and closes on 30th September 2015. Full applications will be invited from 30th November 2015 to 31st may 2016. The intention is for the schemes to open and close regularly up to 2020.

Other funding available may include support for entry into *Quality schemes; Risk Management* – subsidising insurance that will extend to losses incurred due to bad weather; *Restoration of Forestry Potential* – support for woodland and habitat restoration to mitigate natural disasters.

Human & Social Capital Measures

The main interventions available under this element include:

Knowledge Transfer & Innovation and Advisory Services – A new Farming Connect programme will commence in October 2015. It will be delivered by Menter a Busnes and Lantra working with other key organisations in Wales including IBERS. At the time of writing not all the details were known, but the new framework will deliver specialist advisory service providing subsidised business and technical support to eligible agricultural, forestry and food manufacturing businesses. Lantra will be responsible for delivering a new subsidised lifelong learning and development programme. The service is expected to include professional development and training, demonstration, coaching, workshops, specialist events and short-term farm exchanges study tours aimed at SMEs and micro enterprises building on the current Farming Connect service (see below).

Co-operation funds will be available support for co-operation between businesses to aid short supply chains and local markets including those for biomass production. Also support for new and emerging Producer Groups is expected under this funding stream which will build on the Supply Chain Efficiencies Scheme and previous provisions for this kind of work under Farming Connect. At the time of writing details had not been released, but the window for Expressions of Interest was expected to open on 3rd August and close on 14th October 2015.

LEADER & Local Development - LEADER Local Action Groups (LAGs) are able to use a community-led local development approach to encourage innovation and achieve rural development. Under the Rural Community Development Fund (RCDF) the Welsh Government will offer grants, primarily aimed at LEADER Local Action Groups (LAGs) and other community-Based organisations for investment funding across a wide range of interventions designed to prevent poverty and mitigate the impact of poverty in rural communities, improving conditions which can lead to future jobs and growth. The intital Exprssion of Interest window is now open for this scheme and closes on 31st January 2016.

Technical Assistance

Under this element funds will be available for:

- *Wales Rural Network* – building on the existing scheme to help communicate the opportunities available under the WRDP

- *Glastir Support* – Farmers will be able to get Technical advice and the existing Commons Development Officers' roles will be expanded

WALES 2007 - 2013

The following schemes were operating under the previous WRDP and may continue in a similar format under the new WRDP and therefore brief details have been included below:

Glastir will continue in a similar format – see earlier

The *Young Entrants Support Scheme* (YESS) started in 2010. It is available to young farmers (less than 40 years) who are or have just set up as head of a holding for the first time. It provides grant aid of 50% of eligible expenditure up to a maximum of £15,000 whichever is less. It also provides access to a dedicated Young Entrant's Business Enabler Service for advice on training, knowledge transfer and joint venture opportunities together with sign-posted access to funded mentoring services from established farmers and/or processors.

The other main support for farmers in Wales is through *Farming Connect.* This offers one-to-one support, guidance, advice and training. Up to five days subsidised support is available to produce a Whole Farm Plan. A subsidised Skills Development Programme is delivered by Lantra to provide access to practical and regulation linked courses. Through the Farm Advisory Service, help is provided to meet cross compliance measures.

SCOTLAND 2014 - 2020

The Scottish Rural Development Programme (SRDP) 2014-2020 received approval from the European Commission (EC) in May 2015. The specific priorities of the new SRDP 2014-2020 are;
- Enhancing the rural economy
- Supporting agricultural businesses
- Protecting and improving the natural environment
- Addressing the impact of climate change

- Supporting rural communities

Up until 2020 there will be about £1.3bn available under the SRDP. The majority of funds will go towards supporting those farming in the hills and agri-environment payments. Below is a summary of the schemes and the budgets available to fund them;

Less Favoured Area Support Scheme (LFASS) (£459m) - Under the SRDP 2014-2020 the LFASS will continue in a similar format to the scheme which operated under the previous Programme. Although, a new scheme will be introduced by 2018 that will support the new 'Areas with Natural Constraints' (ANCs) land designations as required by the European Commission. It is recognised that there is a problem with destocking in the remotest hill areas. Various policy options have been considered, the latest changes were made to the LFASS in 2011. These included an increase in the payment rates for the Standard Areas and an update of the historic reference on which payments are based. At the same time a new grazing category was introduced for land not currently designated, together with a new variable minimum stocking rate to ensure payments are targeted towards active producers.

The LFASS is applied for on the annual Basic Payment Scheme application form. Eligible hectares are adjusted for non-ring fenced dairy land, variable minimum or maximum stocking density restrictions, grazing category and an enterprise mix multiplier. The adjusted hectares are then paid at the payment rates below depending on the grazing category and location of the land. *There is a minimum payment of £385.*

LFASS Payment Rates

£ per adjusted Hectare	Grazing Category	
	A & B	C & D
Very Fragile	71.35	63.00
Fragile	62.10	54.51
Standard	52.16	34.12

The payment rates have been maintained until 2018, although these may have to be reduced to ensure total payments stay within the £65.5m annual LFASS budget.

Agri-environment Climate Scheme (£350m) – This scheme provides targeted support for land managers to undertake management and capital work for environmental purposes. It will continue with some of the practices supported under the previous Rural Priorities scheme (see below). Support for organic conversion and maintenance is provided for under this scheme. Applicants can also choose from options to support environmental management on arable, grassland, upland, peat, moorland & heath, wetland & bog, farmland habitats & features, small units, control of invasive non-native species, managing water quality & flood risk, public access, capital items and the management of scheduled monuments. This includes £10million of targeted support for slurry stores (available from 2016) and £6million for footpaths and other works to support access management.

Most applications will need a Farm Environment Assessment (FEA). This will record the important environmental features on the holding and help plan what to include in the application. Funding is available to complete the FEA. Support under the Agri-environment Climate Scheme is geographically targeted and it will be necessary to check which of the 60 plus options are available in the applicant's area before applying. Applications are made on line. The first application window closed on 12th June 2015. From 2016 the scheme is expected to be open for applications from January to March. Claims are made annually on the SAF. Funds to help deliver landscape-scale environmental benefits may be available under the Environmental Co-operation Action Fund (see below). This scheme will be delivered by RPID and Scottish Natural Heritage.

Forestry Grant Scheme (£252m) - The Forestry Grant Scheme (FGS) will support the creation of new woodlands, contributing towards the Scottish Government's target of 10,000 hectares of new woodlands per year and the sustainable management of existing woodlands. Support will be available under eight categories;

- Woodland creation - to support the creation of new woodland that will bring economic, environmental and social benefits. There are nine options. There is an initial planting payment (range from £560/ha to £3,600/ha) and an annual maintenance payment for five years (range from £96/ha to £624/ha). There are also a range of capital grants available for operations such as fencing and tree protection. There is no Farm Woodland Premium payment, but land remains eligible for BPS
- Agroforestry - support creation for small scale woodlands (0.25-5ha per holding) on agricultural pasture or forage land which will allow for a mix of trees and sheep grazing.
- Woodland Improvement Grant - there are five options in this category. These aim to support forest management, activity to enhance the environment and the public's enjoyment of existing woodlands (Woodlands in and Around Towns (WIAT))
- Sustainable Management of Forests - there are nine options in this category. These aim to support the management of existing woodlands with a high environmental value.
- Tree Health - This option provides support to prevent the spread of Chalara ash dieback and *Phytophthora ramorum (P. ramorum)*
- Harvesting and Processing - this category supports the development of the small-scale premium softwood and hardwood processing sector. Funding is available for equipment to increase harvesting in small, undermanaged woods.
- Forest Infrastructure – support for access into undermanaged or small woodlands
- Forestry Co-operation – support to deliver landscape–scale projects involving a number of landowners.

This scheme is being delivered by RPID and Forestry Commission Scotland.

Environmental Co-operation Action Fund (£10m) - This will provide funds to help rural businesses work together to deliver larger (landscape- scale) environmental benefits which could not be achieved by businesses on their own. This scheme will be delivered by RPID, Scottish Natural Heritage and Forestry Commission Scotland.

New Entrants Support (£20m)
This scheme will provide start-up grants for new and young entrants through three schemes;

- Young Farmers Start-Up Grant Scheme - aimed at young farmers or crofters who are starting an agricultural business for the first time or who are taking over an existing agricultural business. Applicants must be between 16 years of age and under 41 years of age at the point of application. They must have at least an NVQ level 2 or equivalent qualification in agriculture or a minimum of five years agricultural experience. The business must demonstrate future standard outputs in the range of €10,000 to €600,000 (the level of output that could be expected on the average farm under 'normal' conditions). The level of grant is €70,000. There is an initial payment of €63,000 with the remaining being paid once business 'milestones' have been reached.
- New Entrants Start-Up Grant Scheme – aimed at farmers and crofters who have started their business within 12 months prior to applying for the scheme. There is no upper age limit but applicants must be at least 16 years old. They must farm at least 3 hectares and demonstrate estimated standard outputs in the range of €600 to €9,999. The total grant is €15,000. There is an initial payment of €12,000 and the remaining payable on reaching business plan 'milestones'.
- New Entrants Capital Grant Scheme - open to farmers and crofters who have been head of an agricultural business for up to five years before the application for support.

Funding can be used for capital projects, such as the construction or improvement of agricultural buildings. The total amount of grant aid available in any two-year period is individuals; up to £25,000 and groups; up to £125,000.

This support will be delivered by RPID, Scottish Natural Heritage and Forestry Commission Scotland. Additional support and mentoring will be delivered through the Advisory Service from 2016 (see below).

Beef package (£45m) - This is a new five year scheme and is different from the Scottish Beef Suckler Support Scheme (see Top-up Schemes above in Section 4 Basic Payment Scheme). The aim of this scheme is to see economic and environmental improvements in the beef sector. There will be £32.5 million for support towards genetic resilience, plus targeted support for the beef sector through Knowledge Transfer and the Innovation Fund and the Advisory Service.

Crofting Agricultural Grant Scheme (£14m) - Crofting will continue to be supported under the new SRDP. This scheme will provide grants to crofters to make improvements on their crofts which will help to sustain their business. The total grant available in any two year period is £25,000 for individual crofters and up to £125,000 for groups of crofters. This scheme will be delivered by RPID, Scottish Natural Heritage and Forestry Commission Scotland. In addition the ***Croft House Grant Scheme*** provides grants to crofters to improve and maintain standards of crofter housing.

Small Farms Grant Scheme (£6m) - This scheme will offer targeted support for small farms that face similar issues as crofters regarding sustainability. To be eligible the applicant(s) must be head of a holding between 3 and 30 hectares. The total grant available in any two year period is £25,000 for individual small farmers and up to £125,000 for groups of small farmers.

Advisory Service (£20m) - available from 2016, this service will build on the support currently available under the Whole Farm Review Scheme, providing advice and assistance to farmers, crofters, forest holders and other land managers. The service will be tendered out and will feature a national scheme offering advice on sustainability and resource efficiency. There will also be one-to-one consultancy and targeted advice on conservation and biodiversity.

Knowledge Transfer and Innovation Fund (KTIF) (£10m) - support will be available to organisations to deliver vocational training, coaching, workshops, courses and farm visits designed to promote skills development and knowledge transfer. In addition funds may be available to cover the running costs of 'operational groups' which deliver improvements in competitiveness, resource efficiency, environmental and sustainability in the farming and forestry sector.

LEADER (£86m) - provides support to individuals, communities and businesses to come together to design and implement Local Development Strategies across Scotland. Support will be made available through Local Action Groups (LAGs) who will work with communities and businesses to help them achieve their ambitions. In Scotland 21 LAGs will be implementing Local Development Strategies. £20million has been allocated for specific support for small business growth, including £10 million for farm and croft diversification, which will also be made available through LEADER.

Food Processing, Marketing Co-operation (£70m) - In recognition of the fact that the food and drink industry is a key growth sector for Scotland. This scheme will continue to provide support for SMEs in the food and drink sector with start-up grants for new enterprises, and business development grants. This scheme will be delivered through the Scottish Government's Food and Drink Division.

Technical Assistance (£15m provisional) - Including the Scottish Rural Network for supporting and promoting rural development through the sharing of ideas and best practice. This includes SRDP implementation, evaluation and monitoring.

Broadband (£9m) - Funding will be available to provide support for delivering broadband in rural areas. Delivery options are currently being explored.

Application Process
Under the new Rural Development Regulation there is a change to the application process. Apart from applications to the LFASS, there will be two levels of entry;
- Level 1 – applications for grants up to £75,000 with continuous local approval. For forestry the threshold will remain at £750,000
- Level 2 – applications for grants above £75,000 which will be considered nationally by an expert panel. Applications will also be limited to one per holding, per scheme, per year. This is to ensure that funding is spread more fairly in the future.

SCOTLAND 2007 - 2013

The schemes below were available under the previous Rural Development Programme, some agreements will continue until the contract comes to an end even though the schemes are now closed to new applications.

Rural Development Contracts - Previously the SRDP was delivered through a single mechanism known as Rural Development Contracts (RDCs), this was divided into three tiers:
- Tier I: The Single Payment Scheme – through the cross-compliance requirements a basic level of environmental protection, food safety and animal welfare is provided.
- Tier II: Land Manager's Options - Farmers chose from a menu of options with application at the same time as the Single Application Form (SAF).
- Tier III: Rural Priorities – This element was discretionary and competitive and it covered agri-environment, organic, farm business, forestry, young entrants and processing and marketing. Some of these agreements will still be running, but is closed to new applications. Those with an agri-environment or organic scheme which ended in 2013 were given a one year extension.

Less Favoured Area Support Scheme (LFASS) - this is still available – see earlier for details

Whole Farm Review - The other main support for farmers in Scotland was the Whole Farm Review, which grants aid for a business review, action plan and implementation, up to £2,400. This will run until the new Advisory Service is available from 2016 – see earlier for details.

NORTHERN IRELAND 2014 - 2020

The Northern Ireland Rural Development Programme (NIRDP) 2014-2020 will have a budget of £623m, this will be allocated across three specific areas:

- *Competitiveness of Agriculture (£287m)* – The Farm Business Improvement Scheme will be the main umbrella scheme. Falling under this will be a portfolio of knowledge transfer and targeted capital investment, central to this will be the Business Investment Scheme (BIS) with up to £200m of funding available.

- *Protecting the Rural Environment (£256)* – The majority of funding in this area will be allocated to agri-environmental measures through the Environmental Farming Scheme (£173.5m). There will also be funding for LFAs and woodland creation and expansion.

- *Developing Rural Economies (£80)* - Funds will be available for a range of measures aimed at encouraging the economic development of rural areas; Rural Basic Services Scheme, Rural Broadband Scheme, Rural Tourism Scheme, Village Renewal Scheme, All Island co-operation scheme, plus running costs for LEADER Local Action Groups.

Note at the time of writing the NIRDP had not received European Commission approval.

ENVIRONMENTAL SCHEME PAYMENTS

There are many agri-environment schemes across the UK which provide annual payments to farmers. The table below summarises the latest payments made for environmental schemes.

Environment Schemes Payments, 2014 (provisional)

		£ Million
England:	Organic Farming Scheme (c)	0
	Environmentally Sensitive Areas (c)	7
	Countryside Stewardship (c)	7
	Uplands Transitional Payment (c)	1
	Environmental Stewardship Scheme	377
Wales:	Organic Farming Scheme (c)	4
	Environmentally Sensitive Areas(c)	0
	Tir Gofal (c)	18
	Tir Cynnal (c)	0
	Glastir	26
Scotland:	Organic Aid Scheme (c)	0
	Environmentally Sensitive Areas (c)	0
	Rural Stewardship (c)	0
	Less Favoured Area Support Scheme	66
	Land Management Contract Scheme (c)	0
	Land Managers Options	5
	Rural Priorities (c)	35
N. Ireland	Organic Farming Scheme (c)	0
	New Environmentally Sensitive Areas	5
	Countryside Management Scheme	17
	Less Favoured Area Compensatory Allowances	25

Source: DEFRA, SGRPID, DARD, WAGDEPC. Agriculture in the UK 2014.
  (c) Schemes that are now closed to new entrants.

IV.   LABOUR

1.   LABOUR COST

There are 8 National (UK) Bank Holidays in 2016; New Year's Day, Good Friday March 25, Easter Monday March 28, May Bank Holiday May 2, Spring Bank Holiday May 30, Summer Bank Holiday August 29, Boxing Day December 26 and December 27.

Agricultural workers are subject to the National Minimum Wage (NMW) as follows:

Minimum Wage	25 and Over	21 and over	18-20	Under 18	Apprentice *
1 Oct 2014 to 30 Sept 2015		£6.50	£5.13	£3.79	£2.73
1 Oct 2015 to 30 Mar 2016		£6.70	£5.30	£3.87	£3.30
Living Wage 1 April 2016	£7.20**	£6.70	£5.30	£3.87	£3.30

*   *This is for apprentices under 19 or in their first year.*

** *This will rise to £9.00/hour by 2020.*

There are some occasions when the minimum wage is applicable in agriculture. Many farmers are paying a higher wage than legally necessary to attract greater calibre staff. More qualified workers such as machinery operators and livestock handlers command a premium.

STATUTORY MINIMUM WAGE RATES - ENGLAND

The Agricultural Wages Board (England & Wales) ended in 2013 (Scotland, which has its own AWB is not affected). There will be few or no changes to existing agricultural workers contracts, changes to employment contracts should be made with mutual consent.

Workers Employed before 30th September 2013

Terms and Conditions under the Agricultural Wages Order (AWO) remain in place (unless there is a variation to the employee's terms and conditions of employment). For workers employed prior to 30th September 2013 (end of the Agricultural Wages Board AWB) contracts must not be changed without the consent of both parties. For workers classified as Initial Grade under the 2012 AWO and employed before the 30th September 2013 the minimum wage increases in line with the National Minimum Wage.

Workers Employed after 30th September 2013

Employers can decide on the rate of pay increases and other employment related benefits, with no standard increases dependent on skill level, responsibilities or qualifications.

STATUTORY MINIMUM WAGE RATES - SCOTLAND

The Scottish Agricultural Wages Board (SAWB) continues to operate. The following rates to apply from the 1st October 2014;

- £6.50/hour for those in the first 26 weeks of employment (£9.75/ hr overtime)
- £7.14/hour for those employed for more than 26 weeks by the same employer. (£10.71/ hr overtime)
- £3.96/hour for workers who undertake a Level 2 Apprenticeship in Agriculture
- Dog allowance is £5.41/week for each dog up to 4.

The following rates have been proposed to apply from the 1st October 2015;

	39 Hr Weekly Rate	Hourly Rate*	Overtime per Hour
	£	£	£
1st 26 weeks of employment..................	261.3	6.70*	10.05
Employed for over 26 weeks	282.36	7.24	10.86
Level 2 Modern Apprentice in Agri......	156.78	4.02	6.03

Appropriately qualified workers add 1.10/hr
Those owning dogs as part of their work 5.49/dog/week (up to 4 dogs)
Accommodation provision (other than a house) £5.35/day off-set
* *In line with the National Minimum Wage*

STATUTORY MINIMUM WAGE RATES - WALES

Whilst the abolition of the Agricultural Wages Board applied to both England and Wales, the Welsh Government has decided to establish its own Wages Board for Wales. Details of the news provisions are not yet available. In the meantime, the rates and rules of the final Agricultural Wages Board continue to apply in Wales. Payment rates are set out in the table below;

Normal Hours (Standard Rates) as if under AWB Rules (to 2013)

Grade		39 Hr Weekly Rate	Hourly Rate*	Overtime per Hour
		£	£	£
1.	Initial Grade Over 16 years	261.30	6.70*	10.05
	Under 16 years	-	3.87*	5.81
2.	**Standard Worker**............	**271.44**	**6.96**	**10.44**
3.	Lead Worker	298.74	7.66	11.49
4.	Craft Grade......................	320.19	8.21	12.32
5.	Supervisory Grade...........	339.30	8.70	13.05
6.	Farm Management Grade	366.60	9.40	14.10
Apprentice:	Year 1..............................	139.23	3.57	5.36
	Year 2 ~ 16-17 years	143.52	3.68	5.52
	Year 2 ~ 18-20 years	194.22	4.98	7.47
	Year 2 ~ 21 years and over	241.41	6.19	9.29

* *No changes have been made to Welsh AWB figures because of legal delays, but the minimum wage increased meaning lowest figures increase accordingly.*

For night work between 7pm and 6am a premium of £1.36 per hour is payable more than their basic pay rate. If a worker keeps a dog for their job, an additional £7.63 a week is payable for each dog.

TYPICAL ANNUAL LABOUR COST

Estimated for 2015/16 (from 1st October), based on a Standard Worker with a 2% rise.

Average Labour Costs	Weekly	Annual	Hourly
	£		£
Basic standard worker rate (1)	286.95	14,922	8.50
National Insurance Contribution and Employers Liability Insurance (2, 3)	42.47	2,208	1.26
Minimum Cost (4)	**329.42**	**17,130**	**9.76**
Overtime, average 10 hrs per working week (45) @ £11.44 (+ NIC, ELI)	109.64	5,702	
Typical cost inc. Overtime (5, 6)	**439.06**	**22,831**	**10.35**

1. This is based on the 'Standard Worker', inflated by 2% for 2 years as if pay rises continued yearly since the end of the AWO, giving the hourly wage of £7.36 per hour worked.

   Hours work, excluding overtime, based on 45 weeks (of 39 hours) per year = 1,755 hours, i.e. statutory holidays (23 days), public holidays (8 days) and illness (3 days), have been deducted.

2. NIC = National Insurance Employer Contribution = 13.8%

3. ELI = Employer's Liability Insurance = 1.0%

4. *Annual cost of cottages* (or net value), value of perquisites, contribution towards payment of the council tax, etc., would have to be added where appropriate.

5. *Hours including overtime;* based on 1755 + 450 (10 hours/week) = 2,205 hours per year

6. *Total average worker's gross earnings* on the above assumptions = £19,888 a year.

2.   LABOUR HOURS AVAILABLE FOR FIELD WORK

This section calculates the theoretical maximum time a single worker could spend on field-work per month in 2016.

Hours available for field-work per worker per month in 2016

	Total Ordinary Hours (1)	Adjusted Ordinary Hours (2)	Per cent workable (3)	Available Hours (4,5)		Total Available Hours (6)		percent o/t at w-ends (7)
				Ordinary	Overtime			
Jan	160	142	50%	71	31 (60)	102	(131)	100%
Feb	168	149	50%	75	30 (63)	105	(138)	75%
Mar	168	152	60%	91	65 (63)	157	(154)	53%
Apr	168	152	65%	99	74 (63)	173	(162)	46%
May	160	147	70%	103	108 (80)	210	(183)	49%
Jun	176	161	75%	121	106 (88)	227	(209)	39%
Jul	168	154	75%	116	113 (84)	229	(200)	45%
Aug	176	161	75%	121	111 (88)	232	(209)	42%
Sep	176	161	70%	113	99 (88)	212	(201)	39%
Oct	168	152	65%	99	78 (63)	177	(162)	49%
Nov	176	156	50%	78	33 (66)	111	(144)	69%
Dec	160	142	50%	71	31 (60)	102	(131)	100%

1.   *Ordinary Hours:* 8 hours per work day (less 8 bank hols). No deductions have been made for other holidays because they may be taken at various times of the year.

2.   *After deducting* for illness (5% Nov. to Feb., 3% March, April and Oct., 2% May to Sept.), and for contingencies and non-delayable maintenance (½ hour/day).

3.   *Per cent Workable:* accounts for severe weather, soil conditions e.g. waterlogging etc.

4.   *Available Ordinary Hours:* Adjusted Ordinary Hours x Percentage Workable.

5.   *Available Overtime Hours: Daylight hours above working day (8 hours)* to a maximum of 4 hours per day and 12 to 14 hours at weekends according to season. Same adjustments for illness and percentage workable. Figures in brackets indicate hours available if headlights used, up to 4 hours/day (summer) and 3 hours/day (winter).

6.   *Total Available Hours:* Percentage overtime without headlights available from weekend work as opposed to evenings.

7.   *Overtime at weekends:* out of hours fieldwork that is undertaken in daylight.

Additional Notes

8.   *Figures relate to medium land.* The percentage workability will be higher with light soils, less with heavy soils. On heavy soils, land may be almost 100% unworkable from late November to early March (or later, according to the season), particularly if un-drained. A rough estimate of variations in workability according to soil type (compared with the figures above) is as follows.

Heavy land - March, October, November: 30% less; April: 20% less; September: 10% less; May to August: no difference. Light land — October to April: 15% more; May and September: 10% more; June to August: no difference.

9.   *It must be remembered that indoor work,* e.g. livestock tending or potato riddling, can be continued over the full working week, i.e. the hours available are the Adjusted Ordinary Hours, plus overtime adjusted back for workability. Also, some handwork in the field has to continue even in rain, e.g. sprout picking.

10.   *Percentage workability* varies according to the particular operation, e.g. compare ploughing and harvesting.

3. SEASONAL LABOUR REQUIREMENTS

CROPS AND GRASS

On the following pages, data on labour requirements for various crops and types of livestock are given. Two levels are shown: average and premium.

The average figures relate to the whole range of conditions and commercial farm sizes, i.e. small and medium-sized farms as well as large; the figures give all farms equal weight.

The premium rates do not denote the maximum rates possible, for instance by the use of especially high-powered tractors under ideal conditions, but relate to rates of work estimated to be obtainable over the whole season, averaging good and bad conditions, with the use of wide implements, relatively large tractors (150hp (111kW) to over 180hp (134kW)) and high capacity equipment in up to 8 hectare fields and over, where no time is wasted. Most farmers with more than 200 hectares (500 acres) of arable land ought to achieve at least the premium levels shown. Those with over 400 hectares (1,000 acres) will have still bigger machines and therefore faster work rates, and thus require 15 to 25% less labour than even the premium levels given.

The rates of work include:

- preparation,
- travelling to fields,
- minor breakdowns and
- other stoppages
- They relate broadly to medium and medium-heavy land

Some jobs, such as ploughing, may be done more quickly on light soils. Operations such as combine harvesting can obviously vary according to many factors to do with the topography and other natural features of the farm.

The usual times of year when each operation takes place are shown; these relate to lowland conditions. They will obviously vary between seasons, soil types, latitude and altitude. In particular, light land can be ploughed over a longer winter period and a high proportion of cultivations for spring crops may be completed in February in many seasons. All such factors must be allowed for in individual farm planning. Conditions in different seasons will also affect, for instance, the number and type of cultivations required in seedbed preparation. Typical monthly breakdowns of requirements are given for various crops.

To illustrate the type of questions that need to be asked for full details of seasonal labour requirements on the individual farm, critical questions affecting timing are listed for cereals.

Note: This data is now old and little new research has been completed to replace it with. However, productivity per labour unit has increased since then.

Winter Cereals

Operations	Labour-hours per hectare		Time of Year
	Average	Premium	
Plough (1)............................	1.4	1.0	July to October (according to previous crop)
Cultivate (often power harrow).	1.0	0.7	September to October (according to previous crop) (½ Aug if ploughed in July)
Drill (often with power harrows followed by roll)	1.1	0.7	Mid-September to 3rd week October (according to previous crop and soil)
Apply Fertiliser........................	0.3	0.2	
Spray	0.3	0.2	October-November
Top Dress (three times [2]).......	0.9	0.6	March and April
Spray (three or four [2])............	1.0	0.5	March-June
Combine, Cart Grain, Barn Work	2.5	1.9	Mid-Aug to approx. 10th Sept
Later Barn Work (3)	0.7	0.4	September to June
Total..	**9.2**	**6.2**	
Straw: Bale	1.3	0.8	Mid-August to end
Cart	3.5	2.6	September

Typical Monthly Breakdown

Month	Average	Premium	Notes
October....................................	2.4	1.7	Approx. 60% of Ploughing,
November.................................	—	—	Cults., Drill, Harrow
December	—	—	
January	—	—	
February	—	—	
March	0.4	0.2	Part Top Dress
April	0.8	0.5	Part Top Dress, Spraying
May	0.3	0.2	Spraying
June	0.3	0.2	Spraying
July...	—	—	
August	1.7	1.3	⅔ of harvesting (4)
	(+2.4 Straw)	(+1.7 Straw)	
September (harvest).................	0.9	0.6	⅓ of harvesting (4)
	(+2.4 Straw)	(+1.7 Straw)	
September (prepn. drill)............	1.7	1.1	40% of Ploughing, Cults., Drill, Harrow

1. *Some cereal crops* are direct drilled or drilled after reduced, or minimal, cultivations, i.e. without traditional ploughing. Direct drilling reduces man-hours per hectare by about 2.5 (average) or 1.8 (premium), and minimal cultivations by about 1.2 (average) and 0.9 (premium).

2. *This is for winter wheat;* winter barley will often have one less top dressing and spraying and oats two less. Also see next page for harvest times for winter barley and oats.

3. *Later barn work* is excluded from monthly breakdown.

Spring Cereals

	Labour-Hours per hectare		
Operations	Average	Premium	Time of Year
Plough (1).....................................	1.4	1.0	July to October (according to previous crop and soil type)
Cultivate (often power harrow)...	1.0	0.7	March (½ in second half February on light land)
Apply Fertiliser...........................	0.3	0.2	
Drill (often with power harrow), plus roll	1.2	0.8	March (½ at end February on light land)
Top Dress (once, some possibly twice)	0.4	0.2	
Spray (two or three)...................	0.7	0.3	May
Combine, Cart Grain, Barn Work	2.4	1.8	Last ¾ of August (affected by variety and season)
Later Barn Work (2)	0.6	0.4	September to June
Total..	**8.0**	**5.4**	
Straw: Bale (unmanned sledge)	1.3	0.8	Mid-August to end
Cart...	3.5	2.6	September

Typical Monthly Breakdown

Month	Average	Premium	Notes
October.....................................	0.4	0.3	Ploughing. How much in
November.................................	0.8	0.5	October depends on area
December	0.2	0.2	W. Wheat, Potatoes, etc.
January	—	—	
February	—	—	
March	2.4	1.6	All Cults. Drilling, Rolling, (nearly half in February on light land)
April	—	—	
May	1.1	0.6	Spray and Top dress
June	—	—	
July...	—	—	
August (3).................................	2.4 (+2.6 Straw)	1.8 (+1.8 Straw)	Harvesting
September.................................	— (+2.2 Straw)	(+1.6 Straw)	

1. *Autumn drilling* preferable if possible to allow frost to crumble soils

2. *Later barn work* excluded.

3. *This is for spring barley*; spring wheat and oats partly September.

Crop Timings in a Normal Season:

Winter Wheat

Drilling mid-September to 3rd week October.

Harvesting mid-August to approx. 10th September.

Winter Barley

As for winter wheat, except that:

- Ploughing unlikely to start before cereal harvest, as usually follows a cereal crop.
- Harvesting some weeks earlier: mid-July to approx. 10th August.

Winter Oats

As for winter wheat, except that:

- Drilling usually first full half of October.
- Harvesting earlier (late July or first half of August).

Spring Barley

Drilling end of February to very early April

Harvesting last half of August to early September

Spring Wheat

As for spring barley, except that:

- Drilling on average 1-2 weeks earlier (should finish in March) - lose more if later than barley.
- Harvesting, on average, 2 weeks later: last week August/first half of September (two-thirds in September).

Spring Oats

As for spring barley, except that:

- Drilling usually a little earlier.
- Harvesting is later than spring barley, earlier than spring wheat: end of August/beginning of September.

Critical Questions affecting Timing for Spring-sown Cereals

1. Previous crops.
2. Will the crop be ploughed traditionally, chisel ploughed, subsoiled, minimally cultivated, or direct drilled?
3. Months when winter ploughing is possible, on average (where relevant).
4. Is spring ploughing satisfactory (where relevant)?
5. Average period of cultivations and drilling.
6. Earliest dates for starting and finishing spring cultivations/drilling and latest dates for starting and finishing cultivations/drilling, ignoring extreme seasons (1 year in 10).
7. Effect on yield if drilling is delayed.
8. Is the crop rolled (a) within a few days of drilling or (b) later?
9. (a) Average period of harvesting.
   (b) Earliest dates for starting and finishing harvest, and latest dates for starting and finishing harvest, ignoring extreme seasons (one year in ten).

Critical Questions affecting Timing for Autumn-sown Cereals

1. Previous crops (affects time available and need for ploughing and cultivations).

2. Will the crop be ploughed traditionally, chisel ploughed, subsoiled, minimally cultivated, or direct drilled?
3. Earliest and latest drilling date, by choice.
4. Effect on yield if drilling is delayed.
5. Autumn weed control?
6. In the spring: (a) whether crop is rolled, and when,
   (b) whether crop is harrowed, and when,
   (c) time of top dressings,
   (d) number of spray applications.
7. (a) Average period for harvesting.
   (b) Earliest dates for starting and finishing harvest, and latest dates for starting and finishing harvest, ignoring extreme seasons (1 year in 10).

Maincrop Potatoes

Operations	Labour-Hours per hectare		Time of Year
	Average	Premium	
Plough	1.4	1.0	September to December
Cultivating, Ridging, De-stoning/			
Clod Sep. (as required)	6.5	5.0	March, early April
Plant and Apply Fertiliser (1)	4.5	3.5	Last quarter of March, first
Apply Herbicide	0.3	0.2	three-quarters of April
Spray for Blight (av. 6 times)	1.2	0.9	July, first half August
Burn off Haulm	0.3	0.2	End September, early October
Harvest, Cart, Clamp (2).............	15.0	10.0	End September, October
Work on Indoor Clamp...............	4.8	3.2	November
Riddle, Bag, Load.......................	40.0	30.0	October to May
Total..	**74.0**	**54.0**	

1. *Automatic planter.* Hand-fed planters: approx. 12hrs plus 8 (could be casual labour).
2. *Mechanical harvester,* excluding up to 25 hours for picking off on harvester - usually casual labour. None may be needed on clod and stone-free soils. Hand harvesting: additional approx. 80 hours of casual labour.

Typical Monthly Breakdown

Month	Average	Premium	Notes
October..	12.2	8.2	80% of harvest, ½ burn off
November....................................	5.9	4.0	Clamp work and ¾ plough
December	0.3	0.2	¼ plough
January	—	—	
February	—	—	
March	7.8	6.0	All fert', ½ cults', ¼ plant
April	3.5	2.7	½ cult's, ¾ plant
May	—	—	
June	—	—	
July...	0.9	0.7	3 blight sprays
August..	0.3	0.2	1 blight spray
September...................................	3.1	2.0	20% harvest, ½ burn off

These figures exclude casual labour and riddling.

Early Potatoes

Operations	Labour-Hours per hectare		Time of Year
	Average	Premium	
Plough	1.4	1.0	September to December
Cultivating, etc.	6.5	5.0	Late February, early March
Plant and Apply Fertiliser...........	4.5	3.5	Late February, early March
Apply Herbicide	0.3	0.2	1st half March (some in February on light land or in early season)
Further Spraying..........................	0.3	0.2	
After-Cultivation/Spray	0.3	0.2	April, early May
Harvest, bag, load......................	30.0 (1)	25.0 (2)	2nd week June onwards. All June or till mid-July

1.   Excluding 80 hours picking—usually casuals.

2.   Excluding 60 hours picking—usually casuals.

Second Early Potatoes

Operations	Labour-Hours per hectare		Time of Year
	Average	Premium	
Plough	1.4 (1)	1.0 (1)	September to December
Cultivating, etc	6.5 (1)	5.0 (1)	March
Plant and Apply Fertiliser...........	4.5 (1)	3.5 (1)	March
Apply Herbicide	0.3 (1)	0.2 (1)	Half 2nd half March, half 1st half April
Further Spraying..........................	0.9 (1)	0.7 (1)	End April, May, early June
Harvest	15.0 (1)	10.0 (2)	Mid-July to end August

1.   *Spinner or elevator-digger*, excluding picking and riddling—usually casual labour.

2.   *Mechanical harvester*, excluding picking off on harvester/riddling - usually casual.

Sugar Beet

Operations	Labour-Hours per hectare		Time of Year
	Average	Premium	
Plough	1.4	1.0	September to December
Seedbed Cults.............................	3.2	2.2	Mainly March (some early April. Some late February in good seasons)
Load, Cart, Apply Fertiliser........	0.7	0.4	
Drill (and Flat Roll)	1.8	1.1	Between mid-March and mid-April
Spray (herbicide: pre- and post-emergence)	0.6	0.3	Late March/April
Spray (x 2)...................................	0.6	0.3	May/June
Spray (aphis)...............................	0.3	0.2	July
Harvest (machine)	14.0	9.0	End September, October, November
Load	3.4	2.5	End September to early January
Total..	**26.0**	**17.0**	

Typical Monthly Breakdown

Month	Average	Premium	Notes
October.............................	7.2	4.6	45% harvest; + loading
November	8.2	5.3	45% harvest; ¾ ploughing; + loading
December	1.0	0.8	¼ ploughing; + loading
January	0.5	0.4	Loading
February	—	—	
March	3.8	2.3	Fert., most cults., some drilling
April	2.5	1.7	Some cults., most of drilling
May	0.3	0.2	Spray
June	0.3	0.15	Spray
July..................................	0.2	0.15	Spray
August	—	—	
September........................	2.0	1.4	10% harvesting; + loading

Vining Peas

Operations	Labour-Hours per hectare		Time of Year
	Average	Premium	
Plough	1.4	1.0	September to December
Cults, Fert. and Drill..................	2.3	1.6	Mid-Feb. to April
Post Drilling and Spraying..........	1.5	0.8	
Harvesting	19.0	14.0	July and early August
Total..	**24.2**	**17.4**	

Drilling is staggered in small areas through the season, ranging from early varieties to late varieties.

Dried Peas

Month	Labour-Hours per hectare		Notes
	Average	Premium	
October...............................	1.2	0.8	
November.................................	0.8	0.5	Stubble cult., Plough
December	—	—	
January	—	—	
February	0.2	0.1	Cult. x 2, harrow; drill & fert.
March	2.8	1.9	(80% March); light harrow
April	0.6	0.4	roll; and spray
May	2.5	1.2	
June	0.2	0.2	Scare pigeons; spray
July..	1.8	1.1	Possible spray desiccant;
August	2.2	1.3	combine and cart, dry
September..................................	0.5	0.3	Stubble cult.

Assumes direct combining.

Field Beans

Winter Beans

Operations	Labour-Hours per hectare		Time of Year
	Average	Premium	
Broadcast Seed	0.6	0.4	
Apply Fertiliser...........................	0.3	0.2	
Plough	1.4	1.0	September/October
Power Harrow.............................	1.0	0.8	
Spray (pre-emergence)	0.3	0.15	
Spraying (two or three times)	0.8	0.35	Spring
Combine and cart and			
Barn-work...................................	3.0	2.4	August

Spring Beans

Operations	Labour-Hours per hectare		Time of Year
	Average	Premium	
Plough	1.4	1.0	September to December
Cultivate (often power harrow)...	1.0	0.7	
Apply Fertiliser...........................	0.3	0.2	
Drill, Roll	1.2	0.8	End Feb, early March
Spray (two or three times)	0.8	0.4	
Combine and cart and			
Barn-work...................................	3.0	2.4	September

Winter Oilseed Rape (*Desiccated*)

Month	Labour-Hours per hectare		Notes
	Average	Premium	
October............................			
November.........................	0.6	0.3	Spray herbicide and
December			insecticide if necessary
January	—	—	
February	—	—	
March			
April	0.8	0.4	Top dress twice
May	—	—	
June	—	—	Desiccate (1st half July);
July..................................	2.4	1.7	combine (½ 2nd half July
August	2.0	1.4	½ 1st half Aug.); dry
August	1.6	0.9	Cults. (x 2), spray, drill, fert.;
September	1.6	0.9	harrow, roll, barn work (0.5)

Herbage Seed (*first production year*)

Undersown

Operations	Labour-Hours per hectare		Time of Year
	Average	Premium	
Undersown	0.6	0.4	March, April
	(0.6	0.4)	Straight after drilling
Roll..	0.4	0.3	September
	0.4	0.3	Late February, March
Harvest (by Combine): Mow	1.4	0.9	3 to 4 days before combining
Combine and Cart.......................	4.5	3.5	Ital. Ryegrasses and Early *Perennials: late July. Intermed. Perennials: late July/early August. Late Perennials/White Clover: mid-August*
	6.0	4.5	Meadow Fescue: early July
	7.0	5.0	Cocksfoot: early July
	10.0	7.0	Timothy: mid-August Red Clover: late September

Direct Drilled in Autumn

Operations	Labour-Hours per hectare		Time of Year
	Average	Premium	
Plough	1.4	1.0	
Seedbed Cults.............................	2.2	1.6	Depends on previous crop—
Load, Cart, Apply Fertiliser........	0.3	0.2	Usually July or August
Drill (with harrows behind)	0.8	0.6	As early as previous crop allows. This may be up to mid-Sept for ryegrass without detriment to the yield.
Roll (soon after drilling).............	0.6	0.4	Meadow fescue and cocksfoot are best sown no later than July and it is risky to sow Timothy much later than this.

Grass

Production

Operations	Labour-Hours per hectare		Time of Year
	Average	Premium	
Plough	1.4	1.0	Autumn drilling: may not
Seedbed Cults.............................	2.2	1.6	
Load, Cart, Apply Fertiliser........	0.3	0.2	
Drill*	0.7	0.5	Mid-March to mid-April (1) or end July to mid-Sept.
Roll..	0.6	0.4	Soon after drilling
Load, Cart, Apply Fertiliser* (three lots)	0.9	0.6	March to mid-August (2)
Top*	1.3	0.8	Mid-June to mid-July; if grazed only.

1. * These operations apply only where the seeds are undersown in a spring cereal crop soon after drilling. One extra harrowing and rolling is needed if undersown in an autumn-sown cereal crop.
2. *Spring drilling* may continue to mid-May to enable extra cleaning cultivations or the application of farmyard manure.
3. *P. and K.* may be applied in September - especially on undersown ley in year sown.

Conservation

Operations	Labour-Hours per hectare		Time of Year
	Average	Premium	
Plough	1.4	1.0	Autumn drilling: may not
Hay (5.5 tonnes per hectare)			
Mow	1.2	0.9	
Turn, etc	2.6	1.9	Two-thirds June, one-third
Bale	1.3	0.9	July
Cart..	6.0	4.5	
Total per hectare	11.1	8.2	
Total per tonne............................	2.0	1.5	
Silage (17 tonnes per hectare)			
Mow	1.2	0.9	
Turn, etc	0.7	0.5	Two-thirds May, one-third
Load......................................	2.3	1.7	June
Cart..	3.0	2.3	
Clamp	2.3	1.7	
Total per hectare	9.5	7.1	
Total per tonne............................	0.56	0.42	

Specialised Equipment Prices for Grass Conservation: see page 163.

Typical Monthly Breakdown

Production (figures averaged over the life of the ley)

	1-year ley undersown in spring		3-year ley undersown in autumn (1)		1-year ley drilled		3-year ley drilled	
	Ave.	Prem.	Ave.	Prem.	Ave.	Prem.	Ave.	Prem.
March	0.9	0.5	0.7	0.5	0.6	0.3	0.6	0.3
April	0.9	0.5	0.7	0.5	0.6	0.3	0.6	0.3
May	0.6	0.3	0.6	0.3	0.6	0.3	0.6	0.3
June	0.6	0.3	0.6	0.3	0.6	0.3	0.6	0.3
July	0.6	0.3	0.6	0.3	0.6	0.3	0.6	0.3
August	0.3	0.2	0.3	0.2	5.0	3.4	1.9	1.4
September...	0.6	0.3	0.3	0.2	3.2	2.2	1.4	1.0

1. *If ploughed after a cereal crop,* drilled early August to mid-September.

	1-year ley drilled in autumn (1)		3-year ley drilled in spring		Permanent Pasture	
	Ave.	Prem.	Ave.	Prem.	Ave.	Prem.
March	3.0	2.1	1.4	1.0	0.6	0.3
April	1.8	1.2	0.9	0.7	0.6	0.3
May	0.3	0.3	0.6	0.3	0.6	0.3
June	0.6	0.3	0.6	0.3	0.6	0.3
July	0.6	0.3	0.6	0.3	0.6	0.3
August	0.3	0.2	0.2	0.2	0.3	0.2
September..........	—	—	—	0.2	0.2	0.2
October.............	0.9	0.5	0.6	0.3	—	—
November..........	1.4	1.0	1.0	0.3	—	—
December	0.7	0.5	0.6	0.2	—	—

Conservation

	Hay				Silage			
	per hectare		per tonne		per hectare		per tonne	
	Av.	Prem.	Av.	Prem.	Av.	Prem.	Av.	Prem.
May	—	—	—	—	6.3	4.7	0.37	0.28
June	7.4	5.6	1.3	1.0	3.2	2.4	0.19	0.14
July	3.7	2.6	0.7	0.5	—	—	—	—

Kale

Production

Operations	Labour-Hours per hectare		Time of Year
	Average	Premium	
Plough	1.4	1.0	September onwards
Seedbed Cults.............................	2.2	1.6	March, April, early May
Fertiliser	0.3	0.2	April, early May
Drill...	1.3	1.0	May
Roll..	0.6	0.4	Straight after drilling
Spray (weed killer)	0.3	0.2	6 weeks after drilling

Catch Crop

Kale may be drilled up to the first week of July; the crop will be smaller but either an early bite or silage crop may have been taken from a ley earlier in the year, or the ground may have been fallowed and thoroughly cleaned during the spring and early summer. The smaller crop is also easier to graze using an electric fence.

The above operations will still apply although the times of the year will obviously be different, but there may be an additional three or so rotavations and two or three heavy cultivations if fallowed for the first half of the year or ploughed after an early bite. This means approximately an extra 10 (average) or 8 (premium) man-hours per hectare in April, May, June.

FIELD SCALE VEGETABLES

(Labour hours per hectare unless otherwise stated)

Cabbage Transplanting	Hand 150-160. Spring cabbage, Sept.-Oct.; summer, April; autumn, May-June
	Machine (3.5 gang). Spring cabbage 75, summer 85, autumn 100.
	Pulling and dipping plants. 20 per hectare transplanted.
Cabbage Harvesting	Early spring cabbage, 210, Feb.-April; hearted spring, 250, April-June; summer, 220, June-July; autumn, 220, Oct.-Dec.
Brussels Sprouts Transplanting	45 (machine) to 55 (hand), May-June.
Brussels Sprouts Picking	320-400: picked over 3-5 times, maximum approx. 3 hectares per picker per season. Early sprouts, Aug.-Dec.; late, Nov.-Mar.
Peas Hand Pulling	475-525 (150 per tonne). Early, June; maincrop, July-Aug.
Runner Beans (Picked)	Harvesting. 625 (175 per tonne), July-Sept.
Runner Beans (Stick)	Harvesting. 675, July-Sept.
Runner Beans (Stick)	Erecting Canes and String. 100-150, May-June.
Carrot Harvesting.	Elevator-digger: 260 (1 man + 12 casuals, 20 hours per hectare). Earlies, July-Aug.; maincrop, Sept.-Feb.
	Harvester: 30 (3 men, 10 hours per hectare). Riddle and Grade: (1° per tonne), Dec.-Feb.
Beetroot Harvest and Clamp.	25, Oct.-Dec. 12-15 man-hours per tonne to wash and pack.

Source: The Farm as a Business, Aids to Management, Section 6: Labour and Machinery. (N.B. This data is now dated, but it is still the latest known to the author.)

LABOUR FOR LIVESTOCK

This data is updated for 2016

Dairy Cows

Time Required per Cow Depending on Yield.

Yield of Cow	5,500	7,000	8,000	9,000
	hours per cow per month			
January	2.0	2.5	3.1	3.8
February	1.9	2.5	3.1	3.8
March	1.8	2.5	3.1	3.8
April	1.6	2.4	3.0	3.8
May	1.6	2.1	2.7	3.5
June	1.6	2.1	2.6	3.2
July	1.6	2.1	2.6	3.2
August	1.6	2.1	2.6	3.2
September	1.6	2.2	2.8	3.5
October	1.8	2.4	3.1	3.8
November	1.9	2.5	3.1	3.8
December	2.0	2.5	3.1	3.8
Total per Cow per Year	21	27.9	34.9	43.2
Average Seconds per Litre	*13.7*	*14.3*	*15.7*	*17.3*

No time is allocated here for dairy young stock. This schedule is based on a 100-cow herd.
Low yielding cows tend to spend more time at grass and less housed. High milk yielders
take more management time.
13.7 seconds per litre = 1 man per 725,000L
17.3 seconds per litre = 1 man per 575,000L
The most labour efficient milk producing operations in the UK achieve over 800,000 litres
per employed man.

Hours staff Requirement per Cow per Year.

	Cow Annual Milk Yield (L)			
	5,500	7,000	8,000	9,000
Cows per Herd				
60	21.9	29.1	36.4	45.0
100	21.0	27.9	34.9	43.2
150	20.0	26.6	33.2	41.1
300	17.5	23.3	29.1	36.0
500	15.0	19.9	24.9	30.9

Labour Cost per Litre

	Cow Annual Milk Yield (L)			
ppl	5,500	7,000	8,000	9,000
Cows per Herd				
60	4.31	4.50	4.92	5.41
100	4.13	4.32	4.72	5.20
150	3.94	4.11	4.50	4.95
300	3.44	3.60	3.94	4.33
500	2.95	3.08	3.37	3.71

Earnings. The average earnings of 'dairy herdsmen' in 2015/16 is estimated to be £29,990 a year and working 2,770 hours (10 hours for 277 days). This includes relief milking etc. but no cover for young stock or fieldwork, such as hay and silage making.

Dairy Followers and Beef

No recent survey work has been published on labour requirements for beef animals and dairy followers. The following data is therefore only 'best estimates'. They are for average performance and average conditions, excluding fieldwork. Substantial variations occur, e.g. through differing management styles or economies of scale with differing herd sizes.

Calves (per head, early weaning)

Age Group	Labour hours per month	
	Average	Premium
0-3 months……………………………………..	2.3	1.6
3-6 months……………………………………	0.9	0.6
(av. 0-6 months………………………………	1.6	1.1)
6-12 months, yarded………………………..	1.1	0.8
6-12 months, summer grazed………………..	0.3	0.2
(av. 0-12 months, during winter (1)………..	1.3	0.9)
(av. 0-12 months, during summer (1)……….	0.9	0.6)

1. *Assuming 6 to 12-month olds housed in winter and grazed in summer, and calvings or calf purchases fairly evenly spaced throughout the year.*

Stores (per head)

Yearling, housed………………………..	1.0	0.7
2 year olds and over, housed……………	1.4	0.8
Out-wintered store………………………	0.7	0.5
12 months and over, summer grazed………..	0.2	0.1

Dairy Followers

(Per 'replacement unit', i.e. calf + yearling + in-calf heifer.) (1)		
During winter…………………………....	2.9	2.0
During summer…………………………….	1.2	0.8

1. *Assuming calvings fairly evenly spaced throughout the year and heifers calving at 2 to 2.5 years old.*

Beef Finishing (per head)

Housed………………………………....	1.8	1.2
Summer Grazed…………………………….	0.2	0.1
Intensive Beef (0-12 months)………………..	1.3	1.0

Suckler Herds (per cow)

Lowland Single suckling (av. whole year) …….	0.9	0.6
Lowland Multiple suckling (av. whole year) ….	2.9	2.1
Upland/Hill Single suckling (av. whole year)….	1.1	0.7

Sheep (per Ewe)

| | Labour hours per month | |
	Average	Premium (4)
January	0.3	0.2
February	0.3	0.2
March	1.0 (1)	0.7
April	0.4	0.25
May	0.3	0.2
June	0.4 (2)	0.3
July	0.2	0.15
August	0.2	0.15
September	0.25	0.15
October	0.25	0.15
November	0.2	0.15
December	0.2	0.15
Total	4.0 (3)	2.75

1. Assuming mainly March lambing.
2. 0.3 if shearing is by contract.
3. A full-time shepherd, i.e. one who did no other work on the farm, would have to have a flock of at least 600 ewes for the average 4 hours per ewe per year to be achieved, assuming full-time assistance during lambing time.
4. In a national survey conducted in 1999 the average annual requirement for flocks exceeding 500 ewes was 2.9 hours.

Pigs

| | Labour hours per month | |
Age Group	Average	Premium
Breeding and Rearing, per sow	1.5	1.20
(Average 130 sows per worker, Premium 160)		
Feeding only, per 10 pigs	1.6	1.25
No. at a time, per worker:		
Average 1,200 per man, Premium 1,600		
No. per year, per worker:		
Average: 6,000 porkers, 4,800 cutters, 4,450 baconers		
Premium: 8,000 porkers, 6,400 cutters, 5,750 baconers		
Breeding, Rearing and Feeding, per sow (with progeny)		
Porkers, average 90 sows per worker, premium 110	2.4	2.0
Cutters, average 80-85 sows per worker, premium 100-105	2.6	2.1
Baconers, average 75-80 sows per worker, premium 95-100	2.8	2.2

Poultry (large scale, automated)

	Labour hours per month
Laying hens: battery cages (18,000 per full-time worker)	1.1 per 100
free range	4 per 100
Broilers: 32,500 at a time per full-time worker*	
(225,000 a year)	1.0 per 100

* additional help needed for catching and cleaning out (included in labour hours/ month)

4.   STANDARD MAN DAYS

Standard Man Days (SMD) is a general estimate of the farm labour requirement per enterprise. A SMD is 2,200 hours per year. This is 45 weeks' work of 39 hours (after holidays, illnesses etc. have been deducted), plus an average of 10 hours overtime per week (45 x 49 = 2,205). These total hours are converted into 275 notional 8-hour Standard Man Days. This figure includes an assessment for overtime but can be increased by further overtime working.

Every farm enterprise requires a number of SMDs per unit of production (per hectare, per cow etc.). The total SMD requirement for each enterprise is therefore calculated by multiplying by the size of the operation. The total labour needed on the holding is the sum of all the individual enterprises. An additional 15% has then traditionally been added to account for general maintenance, repairs and management. The total SMD requirement is then divided by 275 to find the number of full-time employees that will be required. This system can work when the labour requirement is constant during the year – e.g. some livestock enterprises. However, when labour use is seasonal, e.g. most field operations, it does not show the 'peaks and troughs' that are crucial in labour planning. It also fails to reflect that daylight hours, soil conditions, rainfall etc. will alter the amount of time available for fieldwork during the course of the year. SMD also does not recognise the efficiency of larger units, so SMD requirements fall per unit as the enterprise grows.

Crops (per hectare)	S.M.D.s
Winter Feed Wheat..	
Winter Milling Wheat...	
Spring Wheat...	
Winter Feed Barley..	1.15 /
Winter Malting Barley..	1.75 (1)
Spring Malting Barley	
Winter Oats	
Spring Oats...	
Winter Oilseed Rape..	1.10
Spring Oilseed Rape	1.00
Linseed..	1.00
Winter Field Beans..	0.90
Spring Field Beans	0.95
Dried Peas	1.60
Lupins...	1.50
Vining Peas	3.00
Maincrop Potatoes...	9.25 (2)
Early Potatoes...	5.50 (2)
Sugar Beet	3.00
Herbage Seed (Ryegrass)...	1.40
Hops	9.50 (2)
Kale (grazed)	1.40
Silage:~ one cut	1.60 (3)
two cuts	2.80 (3)
Grazing only...	0.40 (3)
Hay for sale	1.80 (3)
Let Keep	0.40 (3)
Bare fallow / set-aside	0.20
Rough Grazing	0.20

Livestock (per head) (4)

Dairy Cows	4.00
Bulls	3.50
Beef Cows (single suckler including calf):	
lowland	1.35
upland/hill	1.68
Cereal Beef (0-12 months) (5)	1.90
18-month Beef (5)	1.60
Grass Silage Beef (5)	1.90
Finishing Suckler bred stores:	
Grass	1.10
Winter	1.10
Calves; to 6 months (5)	1.20
Ewes: lowland	0.50
upland	0.45
hill	0.40
Rams	0.50
Winter Finishing Store Lambs	0.30
Sows (including weaners to 30kg)	2.25
Boars	2.00
Other Bacon Pigs	0.25
Laying Birds: battery cages	0.017
free range	0.06
Pullets reared (5)	0.005
Broilers (5)	0.002

1. 1.15 if straw ploughed in; 1.75 if straw harvested. Highly mechanised larger farms will require no more than 0.75 S.M.D./ha of direct labour for cereals and other combinable crops (assuming straw ploughed in).

2. Excludes casual labour for harvesting.

3. Excludes any reseeding carried out – this is likely to be around 0.6 S.M.D./ha in the year reseeding is carried out.

4. Note that for grazing livestock, the S.M.D.s per head exclude field work, e.g. grass production and silage making, i.e. the labour for these has to be added to give total labour for these enterprises.

5. For these livestock, S.M.D. per annum should be based on numbers produced (sold) during the year. For all other livestock, average numbers on the farm at any one time during the year should be used (i.e. average of numbers at end of each month).

'Other Cattle' can refer to both beef animals and dairy followers (ref. detail on page 186).

This data is dated now and many commercial enterprises will have more efficient working practices, requiring fewer SMD per unit of output or input (hectare or head).

V. MACHINERY

1. AGRICULTURAL MACHINERY PRICES

This schedule is for 2016 purchase of new machinery, net of discounts and ex. V.A.T. Since 2003, machinery price inflation has been significant as a result of dearer raw materials and currency fluctuations. In 2011 and 2012, price changes were minimal. In 2013, machinery costs rose by 1.3% and from 2013 to 2014 increased significantly by over 8%, partly because of higher exhaust cleanliness regulations. Over 2015, it is expected that machinery prices will remain relatively static with small reductions possible on certain items. Prices shown are a range as prices vary between makes and models. Machines with a star '*' denote those used in subsequent 'farmer' cost' calculations.

Tractors	*£ Range*	
(a) Two-Wheel Drive		
80-90 hp	30,300	35,350
90-100 hp	30,300	36,865
(b) Four- Wheel Drive		
* 100-120 hp	43,430	58,580
* 125-140 hp	48,480	64,640
* 150-180 hp	64,640	80,800
180-220 hp	75,750	101,000
225-270 hp	85,850	131,300
(c) High Road Speed (50 Km /hour)		
155-175 hp	70,700	90,900
190-220 hp	82,820	106,050
(d) Crawlers - rubber tracks		
* 230-300 hp	155,540	171,700
340-400 hp	171,700	196,950
450-550 hp	207,050	252,500

Cultivating Equipment

(a) Ploughs			Variable width	
	Mechanical		Hydraulic	
Reversible:	Adjustment		Adjustment	
3-furrow	10,100	12,625	—	
4-furrow	12,120	14,645	14,645	17,170
* 5-furrow	15,655	17,675	18,685	20,705
6-furrow	17,170	22,220	20,200	25,250
7-furrow (mounted)	26,260	29,290	30,300	33,835
8-furrow (mounted)	30,300	35,350	35,350	40,400

(b) Furrow Presses		
1.6-1.8 m double row	3,788	4,293
2.0-2.4 m double row	4,040	5,050
* 2.6-3.0 m double row	5,555	8,080
3.2-3.6 m double row	8,080	11,110
3.8-4.0 m double row	10,100	14,140

(c) *Front Presses (excluding linkage)*

1.5 m single row	2,727	3,232
3.0 m single row	3,788	6,060
* 4.0 m single row — hydraulic folding	6,565	8,585

(d) *Front Press Linkage*

1.0 to 2.0 tonne	4,040	7,070

(e) *Other Cultivating Equipment*

* Sub Soiler 2-3 leg	4,040	5,050
Shakarator (3m)	9,595	13,130
Stubble Cultivator (3m)	7,070	12,120
* (heavy duty) (4m) hydraulic folding	14,140	19,190
(6 m): hydraulic folding	17,170	27,270
(8 m): hydraulic folding	25,000	40,000
8-12m straw rakes (excl. roller)	12,500	25,000
* Spring-tine Cultivator (3-4 m):	2,525	4,040
(5-6 m): hydraulic folding	6,565	10,100
Tine / Disc Cultivator Combinations		
(3-4 m) mounted	12,120	22,220
* (5-6 m) trailed	25,250	45,450
* Disc Harrows (3.6 - 4.4 m): trailed	13,130	21,210
(4.4-6.0 m): trailed folding	25,250	40,400
(8.0-12.0 m): trailed folding	40,000	60,000
* Harrows (5-6 m): light-medium, hydraulic folding	3,030	5,050
* Rotovator (up to 135 hp tractor)	8,080	10,100
(200 hp tractor)	13,130	16,160
Power Harrow (with packer roller)		
(3 m)	7,575	9,595
* (4m)	12,120	15,150
(4-6m): folding	22,220	30,300
* Rolls: Triple gang, hydraulic folding (6 m)	7,575	12,120
Five gang, hydraulic folding (12m)	17,170	22,220

Fertiliser Distributors, Seed Drills, Sprayers

(a) *Fertiliser Distributors*

Mounted Spinners		
(700-1,200 litre): twin disc, hydraulic control	3,030	7,070
(1,300-1,700 litre): twin disc, hydraulic control	5,050	8,585
* (1,650-2,300 litre): twin disc, electronic control	8,080	12,120
(3,200 litre): twin disc, electronic control	12,120	16,160
Bag lifter (850-1,000kg)	2,020	2,525

(b) *Seed Drills*

Grain: 3 m, gravity fed	7,070	10,100
* 3-4 m, pneumatic	13,130	17,170
6 m, pneumatic	18,180	25,250
8 m, pneumatic	40,400	60,600
12 m, pneumatic	65,650	101,000

(c)   *Combined Cultivator and Pneumatic Drill*

	3-4 m	18,180	28,280
	6 m	35,350	65,650
	8 m	70,000	100,000

(d)   *Combined Power Harrow and Pneumatic Drill*

*	3-4 m	18,180	30,300
	6 m	40,400	60,600

(e)   *Direct Drill (6m)* — 30,300   60,600

   Precision Maize Drill (6 row) — 15,150   25,250

(f)   *Sprayers*

	Mounted, 600-800 litre tank, 12 m boom	3,030	6,060
	Mounted, 1,000-1,800 l, 20-24 m hydraulic boom	16,160	25,250
*	Trailed, 2,500-3,000l tank 18-24 m boom	28,280	40,400
	Trailed, 3,000-4,500l tank 24-36 m boom	35,350	65,650
	Self-propelled sprayers,		
	2,500-4,000l, 24-36 m boom	90,900	131,300
	5,000-6,000l tank, 24 - 36m boom	101,000	161,600

Grass Conservation and Handling Equipment

(a)   *Silage Equipment*

*	Forage Harvester: trailed, precision chop	30,300	45,450
	Self-propelled (3 m pick-up 400-600 hp)	151,500	222,200
	Maize attachment, 8 row	32,320	38,380
	Silage Trailer, 12 tonne, tandem axle	10,100	13,635
	Silage Trailer, 14 - 16 tonne, tandem axle	13,130	17,170
	Buckrake (push off)	3,535	7,070

(b)   *Haymaking Equipment*

	Mowers 1.5-1.8 m, 1-2 drum	2,828	3,838
*	Disc Conditioner, mounted (2.4-3.2 m)	8,585	13,635
	trailed (3.2 - 3.8 m)	15,150	18,180
*	Rake: single/double rotor, 3.2m-4.5m range	4,040	7,575
	multiple rotors 8-10m range	20,200	40,400
	Tedder/swather		
*	5-7 m, 4-6 rotors	5,555	9,595
	8-11m multiple rotors	15,150	30,300
	Balers and Bale Handling: see 5(c) and (d) below		

(c)   *Silage Handling Equipment*

	Silage shear bucket	2,020	3,030
	Silage grab	1,768	2,778
	Big Bale Silage Feeder, mounted	10,100	15,150
	Diet-feeder Wagon (6 tonne)	17,170	24,240
	Clamp Silage Mixer (10 tonne)	24,240	30,300

Grain and Straw Harvesting and Handling Equipment

(a) Combines

Engine size hp	Cutterbar width metres (feet)			
220-249	4.5-5.5 (14-18)	....	101,000	141,400
250-299	5.4-6.6 (18-22)	....	121,200	171,700
300-399	6.0-7.7 (20-25)	....	131,300	202,000
400+	7.7-10.6 (25-35)	....	202,000	373,700

(b) Yield monitoring/mapping 8,080   11,110

    Self-levelling options 12,120   18,180

(c) Balers

*   Conventional Balers 10,605   13,130

*   Round balers, twine tying and net wrap 20,200   30,300

*   Big Square Balers 80,800   111,100

(d) Bale Wrappers

       Big Bale Wrapper: trailed 9,090   14,140

       Big Square Bale Wrapper: trailed 20,200   28,280

       Combined Baler and Wrapper 40,400   55,550

     Bale Trailers, 30 ft - 35 ft long 3,535   5,050

     Accumulator, flat 8, mechanical 2,525   4,040

     Big bale accumulator 10,100   15,150

     Big Bale Shredder, silage or straw 6,060   9,090

     Big Square Bale Chasers 60,000   75,000

(e) Drying, Handling, Feed Processing Equipment

     Grain driers and Grain storage:

     Cleaner/grader, 10-20 tonnes/hour 10,100   16,160

     Grain augers 150 mm, 6-8.5 m, with trolley 2,020   3,030

     Grain conveyors, (25-50t/hour) 1,515   2,525

     Hammer mill, 7.5-15 kW 4,040   5,050

     Roller mill, 4-5.5 kW 3,283   4,040

     Mixer, 750-1000 kg 4,545   5,050

     Mill and mixer, 1,000-1,300kg, 3.7-5.5 kW 7,070   9,090

Potato, Sugar Beet and Vegetable Machinery

(a) Potato Machinery

*   De-stoner 45,450   55,550

*   Bedformer, 1 bed 5,050   8,080

     Bed tiller (1 bed) 9,090   13,130

*   Planter: 2 row mounted 12,120   25,250

              6 row 35,350   45,450

     Haulm pulveriser (2 row): 6,565   9,090

*	Harvesters trailed: 2 row elevator manned/unmanned	75,750	101,000
	2 row, self-propelled	151,500	202,000
	4 row, self-propelled	353,500	454,500
	Store loader (heavy duty)	25,250	30,300
	Self-unloading hopper, 3-5 tonnes	11,110	14,140
	Clod separator	11,110	14,140
	Sizer, 5-30 tonnes/hour	11,110	15,150
	Barrel washer, 8-10 tonnes/hour	25,250	35,350
	Roller inspection table, 1.2 x 2.4 m	3,030	6,060
	Weigher, automatic, 8-10 tonnes/hour	7,575	10,100
	Box tipper with cross conveyor	15,150	25,250
	Box filler, automatic	15,150	20,200
	Bag stitcher (hand held)	505	1,515
	Complete out of store grading line: 20 tonnes/hour	60,600	151,500
	30 tonnes/hour	101,000	202,000

(b) Sugar Beet Machinery

*	Precision Drill 6 row (pneumatic)	11,110	15,150
	12 row-18 row (pneumatic)	20,200	40,400
*	Hoe: 6 row-12 row (heavy duty)	8,585	14,140
	Harvesters: Trailed, 2 row, tanker	70,700	85,850
	Trailed, 3 row, tanker	90,900	101,000
	Trailed, 4 row, tanker	95,950	106,050
*	Self-propelled, 6 row, 18 tonne tank	343,400	404,000
	Cleaner-loader, with engine, 1-3 tonnes per minute	20,200	35,350
	Fodder beet harvester	10,100	90,900

(c) Vegetable Machinery

Onion windrower	11,110	13,130
Root crop digger: 1 webb	7,575	8,585
2 webbs	9,090	11,110
Top lifting veg single row, bunker	55,550	70,700
twin row, bunker/elevator	95,950	126,250
four row, elevator	131,300	156,550
four row, self-propelled	343,400	393,900
Leek harvester (mounted)	25,250	40,400

Dairy Equipment

Water heater	808	1,818
Heat recovery unit	2,525	5,050
Plate Cooler	1,515	4,040
Variable speed vacuum pumps	9,090	11,110
Cow collars for heat-time monitoring (£ per cow)	71	91
Electronic auto-shedding systems	8,080	14,140
Auto-dipping and flushing system (£ per stall)	808	1,010

For complete milking parlour costs - see building costs on page 218.

General

	Trailer, 12 tonne tipping; grain/silage	10,100	13,130
*	Trailer, 14t tipping, tandem axle; grain/silage	11,110	16,160
	Grain Chaser Bin - 24t	50,000	60,000
*	F.Y.M. Spreader, (10 - 12 tonne)	11,110	16,160
	(12 - 14 tonne)	15,150	20,200
*	Loaders, front mounted	5,555	9,090
*	Materials Handler, telescopic boom (2.5-3.0 tonne)	40,400	60,600
	Skid steer loader (500-600 kg)	15,150	22,220
	Quad Bikes	3,535	6,565
	Vacuum Tankers (5,000-6,000 litre)	5,050	7,070
*	Low Ground Pressure Tankers (9,000-11,000 litre)	12,120	16,160
	Slurry pump	4,040	5,050
	Slurry separator	28,280	35,350
	Cattle crush	1,010	2,020
	Cattle crush with weigher	2,020	3,030
	Cattle trailer (twin-axle)	3,535	5,050
	Yard scrapers	505	1,010
	Rotary brush (2-2.5 m)	2,020	2,525
*	Flat roll, ballastable (2.5-3 m)	1,263	2,020
*	Pasture topper (2.0-3.0 m)	1,212	2,525
	Hedge cutter:		
*	hydraulic angling; flail head	12,120	18,180
	7.6m reach, 1.3m flail head, double sided	28,280	35,350
	Ditcher: fully slewing	9,595	12,120
	Post hole digger	1,212	2,020
	Post hole driver	1,515	3,535
	Saw bench	1,515	2,525
	Log splitter	808	1,212
	Welder	253	1,515
	Angle Grinder	25	202
	Compressor	253	808
	Farm Security Camera (single basic camera)	101	202
	Farm Security Camera System (automatic and wireless)	1,111	1,414
	Tractor Guidance System (basic)	808	1,515
	Auto-Steer Guidance System	7,070	12,120

2. CONTRACTORS' CHARGES, FARMERS' COSTS AND WORK RATES

Contractors' charges vary widely according to many factors: these are estimates for 2016. Farmer-contractors sometimes charge less than dedicated contractors, since some of their overheads and fixed costs are largely *considered* covered by their own farming operations, but the service may not always be so complete, including specialist advice or access to new technology.

Farmers' own costs (including the value of the farmers' own manual labour) vary even more widely; those given (for 2016) are averages in every respect as costs will vary according to soil types, size of farm, and so on; they are based on accounting cost procedures in that labour, tractor and machinery fuel, repairs and depreciation are included - no allowance has been added for general farm overheads, interest on capital, supervision/management or under-occupied labour during slack times. They assume four-wheel drive 150 hp tractors for moderate field work such as ploughing, cultivations and drilling and 185 hp tractors are assumed for work with a very high power requirement such as heavy discing/cultivating, sub-soiling and deep ploughing. An additional fuel allowance for very heavy work has been added (i.e. higher than the average consumption assumed in the tractor costs schedule). Four-wheel drive 120 hp tractors are assumed to be used for most other operations (these individual tractor costs are shown in the tractor costs schedule on page 204). The figures should not be used for partial budgeting. The machinery used in the calculations for farmers' costs is identified by a 'star' * adjacent to specific items of equipment in the machinery list in the previous section (an average has been used for the purchase price).

The contract charges and average farmers' costs are put side-by-side for tabular convenience, not to facilitate comparisons. Apart from the fact that contractors' charges must cover expenses omitted from the farmers' cost, the advisability or otherwise of hiring a contractor for a particular job depends on many factors (e.g. timeliness), varying widely according to farm circumstances; therefore, there are advantages and disadvantages not reflected in a cost comparison alone.

Assumptions: Contractors' costs are particularly sensitive to many factors including fuel costs, capital machinery prices, and local demand versus competition. Contractors' charges are based on red diesel at 60ppl whilst the farmers' cost calculations are based on fuel at 47ppl. The reason for the difference is because it is unlikely that contractors' charges would reduce due to a small fall in fuel prices. However, many contractors are now making individual arrangements with customers regarding fuel (i.e. prices quoted before fuel – therefore using the farmer's fuel when on site). The contractor charges shown below are inclusive of fuel and do not reflect this trend. Tractor costs are taken from those on page 204. The rates of work include preparation, travelling to and from the fields and allow for minor breakdowns and other stoppages.

Machinery rings. Prices charged by farmers offering services through machinery rings are extremely variable but are generally between average farmers' costs and contractors' charges. There are exceptions, which mainly relate to relatively expensive items of machinery (e.g. precision drills, de-stoners and combine harvesters), where the charges for services offered through machinery rings are close to and often less than average farmers' costs. Machinery and Labour rings are great examples of Joint Ventures that can deliver significant cost savings for all of the farming businesses involved. Structures and circumstances often vary considerably between organisations / groups involved.

Acknowledgement. The estimates for contractors' charges are kindly supplied by the National Association of Agricultural Contractors (as collected through their survey).

*   *All costs below are per hectare unless otherwise stated. The figures represent a national average.*

Average Contractors Charges & Farmers Costs of Performing Mechanical Operations

Operation	Contract Charge £/ha *	Farmer's Average Cost £/ha *	Days Use Per Year	Average Rate of Work (Ha per 8 hr day)
Cultivations				
Ploughing – light land	58.51	56	30	7
– heavy land	63.01	60	30	6.5
-- with furrow press	7.12	9	30	6
Deep ploughing (over 30cm)	70.50	85	25	5.5
Rotovating - ploughed land	68.45	85	18	5
- grass		106	18	4
Sub-soiling/Flat Lifting	58.81	63	10	6
Mole-ploughing – single leg	95.26			
Stubble cultivating	40.77	35	20	12
Discing: Shallow	42.85			
Deep	46.18	46	20	10
Power harrowing – Deep/on ploughing	53.69	43	20	9
Shallow/seedbed prep	50.26			
Spring-tine Harrowing	32.27	21	20	12
Pressing	33.04	25	10	
One-pass tillage train (solo/discordon etc)	68.74	53	20	15
Rolling – flat (grassland)	25.80	19	10	12
– ring (seedbeds)	17.64	14	10	20
Drilling				
Rape drilling with flatlift/subsoiler	66.52	63	10	6
Cereal drilling – conventional	44.53	29	12	14
Combi-Drilling	59.97	56	12	9
Tyre Drill (Vaderstad)	48.18	46	12	18
Direct Drilling	57.20	52	12	15
Sugar beet drilling	53.13	48	5	10
Carrot/Parsnip/Onion Precision Drilling	86.49			
Grass seed (broadcast)	22.66	24	2	11
Grass seeding with harrow (e.g. Opico)	29.38			
Cross drilling grass	79.07			
Chain Harrowing	22.93			
Maize Precision Drilling	45.22			
Maize Drilling Under Plastic	121.08			
Fertilising & Spraying				
Fertiliser distribution	12.06	8	15	45
Extra for variable rate application	3.29			
Lime spreading (per tonne)	4.55/tonne			
Irrigating (excl. water costs) per inch	25.33			
Spraying (based on 200 l/ha & 24m boom)	13.22	11	20	45
Extra if less than 50 acres (20 ha)	4.69			
Liquid Fertiliser	15.15			
ATV spraying	36.00/hr or 11.74/ha			
Slug-pelleting	9.09			
Weed Wiping	25.95			
Avadex Spreading	15.12			

Operation	Contract Charge £/ha *	Farmer's Average Cost £/ha *	Days Use Per Year	Average Rate of Work (Ha per 8 hour day)
Combining				
Combining cereals	86.81	74	14	20.4
Extra for straw chopper on combine	6.52	*Farmer's cost assumes*		
Extra for seeding (Autocast)	9.02	*average of all machine sizes*		
Extra for yield mapping	2.47	*and harvested areas*		
OSR harvesting – out of windrow	86.06			
– direct combining	89.05	74	14	20.4
Combining peas/beans	94.10	74	14	20.4
Combining grain maize	102.13			
Swathing OSR	45.42			
Grain carting to barn (per hour)	38.23/hr	32.18 /hr		
Grass & Forage				
Topping margins per hour	42.67/hr			
Grass topping	32.81	24	3	12
Grass mowing	29.90	30	10	12
Tedding	16.09	14	10	20
Raking	16.70	21	3	20
Forage harvesting only – first cut	67.33	57	6	16
- other cuts	56.19	46	6	20
Forage harvesting, cart (3 trailers) and clamping (1st cut)	128.69			
Whole Crop forage harvesting, cart (3 trailers) and clamping	168.03			
Complete service – mow, rake, forage harvest, cart (3 trailers) and clamp	160.19			
Maize harvesting incl carting (3 trailers) and clamping	169.76			
Extra forage trailer (per hour)	39.36/hr			
Forage box	104.94/hr			
Baling				
Baling (per bale) - 'small'	0.58/bale	0.35 / bale	10	5.6
- 80cm × 70cm	3.58/bale			
- 120cm × 70cm	4.59/bale	4.39 / bale	25	20
- 120cm × 130cm	6.75/bale			
- Round 120cm	2.82/bale			
- Round 150cm	3.45/bale	2.36 / bale	20	13.6
Bale-wrapping – Round 120cm (6 layers)	5.73/bale			
- Round 120cm (with 4 layers)	5.17/bale			
- Round 120cm (without plastic)	2.14/bale			
- Square 120cm × 70cm (6 layers)	6.72/bale			
- Square 120cm × 70cm (4 layers)	5.53/bale			
- Square120cm × 70cm (without plastic)	2.47/bale			
Bale Chaser (per hour)	60.00/hr			

Operation	Contract Charge £/ha *	Farmer's Average Cost £/ha *	Days Use Per Year	Average Rate of Work (Ha per 8 hour day)
Root Crop Operations				
Potato harvesting – harvesting only	778.37	432	20	2
- Harvesting and carting	988.40	689		
De-stoning potato land	259.46	214	18	2.5
Potato ridging	69.19	39	5	9
Potato Planting	197.68	121	16	3
Sugar beet harvesting - harvesting only	227.33	307	20	8
- Harvesting and carting	271.81			
Irrigation (25 mm application / ha)	98.00			
Manure Handling - *see below for telehandler costs for loading*				
FYM spreading – tractor and rear discharge :	42.45/hr	47	per hour	
- tractor and side discharge spreader	38.78/hr			
Slurry spreading – tanker	47.43/hr	47	per hour	
- umbilical	83.00/hr or 2.63/cube			
- extra pump	35.75/hr			
Slurry injection	56.50/hr			
General / Rural Maintenance				
Hedge cutting - flail	34.83/hr	36	per hour	
- saw-blade	48.12/hr	44	per hour	
Hedge laying	15.00/metre			
Fence erection (with materials)				
– post and 4 Barb	4.97/metre			
– post, stock net & 2 Barb	6.11/metre			
– post and 3 rails	16.00/metre			
Quad Bike (including man)		16	per hour	
Tractor + Post Knocker + Man	38.00/hr			
Ditching using 360 deg digger	36.54/hr			
Tractor + trailer + man	39.00/hr	32	per hour	
100 – 150 hp Tractor + man	35.00/hr			
150 – 220 hp Tractor + man	36.06/hr	*See tractor costs schedule*		
220 – 300 hp Tractor + man	48.10/hr	*for farmer's average cost*		
300 hp + Tractor + man	63.75/hr			
Forklift/Telehandler + Man	38.03/hr	29	per hour	
Livestock Husbandry				
Sheep dipping	1.50/head			
Sheep jetting / showering	1.00/head			
Sheep – shearing ewes	1.49/head			
-- rams	3.06/head			
-- crutching	0.74/head			
Sheep ultrasound scanning	1.00/head			
Cattle ultrasound scanning	2.00/head			
Foot trimming – sheep	1.00/head			
- cattle	11.00/head			
- bulls	25.00/head			
Tractor + Man + Feeder Wagon		36	per hour	
Mobile Feed Mixing and Processing (£/t)	19.00/tonne	(crimping at £9.25/tonne)		

Purchase, Hire Purchase and Contract Hire of Machinery

The farmer's cost for the various operations shown in the table above assume the machinery and equipment is purchased outright. There is no interest charge included in the calculations for the capital required to purchase the machinery. However, a farming business may choose to purchase the machinery through a hire purchase (HP) agreement. This is where a deposit is paid up-front followed by a number of monthly or annual payments. The benefits of HP agreements are purely cash flow, allowing a business to spread the cost over say 3 years. For new equipment, the interest charge may be very low or even 0%, whereas using HP agreements to finance used machines will usually incur an interest rate currently of 3-7%. Once the HP agreement ends (i.e. all payments are complete), the farmer owns the item of machinery outright.

Alternatively, some businesses choose to use contract hire (CH) agreements. This involves paying a rental charge for the use of an item of equipment for a set period of time. At the end of the period, the machine is returned to the company (although sometimes opportunities exist to negotiate a price to buy the machine). Contract hire agreements usually include a full service, maintenance and repair plan. The main advantage of these agreements is the ability to plan and budget costs, as the farmer/contractor is 100% confident of the exact cost of operating that machine, with no un-expected repair bills or no need to budget what it will be worth when you come to trade-in the machine. These are becoming popular with large arable and contracting businesses.

Another option which is increasingly popular is to use short-term hire agreements to hire key items of machinery as and when required. For example, many arable businesses contract hire combines and/or additional tractors at harvest time when extra machinery is required. This allows them to access new technology without having large sums of capital tied up in machinery that sits idle for much of the year. The most cost-effective option depends very much on the specific circumstances of the farm business and will be determined by factors such as ability to access capital, annual usage and life expectancy.

Contract Charge for All Operations

For cereals and combinable break crops, 'stubble to stubble' charges (i.e. up to and including combine harvesting and carting the grain to store) are typically £333 to £420/ha (£135-170/acre). Variations depend upon such factors as distance away, area contracted, size of fields, type of terrain, quality of soil, level of inputs and which party provides the storage. Local competition also has a significant bearing on prices, as with all contract charges. Some regions of the UK are very competitive when it comes to certain contract operations, for example hedge cutting or 'tractor and man' provision.

One sometimes views farmers' total power, machinery and labour costs compared with stubble to stubble contractors' charges. It has of course to be remembered that the former include many cost items not included in the latter, e.g. the cost of farm vehicles, fixed plant such as grain stores and general farm maintenance.

Contract Farming Agreements

Generally these are formalised with a written agreement which sets out the terms for the "Farmer" (who can be a landowner or tenant) and a "Contractor". The "Contractor" can be a neighbouring farmer or traditional contractor. "Contractor" remuneration includes a guaranteed basic payment (fee). The basic payment is usually between £210 and £275/ha (£85-£110/acre) for combinable crops and should cover the majority of the fixed costs of the operation. However, it should not offer any margin for the contractor to incentivise him to farm the land to the best of his ability and therefore generate the maximum return to the farmer and contractor through the share of the divisible surplus.

Following deduction of agreement running costs (crop variable costs, drying, insurance, interest charges etc.) and the Farmers Basic Payment, the surplus is split between the 2 parties. The split may typically be 70%-80% to the Contractor and 20%-30% to the Farmer. This incentivises good performance and management from the contractor. A second band of payment rate is sometimes introduced e.g. 50%:50% split above a set level of surplus to enable the farmer to benefit from any significant rises in market prices. This is increasingly the case given the large volatility in cereal prices in recent years.

LIVESTOCK HAULAGE COSTS

The cost of hauling livestock to market, to field, back to winter housing or other movements between grazing is a cost that is often over-looked. The table below demonstrates the farmers cost of hauling livestock per head per journey, for a number of different journey lengths.

Journey Length	£ Per Head Per Journey		
	Ewe	Finished Lamb	Finished Cattle
1 Mile	0.50	0.33	4.96
5 Miles	0.61	0.41	6.13
10 Miles	0.76	0.51	7.58
15 Miles	0.90	0.60	9.04
20 Miles	1.05	0.70	10.50
30 Miles	1.34	0.89	13.42

The costs calculated above include the cost of running a vehicle (pick-up/Landrover), based upon 12,000 miles annual mileage, attributing this cost on a per mile basis to the livestock transport cost (to reflect the fact that the vehicle is also used for many other purposes). The cost of running a livestock trailer (capital cost and repairs/maintenance) is based upon an average sized farm stock trailer with decks, capable of holding 30 ewes, 45 finished lambs, or 3 finished cattle, assuming it is kept for 10 years and used for 40 journeys per year.

In arriving at a cost per head, the calculations assume that the trailer is always fully occupied with one of the above livestock numbers. The costs per head by journey length assume one journey; therefore if the journey to market was 30 miles one-way and no return load was bought back (i.e. an empty trailer), the total cost of transporting those livestock to market would in fact be almost double that shown above (although recognising the fact that towing an empty trailer will use less fuel than when fully loaded). The labour costs calculated above exclude time for loading/un-loading but account for time spent driving between destinations averaging 30mph.

Specialist livestock hauliers charge either on a per day basis or a cost per head for specific journey lengths. As a result, charges vary widely depending upon the specific circumstances, such as distances and the size of groups etc. As a guide, to move breeding sheep from Yorkshire to the Midlands would cost approximately £3/ewe assuming the haulier is able to backload. Costs for hauling lambs to market over a distance of more than 40 miles would cost circa £2.00 - £2.50/lamb and £15-20/head for finished cattle. An articulated lorry and driver, fully equipped for livestock haulage, would typically cost £550-£600/day.

GRAIN HAULAGE COSTS

The average costs per tonne of grain (and oilseed) haulage in Great Britain over six seasons are summarised by the AHDB's haulage survey carried out each December. The summarised results for the years 2008 to 2014 are tabulated below *(there is no data available for 2011)*:

Summary table of the HGCA Haulage Survey Results

	2008	2009	2010	2012	2013	2014
10 miles	£4.83	£4.24	£4.54	£4.28	£4.92	£4.33
20 miles	£5.35	£4.81	£5.03	£4.90	£5.54	£5.03
40 miles	£6.40	£5.95	£6.01	£6.13	£6.76	£6.42
60 miles	£7.45	£7.09	£6.98	£7.36	£7.99	£7.82
100 miles	£9.54	£9.38	£8.94	£9.83	£10.44	£10.61
150 miles	£12.16	£12.23	£11.39	£12.91	£13.51	£14.10

TRACTOR POWER REQUIREMENTS

		hp/acre		hp/ha		kW/Ha	
		av.	prem.	av.	prem.	Av.	Prem.
Combinable crops:	heavy land	1.20	0.85	3.00	2.10	2.24	1.57
	light land	0.90	0.65	2.20	1.60	1.64	1.20
Mixed cropping:	heavy land	1.35	0.95	3.35	2.35	2.50	1.75
	light land	1.00	0.70	2.50	1.75	1.86	1.30

Includes tractors, telehandlers, self-propelled sprayers and combines

UK Agricultural Tractor Sales per Year *(over 50 HP)*

Year	Average Tractor Size HP	Number of Units Sold	Per Cent change y/y
2006	128.3	13,566	+ 3.8%
2007	134.0	15,540	+14.6%
2008	138.1	17,104	+10.1%
2009	143.4	15,013	-12.2%
2010	141.7	13,347	-11.1%
2011	144.3	14,094	+5.6%
2012	148.0	13,951	-1.0%
2013	150.7	12,498	-10.4%
2014	155.1	12,433	-0.5%
2015 (Jan-June)		5,964	-14.1%

(data from the Agricultural Engineers Association).

3. TRACTOR HOURS

Crops	Per Hectare Per Annum	
	Average	Premium
Cereals	8.4	6.3
Plus, Straw	1.6	1.2
Potatoes	18.6	13.9
Sugar Beet	11.6	8.7
Vining Peas	9.4	7.0
Dried Peas	6.9	5.2
Field Beans	6.9	5.2
Oilseed Rape	8.4	6.3
Herbage Seeds:- 3 year crop	5.0	3.7
Hops (machine picked)	120.0	90.0
Kale (grazed)	5.2	3.9
Turnips/Swedes (Folded/Lifted)	10/28	8/22
Fallow	0.8	0.6
Grass Ley Establishment	4.2	3.2
Making Hay	4.8	3.6
Making Silage:		
1st Cut	4.1	3.1
2nd Cut	3.3	2.4
Grazing:-		
Temporary Grass	2.2	1.7
Permanent Grass	1.3	1.0

Livestock	Average Per Head
Dairy Cows	6
Other Cattle over 2 years	5
Other Cattle 1-2 years	4
Other cattle 0.5-1 year	2.25
Calves 0-0.5 year	2.25
Housed Bullocks	3
Sheep (per ewe)	1.25
Store Lambs	0.8
Sows	1.75
Other Pigs over 2 months	1
Laying Birds	0.04

1. *For livestock*, annual requirements are per head requirements above multiplied by average numbers during the year (i.e. average numbers at end of each month).

2. *As with labour,* the number of tractors required by a farm depends more on the seasonal requirements and number required at any one time than on total annual tractor hours. These can be calculated from the seasonal labour data provided earlier in this book. The soil type and size/power of tractors purchased are obviously other relevant factors. All figures are for 2016.

4.   TRACTOR COSTS

Four-Wheel Drive Tractors

	120 h.p.		150 h.p.	
Initial Cost..	£54,035		£64,640	
	per year £	per hour £	per year £	per hour £
Depreciation.....................................	4,323	8.65	5,171	10.34
Insurance...	405	0.81	485	0.97
Repairs and Maintenance.....................	1,351	2.70	1,616	3.23
Fuel and Oil.....................................	2,641	5.28	3,428	6.86
Total	8,720	17.44	10,700	21.40

	185 h.p.		Crawler 265 h.p.	
Initial Cost..	£82,820		£163,620	
	per year £	per hour £	per year £	per hour £
Depreciation.....................................	6,626	13.25	13,090	26.18
Insurance...	621	1.24	1,227	2.45
Repairs and Maintenance.....................	2,071	4.14	4,091	8.18
Fuel and Oil.....................................	4,698	9.40	7,850	15.70
Total	14,015	28.03	26,258	52.52

Figures are estimates calculated for 2016. Depreciation assumes all tractors are sold for 20% of their original value after 10 years of life. The depreciation schedule shown on page 206 demonstrates the average annual fall in value of machinery over its life (column 2 is applicable to tractors). Annual repair costs have been calculated at 2.5% of initial cost for all tractors. This assumes the majority of basic servicing work carried out by the farm's own labour. No interest on capital has been included. Fuel is charged at 47p/litre plus a 5% allowance for oil.

The hourly figures are based on a use of 500 hours per year. A greater annual use than this will mean higher annual costs but possibly lower hourly costs. On some larger farms and within many contracting businesses, many tractors do up to, and even over, 1,000 hours per year. Earlier replacement at a given annual use will increase depreciation costs per hour but should reduce repair costs. The hourly figures are averages for all types of work: heavy operations such as ploughing obviously have a higher cost than light work. The variability of fuel usage is significant depending upon the type of work (light work vs. heavy cultivations) and can vary by up to 80%. The figures shown attempt to depict the average consumption from all types of work.

Typical Contract Hire Charges (see page 200) for tractors are shown below (prices exclude insurance but include repairs/maintenance):

	Short-Term (8-10 weeks)	52 weeks Contract
110 hp tractor:	£430 - £490 / week	£180 - £220 / week
130 hp tractor:	£480 - £560 / week	£230 – £280 / week
165 hp tractor:	£675 - £775 / week	£280 - £330 / week
290 hp tractor (wheeled):	£1,100-£1,375 / week	£350 - £450 / week
130 hp telehandler	£500 - £550 / week	£280 - £330 / week
16 tonne Grain Trailer	£250 – £270 / week or £60-£70/day	

5.   ESTIMATING ANNUAL MACHINERY COSTS

Annual machinery costs consist of depreciation, repairs, fuel and oil, contract charges, and vehicle tax and insurance. These can be budgeted in three ways;

1)   using information on past machinery costs on the farm (e.g. management accounts),

2)   per hectare, by looking up an average figure for the district, according to the size and type of farm. Approximate levels are shown in the tables of whole farm fixed costs (page 218). This is obviously a guide only and masks huge variations between farms.

3)   Fully detailed calculations, costing and depreciating each machine in turn, including tractors, estimating repairs and fuel costs for each, and adding the charges for any contract work. The following tables give, for different types of machinery, estimated life, annual depreciation, and estimated repairs according to annual use.

ESTIMATED USEFUL LIFE OF POWERED MACHINERY IN NORMAL USE

Estimated Useful Life (years)	Annual Use (hours)				
Equipment	25	50	100	200	300
Group 1:					
Ploughs, cultivators, toothed harrows, hoes, rolls, ridgers, potato planting attachments, grain	12+	12+	12+	12	10
Group 2:					
Disc harrows, corn drills, grain drying machines, food grinders and mixers	12+	12+	12	10	8
Group 3:					
Combine harvesters, pick-up balers, rotary cultivators, hydraulic loaders	12+	12+	12	9	7
Group 4:					
Mowers, forage harvesters, swath turners, rakes, tedders, hedge cutting machines, semi-automatic potato planters and transplanters, unit root drills, mechanical root thinners	12+	12	11	8	6
Group 5:					
Fertilisers, combine drills, FYM spreaders, elevator potato diggers, spraying machines, pea cutter windrowers	10	10	9	8	7
Miscellaneous:					
Beet harvesters	11	10	9	6	5
Potato harvesters	—	8	7	5	—
Milking machinery	—	—	—	—	20+

	Annual Use (hours)					
	500	750	1,000	1,500	2,000	2,500
Tractors	12+	12	10	7	6	5
Electric motors	12+	12+	12+	12+	12	12

DEPRECIATION

There are two different methods by which to calculate depreciation rates for agricultural machinery. The **straight line** method takes the difference between the estimated trade-in, second-hand or scrap value of a machine, and the purchase price of the machine. The loss in capital value over the period the machine is retained for is then divided by the age of the machine to arrive at the annual depreciation charge. This can then be used to arrive at the annual % depreciation rate to apply to that machine on a straight line basis over its useful life for budgeting purposes.

Example: If a machine costing £10,000 is retained for 8 years, at the end of which the trade-in value is £2,000, the depreciation has been £8,000. Over 8 years this equates to £1,000 per annum (i.e. 10% per year of the new price).

The **diminishing balances** method takes account of the fact that new machines lose a larger proportion of their capital value in the early years even with modest annual usage. Some estimated percentage rates of depreciation for different machine types under a diminishing balance basis are shown in the table below. *Clearly, in addition to the age of the machine, annual usage has a signifciant effect upon depreciation rates which is not necessarily accounted for below.*

AVERAGE ANNUAL FALL IN VALUE

Age of Machine	Complex. High depreciation rate		Traditional machines		Simple equipment: Low depreciation rate	
	Annual % Dep'n	Total % Dep'n	Annual % Dep'n	Total % Dep'n	Annual % Dep'n	Total % Dep'n
1	37.5	37.5	28	28	22	22
2	25	50	19	38	16	32
3	20*	60	15.3	46	13.7	41
4	16.5†	66	13.3*	53	12	48
5	14.2‡	71	11.8	59	10.8	54
6	12.5	75	10.7†	64	9.8	59
7	11.3	79	9.8	68.5	9.1*	64
8	10.3	82	9.0‡	72	8.4	67
9	9.3	84	8.2	74	7.7	69
10	8.5	85	7.5	75	7†	70

Complex: Machines such as potato harvesters, pea viners, etc.
Traditional Machines: with many moving parts, e.g. tractors, combines, balers, forage harvesters
Simple Equipment: with few moving parts, e.g. ploughs, trailers

* Typical frequency of renewal with heavy use.

† Typical frequency of renewal with average use.

‡Typical frequency of renewal with light use.

These figures have been updated from a survey of machinery sale prices undertaken in 2014. Depreciation is calculated from the new price, asking price of the second hand machine, and its age. The asking price has been discounted by 5% to account for price negotiations. Prices for a variety of machinery and equipment types have been collated and categorised according to complexity.

Example: If a tractor (Traditional Machine) costing £80,000 is 5 years old, the value of the machine has depreciated on average by 11.8% per year, totalling a 59% fall in value. This means the tractor is now worth £32,800. The chart shows the rise of depreciation over the ten year period.

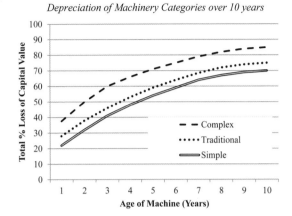

Depreciation of Machinery Categories over 10 years

ESTIMATED ANNUAL COST OF SPARES AND REPAIRS

These figures are based on a percentage of purchase price* at various levels of use

	Annual Use *(hours)*				Additional 100 hours
	500	750	1,000	1,500	use add
	%	%	%	%	%
Tractors	3	3-4	5	7	0.5

	Annual Use *(hours)*				Additional 100 hours
	50	100	150	200	use add
Harvesting Machinery:	%	%	%	%	%
Combine harvesters, self-propelled forage harvesters, self-propelled potato harvesters	1.5	2.5	3.5	4.5	2
Trailed forage harvesters, pick-up balers, potato & sugar beet harvesters	3	5	6	7	2
Other Implements and Machines:					
Ploughs, Cultivators, Toothed harrows, Hoes, Elevator potato diggers	4.5	8	11	14	6
Rotary cultivators, Mowers, Pea cutter-windrowers	4	7	9.5	12	5
Disc harrows, Fertiliser distributors, Farmyard manure spreaders, Combine drills, Potato planters with fertiliser attachment, sprayers, Hedge-cutting machines.	3	5.5	7.5	9.5	4
Swath turners, Tedders, Side-delivery rakes, Unit drills, Flail forage harvesters, Semi-automatic potato planters and transplanters, Down-the-row thinners	2.5	4.5	6.5	8.5	4
Corn drills, Milking machines, Hydraulic loaders, Potato planting Attachments	2	4	5.5	7	3
Grain driers, Grain cleaners, Rolls, Hammer mills, Feed mixers Threshers	1.5	2	2.5	3	0.5

* When it is known that a high purchase price is due to high quality and durability or a low price corresponds to a high rate of wear and tear, adjustments to the figures should be made.

Service Plans

Most tractor manufacturers now offer extended warranties or comprehensive service plans to cover the cost of all servicing, maintenance and repairs beyond the regular manufacturer warranty. This is usually for a pre-agreed period of time or maximum number of hours (usually this expiry date is determined by which comes first). Costs and offerings vary hugely between manufacturers and tractor models but the following gives an approximate guide. A 'standard' maintenance and repair plan for a 130hp tractor doing 500 hours per year for 5 years would cost an average of £1,300-£1,500/year. This is for a 'standard' maintenance and repair plan to include all servicing, most replacement parts, filters, maintenance fluids and routine labour.

There are 'premium' plans available to go a stage further and protect further parts of the machine. There are, however, always exclusions from these agreements such as tyres, glass and provisions for negligence. Given the rising cost of repairs (and machinery dealer labour costs), such plans can be beneficial for farming businesses, particularly contractors who can fix their repair costs. This therefore helps with budgeting and setting prices to charge customers. However, where annual usage is lower, they may not always be economical. Such agreements are a risk management strategy in protecting against large un-expected repair costs. This also gives peace of mind in the knowledge that the services were carried out by a qualified technician at the correct service intervals, rather than by farm staff who may lack knowledge and also can be undertaken on a rather ad-hoc basis, particularly during busy times of the year.

Tyres

The length of time a set of tractor tyres lasts before they need to be replaced will vary significantly depending upon a number of factors. These include soil type (stone content is the main determinant of tyre wear), the amount of yard work undertaken (feeding, loading grain etc), and the amount of road travelling undertaken. Many tractors will do in excess of 5,000 hours on a set of tyres assuming the machine does not do excessive road work. Front tyres on loader tractors are likely to require replacement earlier than rear tyres due to the weight of the loader (and items lifted) and the associated increase in wear that this creates when turning on yard areas. Costs vary significantly between makes and sizes.

As a guide new standard rear tyres for a 130 hp tractor would cost between £700-£1,000 + VAT each and for standard front tyres they would cost in the region of £400-£600 + VAT each. Therefore, the cost to replace the full set of tyres would be approximately £2,700, plus the cost of fitting. This could be done on-farm where the correct equipment is held, otherwise most tyre fitters / tractor dealers would fit these. Typical labour charges for technicians vary between £30/hour to £60/hour. The cost of larger tyres for tractors in the 160-180 hp range, say for 650mm width on the rear, could cost £1,500-£2,200 each including the cost of fitting. Larger and even flotation tyres are becoming increasingly popular for field-work in an attempt to reduce soil compaction. These will cost significantly more to purchase.

BENCHMARK POWER & LABOUR COSTS

One of the key areas where significant differences in costs between businesses is apparent is the fixed costs. However, whilst many fixed costs such as property expenses, administration, rent and finance differ due to farm circumstances e.g. rented vs owner occupied, power/machinery and labour costs can be easily considered as a method of comparing financial performance and business efficiency. The table below gives some benchmark figures for different businesses in different sectors. For dairy, these costs are presented on a pence per litre basis on page 50.

Represents good financial performance	£ Per Hectare				
	Combinable Cropping		**Dairy (120 ha farms)**		
	Large	Small-Medium	Spring Calving	All-Year-Round	Autumn Calving
Power & Machinery	800-2,000 ha	150-500 ha	5,250 l / cow	8,000 l / cow	7,000 l / cow
Fuel	71	82	15	105	48
Light & Heat	20	22	54	68	55
Machinery Repairs	64	52	30	88	61
Contractors	20	27	275	316	309
Hire Costs	4	2	9	14	26
Depreciation	113	128	161	201	158
Total Power Costs	**292**	**314**	**544**	**792**	**657**
Labour					
Paid Labour	67	30	263	372	407
Family Labour	44	104	195	215	135
Total	**111**	**133**	**458**	**587**	**542**
Hectares / FTE	270	190	55	43	46

6.   PRECISION AGRICULTURE

Precision farming is a method of farm management fundamentally centred on responding to very detailed variations in resource capability. The term has been adopted in recent years as a technology to map resource capacity such as land fertility or machinery passes so that each resource unit can be treated individually and precisely to maximise its productive capacity. It is estimated that about two thirds of UK arable land is farmed using precision farming technology, dominated by the larger farms.

Two main technologies exist. The first is nutrient mapping to determine the nutrient balance at a very precise level of field area so that applications can be tailored according to the requirement or yield potential of that precise piece of land. The second is automatic or assisted steering to ensure the machinery covers precisely the right ground without overlaps or leaving gaps. This is also used for controlled traffic; keeping all vehicle types solely on a precise layout of permanent traffic lanes to reduce compaction and soil structure damage.

The cheapest and most cost effective piece of precision farming equipment is a tape measure. For example, measuring the 'operating' width of machinery compared with actual width of bouts to identify overlap is a critical starting point. Precision farming is of most benefit to farmers who are least precise in their resource allocation. This might be through considerable variation of in-field nutrient/soil type variation. Larger, more extensive operations that have less management and labour per hectare to examine and treat each small parcel of land (or other resource) individually, will be able to benefit more greatly through automated measurements of resource capacity such as soil fertility or pH in different areas. They can also benefit more by spreading the capital cost over more hectares.

Economic benefits result from better allocated inputs leading to savings of inputs, or higher yields. Inputs saved could include seed, fertilisers, sprays, machinery use, fuel and labour. Faster work-rates achieved can mean achieving more in periods of optimal weather conditions. Environmental benefits can also be achieved through correct input allocations and less wastage/leaching.

Table of benefits for Assisted Steer Technology (HGCA Review 71)

Level	Arable area	Accuracy	Machines Adapted	cost £/ha	benefit £/ha	net £/ha
Assisted Manual Steer	300 Ha	+/- 40cm	2	1.25	2.50	1.25
Mid-Level DGPS*	500ha	+/- 10cm	2	12	14	2.00
RTK**	500ha high value crops	+/- 2cm	3	20	22	2.00

* DGPS = Differential Global Positioning System   ** RTK = Real Time Kinematic

A HGCA publication 71 (2009) suggests that costs of automated steering might be in the region of the table above, although this will vary considerably between farms and years.

Some service providers now offer mapping of Phosphate, Potash, soil pH and other micro-nutrients using either grid methods or zoning linked to soil conductivity testing (soil type variations). These enable variable rate P, K and lime application, as well as variable seed rates to better target inputs. Such a comprehensive service costs in the region of £8-£11/ha for all mapping services, often costing more in the early years until all zoning has been completed. The cost of individual soil tests for N, P, K and Mg is about £8 per sample. Machine compatibility with control boxes / existing tractor technology is important when considering precision farming techniques/services.

For the variable application of nitrogen fertilisers, either granular or liquid, growers can choose between satellite based imagery systems for green leaf area index mapping or Active Light Source (ALS) tractor mounted sensors. The cost of preparing variable rate nitrogen plans using satellite based mapping services, which convert data into green leaf area/crop biomass maps, is approximately £1.50 per hectare. A number of images are taken during the growing season and applications adjusted accordingly in line with changes in crop development in different areas of the field. Tractor mounted sensors are becoming more popular due to the arguably more accurate real-time data gathered and processed whilst the machine is driving through the crop. By mapping crop biomass levels, nitrogen and sulphur fertilisers can be applied variably, as well as growth regulators and fungicides. Sensor manufacturers claim from long term trial results, savings of up to 20kgN/ha are possible with yield improvements of circa 3% in cereals. The cost of sensors and software are approximately £25,000 per unit, sufficient for a 1,000 ha arable unit.

Godwin R. J. An Economic analysis of the potential for precision farming in UK cereal production Biosystems Engineering, Volume 84, Issue 4 2003

Knight S., Miller P. and Orson J. An up to date cost/benefit analysis of precision farming techniques to guide growers of cereals and oilseeds. HGCA Review 71. 2009

Acknowledgement: thanks to Ian Beecher-Jones 07967 637 985

7.   FIELD DRAINAGE

Estimated for 2016

1. Field drainage is one of those farm investments which has been over-looked in recent years. Most agricultural land has been drained at some point historically, although some will have been done over 100 years ago (clay pipes). Much was re-drained in the 1960's and 1970's when significant grants were available to assist with the capital cost. Despite the age of some of these systems, many still function, although do require regular maintenance. This may include clearing out-falls, cleaning out ditches, or even using high pressure systems to clean field drains (jetting).

2. The costs of installing drains per metre are shown below. These costs include the cost of operating a trenching machine, supplying and laying the perforated plastic pipe to an average depth of 800 mm by trencher with 40/20mm cleaned washed porous fill (drainage stone) laid over the pipe to within 375mm of the surface. Costs as follows:-

60 mm diameter	£4.50 - £5.00/metre
80 mm diameter	£5.50 - £6.00/metre
100 mm diameter	£7.50 - £7.75/metre
160 mm diameter	£9.50 - £11.50/metre

The costs above include the cost of and laying porous backfill (drainage stone). However, in some soil types (very rare), soil can be used as backfill. This could save £2.50-£3.50 per metre in cost depending upon the depth of the trench required to get the falls correct and the type of drainage stone selected. However, porous backfill greatly enhances the effectiveness of drains by keeping the openings in the pipe clear and enabling fast penetration of water into the drain. The choice to use permeable backfill should be dependent on soil type not cost. The above rates apply to comprehensive schemes of 4 hectares or more. Smaller areas and patching up work can cost up to 50% more. This is because of the cost of transporting and tracking trenching equipment across fields for small areas of work. Patching up / repairing old drainage systems is common practise as a cheaper alternative to new comprehensive systems.

Digging new open ditches (1.8m top width, 1.25m depth) costs £2.20-£3.00 per metre compared with improving existing ditches at £1.20 to £1.80 per metre depending upon the amount of material that needs to be removed. However, most contractors would charge on an hourly basis for this work with a 360 digger at approximately £35/hour.

Mole draining will cost in the region of £80-£100 per hectare (see contractor charges). Mole draining is effectively a secondary drainage method which is used where a drainage system already exists. The mole plough creates a cavity for the water to travel through. This practise is best suited to heavy land / clay based soils, where mole cavities will remain in place for some time.

3. *Total Costs* per hectare for complete schemes will vary depending on the distance between laterals, soil type, size of area to be drained, region of the country and the time of year when the work is to be undertaken. The cost of a scheme with 20m spacing between laterals and using permeable backfill will typically be in the range of £2,200 to £3,200 per hectare (£900-£1,300 per acre). Comprehensive schemes using little / no permeable backfill will cost circa £1,300 - £1,800 per hectare. Backfilling with soil, rather than with permeable material (washed gravel), may reduce the cost by almost half but is only possible on certain soil types. Certain soil types which are particularly suitable for mole drainage may permit spacing between laterals to be increased to 40m or even 60-80m in some instances. Where this is possible costs will be reduced proportionately.

Acknowledgement: thanks to Rob Burtonshaw 01926 651540

8. IRRIGATION COSTS

Estimated for 2016

Capital Costs

1. Pumps (delivering from 20 to 200 cubic metres per hour from a surface water source), complete with monitoring equipment:-

Tractor PTO driven (pump only)	£800 - £4,000
Diesel engine driven pump unit	£12,500 - £25,000
Electric motor driven pump unit	£22,000 - £32,000
Optional remote/wireless monitoring controls	£500 - £1,500
Variable speed drive option – fitted to electric motor	£800 - £5,000

Individual pumps for mounting on diesel engines range in price from £2,000 to £11,000 for capacities of between 50 and 250 cubic metres per hour. A sophisticated system, including pump house, pumps and control equipment to feed an irrigation system from a reservoir to cover a total area of approx. 400 ha (as and when required) would cost approximately £30,000 - £40,000 to construct and install.

2. Pipelines (averages £ per metre):-

Portable: (excl. valve take offs) 50mm: £4.00; 75 mm: £5.25; 100 mm: £7.50; 125 mm: £8.75; 150 mm: £11.00.

Permanent underground galvanised pipe 12 bar rating (supply and laying) per metre: 80 mm: £10.00 - £13.50; 100 mm: £15.00 - £19.50; 150 mm: £25.00 - £32.00; 200 mm: £54.00 - £62.00.

Hydrants: 100 mm x 100 mm: £200-£275; 150 mm x 125 mm: £310-£430.

3. Application Systems:-

(a) Hose reel systems (average cost per machine) complete with rain gun:

	Hose Length	Output	Acre Inches Per Day	Manual Controls	Electric Controls
Small	180-250m	5-25m³/hr	4.5-5.5	£8,500 - £9,500	
Medium	300-400m	40-80m³/hr	17-20	£19,000 - £21,000	+ £3,000
Large	450-650m	70-120m³/hr	28-33	£40,000 - £45,000	

(b) Irrigation booms (average cost per unit):

Small	14m boom (20m wetted width)	£2,000 - £3,000
Medium	30m boom (40m wetted width)	£5,000 - £8,000
Large	50m boom (60m wetted width)	£8,000 - £15,000

(c) Pivot and linear systems:

Small Linear	200m width	£45,000 - £55,000
Large pivot	600m radius (100ha approx.)	£60,000 - £85,000

(d) Traditional portable hand move sprinkler systems (very specialist and not widely found):

75mm diameter, sprinkler line assemblies:

1 move/day/six day cycle	£800 - £1,100/ha
2 moves/day/six day cycle	£400 - £550/ha
3 moves/day/six day cycle	£300 - £375/ha

(e) Solid set sprinkler lines – semi-permanent systems (very specialist and not widely found):

63mm dia. pipework assemblies at

18m x 18m triangulated spacing	£1,500 - £1,800/ha
As above but with infra-red automated hand-held controls	£1,700 - £2,100/ha

(f)   Specialist Drip Irrigation systems typically use a tape. 25mm tape (excluding the header mains, control valves and filtration equipment) will cost approximately £0.50-£0.55 per metre.

4.   Total:

If no source works are needed, as with water from a river, or pond, total capital costs are likely to vary between £1,200 and £2,300 per hectare requiring irrigation at regular intervals, depending on the site layout, levels of sophistication and automation of the system installed. The capital cost of constructing a reservoir to store irrigation water, usually filled during the winter, is typically in excess of £1.25/m^3 for clay-lined reservoirs (although considerable variations will exist depending on precise circumstances). Lining and fencing could double this cost. This cost could be off-set partly by the sale of sand / gravel depending upon the location. In addition, there may be a need for pump houses and other infrastructure depending upon the circumstances. New time limited abstraction licences are difficult to obtain, especially for summer abstraction. Hence there is an increasing trend towards constructing reservoirs that can be used to store water abstracted during the winter months.

Water Sources

An abstraction licence is required if more than 20m^3 (4,400 gallons) of water per day are taken from surface or underground sources. Once an abstraction licence is obtained, the licence holder must comply with its conditions. *The rules and charges below are based upon the abstraction charges scheme for 2014/15. The Environment Agency was unable to provide the new details for 2015/16 at the time of writing.* A temporary abstraction licence is sufficient if more than 20m^3 of water per day is to be taken for less than 28 days, whereas a full abstraction licence is required if more than 20m^3 of water per day is to be taken for more than 28 days. If abstracting more than 10m^3 per day in Scotland, you must obtain authorisation from SEPA. If abstracting less than 10m^3 per day in Scotland, and comply with certain General Binding Rules (GBR), you do not require authorisation. Abstraction charges vary widely calculated by a formula combining the following factors together:

* Volume – annual licensed
* the Source Factor; whether the source is Environment Agency unsupported, supported or tidal
* The Season Factor; summer, winter or all year round
* The loss factor – high, medium, low or very low, depending upon what the water is authorised to be used for under the licence
* A minimum annual charge of £25

There were 22 regions 'supported' by the Environment Agency in 2014/15. Abstraction from these rivers is 3 times dearer than 'unsupported' sources. Abstraction from tidal sources costs 20% of 'unsupported' sources.

Winter abstraction charges (authorised for abstraction between 1st November to 31st March) cost 16% of all-year abstraction charges. Summer charges (1st April to 31st October) are 160% of the all-year charge.

An application charge of £135 and advertising administration charge of £100 is due, alongside an annual subsistence charge which comprises the Standard Unit Charge (SUC) and the Environmental Improvement Unit Charge (EIUC). Annual subsistence charges are not payable for temporary licences. The charges for 2014/15 were as follows:-

Region (£/1000m³)	Standard Unit Charges	Environmental Improvement Unit Charge (EIUC)
Anglian	27.51	9.96
Midlands	14.95	6.19
Northumbria	29.64	0.00
Yorkshire	11.63	0.00
North West	12.57	8.91
Southern	19.23	8.26
South West inc. Wessex	19.71	0.00
Thames	13.84	8.24
Natural Resources Wales	15.16	0.00

Most abstractors must provide the Environment Agency with accurate records (known as 'returns') of how much water is taken in order to enable them to balance water resources between different users and check compliance with licence conditions. If a licence is in place and you have not extracted any water, a 'nil' return must be submitted. It is a cross-compliance breach to not submit an abstraction return form.

Water Costs

A typical extraction cost for a non-tidal, non-supported farm in East Anglia for 25mm per hectare (250m³ per hectare) would be £1.65/ha for winter abstraction only (0.66p/m³), £10.31/ha for all year abstraction (4.12p/m³) and £16.49/ha (summer only abstraction) (6.60p/m³). The same for an acre-inch would equate to £0.68, £4.24 and £6.78 respectively. This is clearly just the cost for the water. The capital invested plus the labour and any power requirement should also be accounted for which will vary according to individual circumstances. Mains water at 155p per m³ would cost £388 per application of 25mm per hectare (£159/acre inch).

Overall Operating Costs

Because of variations in individual farm circumstances in terms of source works and the irrigation system used, the overall cost of applying 25mm per hectare can range widely, from £85 to £155/ha. Very sophisticated systems distributing mains water over intensive specialist crops could be much more expensive.

Conversions and Calculations

The (approximate) imperial equivalents for metric values commonly used in irrigation are as follows:

- 1 cubic metre = 1,000 litres = 220 gallons (1 million gallons = 4,546 cubic metres).

- A pump capacity of 100 cubic metres per hour is equivalent to 22,000 gallons per hour (367 gallons per minute).

- 1,000 cubic metres is sufficient to apply 25 millimetres of water over 4 hectares, which is approximately equivalent to applying 1 inch over 10 acres. An acre inch is therefore 100 cubic meters (22,000 gallons), or a hectare centimetre is 100 cubic meters.

- The cost/volume conversion from a hectare of 25mm depth to an acre-inch is 0.411 or 2.433 from an acre-inch to a hectare 25mm.

9.   GRAIN DRYING AND STORAGE COSTS

Drying (estimate for 2016)

Capital Costs: vary widely according to type and capacity of drier. A standard 20 tonne per hour continuous flow drier, suitable for a 500 hectare arable unit would cost in the region of £110,000 – £160,000 including the wet bin and associated handling requirements (to feed the drier and empty it). Over 15 years, this capital cost represents £2.54 for every tonne of grain regardless of drying requirements (assuming no residual value). Amortised (i.e. cost to repay capital and interest) at 5% and assuming only 75% of the grain requires drying, over the 15 year period, this figure rises to £4.88/tonne dried. This figure changes dramatically with changes to throughput and longevity.

Annual fixed costs: being fitted and immobile, grain dryers have a low resale value (however mobile dryers do have good second hand value). *Depreciation* is calculated as the capital value divided by the longevity and tonnes per year. *Maintenance* tends to be low at around 2% of purchase value, rising as the dryer ages. *Insurance*; 1.25% of current value.

Running costs: *Fuel*: A useful 'rule of thumb' is 1.50 litres of fuel per 1% moisture per tonne. However, this will vary considerably between different machines and drying systems. Thus drying each tonne by an average of 5% at 47ppl will cost £3.53 per tonne in fuel. *Electricity* use is 17.5Kw/hr for the burner and dischargers, as much again for the handling apparatus, totalling 35Kw/hr. Over a season, (approximately 134 hours use) at 12p/kWh is £563. This represents £0.21 per tonne of grain dried (75% dried). Little labour is required for modern automatic driers. There could be a further cost requirement to cool the grain in store after being dried. This cost varies depending upon the system used – pedestals or on-floor blowing are common. The cost of suitable fans vary but can be obtained for £1,500 - £4,000 depending on requirements. With the introduction of the Renewable Heat Incentive, there are now opportunities to use renewable fuels (woodchip, straw) to reduce drying costs. There are a number of burners on the market which are fired by renewable fuels that produce hot air to then dry grain. There is even a market for using drying systems to dry woodchip fuel to utilise grain drying facilities when not required for combinable crops.

Overall operating costs for a fixed machine of 20t/hr output (on a 500 ha arable farm) therefore equate to £8.45 per tonne of grain dried (assuming 75% dried). Per tonne of total grain produced by the farm the cost is £6.34. *Mobile batch driers are much cheaper to buy, in the region of £35-45,000 for a 16t – 20t machine, but these can require more handling of grain (forklift and trailers) unless they are automatic and sited suitably. Therefore the capital costs per tonne are often much lower but the running costs can be much higher. These machines are popular on many farms, however, offering flexibility and are a viable alternative where a suitable electrical connection is not available.* There has been considerable investment in grain storage and drying facilities in recent years, which has been much needed, with many businesses having old and often inefficient facilities.

Central grain stores offer grain drying services for about £7.00 to £12.00 per tonne for 5% moisture drying for members and non-members respectively. Contractors' charges are typically around £12.00 – 16.00 per tonne for drying grain by 5% moisture.

Storage (estimate for 2016)

Capital Costs: from approximately £85 per tonne (on-floor concrete floor and concrete walling) to £170 per tonne (on-floor storage in a purpose-built building with drying floor and stirrers). This cost can rise to over £300 per tonne for an elaborate plant, including pit, elevator, conveyors, ventilated storage bins, catwalk etc. in a new building. *See page 228.*

Depreciation and Interest: £250/t depreciated over 25 years is £10.00/t per year. Interest/opportunity cost of £250/t at 5% is £6.25/t/year (i.e. on the average capital employed). *Fuel and Repairs:* £2.50 per tonne (1%). *Interest on Grain Stored*: 56p/month with grain at £135/t at 5% interest.

Contract Storage: typically £1.50 - 2.50/t per month with a handling charge of around £2.00 - £2.50 per tonne for loading into store and out of store. Large grain merchants offer storage including haulage for around £10/t for the four month period September to December (giving flexibility on marketing where no on-farm storage is available) with a further charge of £1.50/t per month for every additional month stored prior to sale post-Christmas. Alternatively farmers can choose to buy into farmer owned co-operative grain store operations. Costs vary depending upon membership structures but are in the region of £100-£110/t for membership storage rights, plus annual handling charges (including haulage) of typically £10-£12/t. Additional drying charges normally apply for grain delivered with a moisture content in excess of 16%.

VI.   OTHER FIXED COSTS DATA

1.   WHOLE FARM FIXED COSTS

The following are a broad indication of the levels of fixed costs per hectare (acre) for various types and sizes of farm, estimated for 2016, including the value of unpaid family manual labour, including that of the farmer and his wife. The figures are based on the actual results from the Farm Business Survey (FBS) for the 2013-14 year (February to February), adjusted for subsequent changes in costs. The FBS is based on a sample of farms which does change over time, so there is not a consistent sample. This just emphasises that the costs given below should be used only as an indication and must be adjusted according to individual situations; see also further notes on the use of this data below.

The FBS is conducted by a consortium of Universities and Colleges across England on behalf of Defra. Although the survey is limited to England, the figures within this section are likely to be broadly applicable to most parts of the UK. The FBS has undergone an overhaul in recent years. Specific regional reports are no longer published - although they can be accessed via the FBS website (see www.farmbusinesssurvey.co.uk).   In addition, the farm types have been standardised across the country. They are now based on Defra's standard farm classifications. This has meant that some categories of farm have disappeared (mainly the 'mixed' ones such as dairy & arable, and arable & lowland livestock). All of these costs can of course vary widely according to many factors, especially the intensity of farming, e.g. the number of cows per 100 hectares on dairy farms, or the hectares of intensive crops on general cropping farms.

The figures provided are averages. 'Premium' farms of the same level of intensity can have labour, machinery and general overhead costs at least 20% lower. However, the most profitable farms are often more intensive. They therefore have higher fixed costs associated with the great intensity - but with substantially higher total farm gross margins. Thus it is the net amount (Gross Margin – Fixed Costs) that matters.

The 'small' farm categories relate only to full-time holdings and do not include very intensive holdings occupying very small areas.

The term 'fixed costs' is used here as it is in gross margin analysis and planning; a full explanation of the differences between fixed and variable costs in this context is given on pages 1 and 2. Note that all casual labour and contract work has been included under fixed costs. In calculating enterprise gross margins on the individual farm these costs are normally allocated as variable costs if they are specific to a particular enterprise and vary approximately in proportion to its size, i.e. are approximately constant per hectare of a particular crop or per head of livestock. Otherwise they are included as fixed costs. In both cases, however, they could be regarded as substitutes for regular labour and/or the farmer's own machinery - which are both items of fixed cost. It is therefore simpler if both are included, fully, as fixed costs. If one is comparing results from accounts set out on a gross margin basis, and some or all of the casual labour and contract work have been included as variable costs (especially on cropping farms, e.g. for potato harvesting using casual labour or a contractor's machine), the necessary adjustments need to be made in making the comparisons.

Notes on the Schedules

1. *Unpaid Labour:* Refers to the value of unpaid family manual labour, including that of the farmer and his wife.

2. *Machinery Depreciation:* This is based on current (i.e. replacement) cost. This gives a truer reflection of the real loss of value of machinery (as is apparent when replacement becomes necessary). It also allows easier comparison between different businesses.

However, many farm accounts calculate depreciation on the 'historic' (i.e. original) cost of the machinery. This will tend to produce a lower figure. Depending on the age of the machine, and bearing in mind recent strong increases in machinery prices, the historic method may underestimate depreciation by 10-20%. Note that both the Depreciation item and Repairs include vehicles.

3. *Leasing Charges:* The capital element, but not the interest, is included in depreciation; the proportion paid as interest varies according to the rate of interest paid and the length of the leasing period, but is typically 7%-10%.

4. *Machinery Running Costs:* This includes fuel, oil, repairs, servicing and vehicle tax and insurance. Separate figures for these elements are no longer available. As a general rule, fuel might make up a little over half of all such costs.

5. *General Overheads:* include general farm maintenance and repairs, office expenses, water, insurance, fees, subscriptions, etc.

6. *Rent & Interest:* Rent now only relates to the actual rent paid by the average farm in that particular category. It is no longer an imputed rent for all land farmed by the business; thus, a fully owned-occupied farm will have no rental costs. Interest used to be excluded but now actual interest paid by the average farm in that particular category is shown.

In making comparisons with fixed costs taken from farm accounts it is important to note that in the figures below unpaid manual labour is included; farm accounts will rarely include this. Also the figures below include average rent and interest; in farm accounts these will vary widely depending on the farm tenure and borrowing. Very low 'target' figures given in press articles often omit these items and can therefore be misleading; usually, too, they relate only to large, very well appointed farms. If an 'opportunity cost' for owner-occupied land (often fully paid for many years ago) is included, then the cost level rises further. Note too that the figures given below do not include management, whether paid or unpaid. The margin after deducting the fixed costs below from the total gross margin plus any other farm receipts represents the total return to management and own capital in the business.

Labour, machinery and buildings are the main items of 'fixed' costs subject to change with major alterations in farm policy. Each has a separate section in this book.

Mainly Dairying

	Under 75 ha (Under 185 acres)		75 - 125 ha (185 - 310 acres)		Over 125 ha (Over 310 acres)	
Regular Labour (paid)	90	(36)	180	(73)	315	(127)
Regular Labour (unpaid)	680	(275)	355	(144)	185	(75)
Casual Labour	30	(12)	45	(18)	35	(14)
Total Labour	**800**	**(324)**	**580**	**(235)**	**535**	**(217)**
Machinery Depreciation	175	(71)	200	(81)	185	(75)
Machinery Running Costs	160	(65)	205	(83)	220	(89)
Contract	120	(49)	150	(61)	180	(73)
Total Power & Machinery...	**455**	**(184)**	**555**	**(225)**	**585**	**(237)**
Farm Maintenance	50	(20)	80	(32)	80	(32)
Water & Electricity	160	(65)	170	(69)	145	(59)
General Overhead Expenses ..	95	(38)	80	(32)	80	(32)
Total Overheads	**305**	**(123)**	**330**	**(134)**	**305**	**(123)**
Rent & Interest	135	(55)	200	(81)	235	(95)
Total Fixed Costs	**1695**	**(686)**	**1665**	**(674)**	**1660**	**(672)**

	Mainly Cereals					
	Under 175 ha		175 - 300 ha		Over 300 ha	
	(Under 430 acres)		(430 - 740 acres)		(Over 740 acres)	
Regular Labour (paid)	55	(22)	65	(26)	110	(45)
Regular Labour (unpaid)	225	(91)	155	(63)	95	(38)
Casual Labour	10	(4)	10	(4)	10	(4)
Total Labour	**290**	**(117)**	**230**	**(93)**	**215**	**(87)**
Machinery Depreciation	125	(51)	135	(55)	130	(53)
Machinery Running Costs	105	(42)	130	(53)	120	(49)
Contract	95	(38)	80	(32)	65	(26)
Total Power & Machinery...	**325**	**(132)**	**345**	**(140)**	**315**	**(127)**
Farm Maintenance	35	(14)	20	(8)	30	(12)
Water & Electricity	65	(26)	60	(24)	55	(22)
General Overhead Expenses ..	90	(36)	70	(28)	80	(32)
Total Overheads	**190**	**(77)**	**150**	**(61)**	**165**	**(67)**
Rent & Interest	105	(42)	125	(51)	120	(49)
Total Fixed Costs	**910**	**(368)**	**850**	**(344)**	**815**	**(330)**

Large-Scale Cereal Farms (over 500 ha (1,250 acres))

Data from the Farm Business Survey indicates there are further economies of scale for cereals farms at even larger farm sizes. There are likely to be wide variations depending on the precise scale of these businesses (some of which are very large). The following figures may be used as a guide; Labour - £160 per ha (of which paid labour £105); Power & Machinery - £280 per ha; Other Overheads - £180 per ha; Rent & Interest - £140 per ha. This totals £760 per ha (£308 per acre).

Data for larger-scale General Cropping farms (see below) is not so conclusive. Costs on a 'per ha' basis do not necessarily seem to fall as farm size increases. This may be due to the larger proportion of (higher cost) root crops and vegetables seen on larger farm sizes.

General Cropping

	Under 150 ha (Under 370 acres)		150 - 225 ha (370 - 560 acres)		Over 225 ha (Over 560 acres)	
Regular Labour (paid)	70	(28)	90	(36)	140	(57)
Regular Labour (unpaid)	310	(125)	220	(89)	170	(69)
Casual Labour	15	(6)	35	(14)	50	(20)
Total Labour	**395**	**(160)**	**345**	**(140)**	**360**	**(146)**
Machinery Depreciation	145	(59)	150	(61)	165	(67)
Machinery Running Costs	145	(59)	160	(65)	170	(69)
Contract	120	(49)	110	(45)	90	(36)
Total Power & Machinery...	**410**	**(166)**	**420**	**(170)**	**425**	**(172)**
Farm Maintenance	25	(10)	35	(14)	45	(18)
Water & Electricity	85	(34)	90	(36)	90	(36)
General Overhead Expenses ..	65	(26)	95	(38)	65	(26)
Total Overheads	**175**	**(71)**	**220**	**(89)**	**200**	**(81)**
Rent & Interest	130	(53)	130	(53)	145	(59)
Total Fixed Costs	**1110**	**(449)**	**1115**	**(451)**	**1130**	**(457)** *

With potatoes and/or sugar beet and/or field vegetables; grade 1 or 2 land.

Mainly Sheep/Cattle (lowland)

	Under 90 ha (Under 220 acres)		90 - 125 ha (220 - 310 acres)		Over 125 ha (Over 310 acres)	
Regular Labour (paid)	25	(10)	50	(20)	40	(16)
Regular Labour (unpaid)	470	(190)	360	(146)	270	(109)
Casual Labour	10	(4)	15	(6)	20	(8)
Total Labour	**505**	**(204)**	**425**	**(172)**	**330**	**(134)**
Machinery Depreciation	90	(36)	95	(38)	110	(45)
Machinery Running Costs	90	(36)	95	(38)	115	(47)
Contract	60	(24)	55	(22)	60	(24)
Total Power & Machinery...	**240**	**(97)**	**245**	**(99)**	**285**	**(115)**
Farm Maintenance	30	(12)	30	(12)	30	(12)
Water & Electricity	65	(26)	70	(28)	65	(26)
General Overhead Expenses ..	60	(24)	50	(20)	45	(18)
Total Overheads	**155**	**(63)**	**150**	**(61)**	**140**	**(57)**
Rent & Interest	75	(30)	80	(32)	105	(42)
Total Fixed Costs	**975**	**(395)**	**900**	**(364)**	**860**	**(348)**

	Mainly Sheep/Cattle (upland)					
	Under 130 ha		130 - 200 ha		Over 200 ha	
	(Under 320 acres)		(320 - 490 acres)		(Over 490 acres)	
Regular Labour (paid)	15	(6)	20	(8)	20	(8)
Regular Labour (unpaid)	345	(140)	230	(93)	180	(73)
Casual Labour	10	(4)	10	(4)	15	(6)
Total Labour	**370**	**(150)**	**260**	**(105)**	**215**	**(87)**
Machinery Depreciation	65	(26)	55	(22)	65	(26)
Machinery Running Costs	60	(24)	55	(22)	65	(26)
Contract	20	(8)	20	(8)	20	(8)
Total Power & Machinery...	**145**	**(59)**	**130**	**(53)**	**150**	**(61)**
Farm Maintenance	15	(6)	10	(4)	15	(6)
Water & Electricity	40	(16)	35	(14)	35	(14)
General Overhead Expenses ..	20	(8)	20	(8)	20	(8)
Total Overheads	**75**	**(30)**	**65**	**(26)**	**70**	**(28)**
Rent & Interest	40	(16)	55	(22)	65	(26)
Total Fixed Costs	**630**	**(255)**	**510**	**(206)**	**500**	**(202)**

Other Farm Types

The other main DEFRA farm types are '*Mixed*', *Pigs*, *Poultry and Horticulture*. As the name suggests, the mixed category includes all farms where one enterprise is not sufficiently dominant for it to be allocated to one of the categories above. As it includes many different mixes of enterprises, the figures are unlikely to be useful for budgeting purposes.

Due to the intensity and variability of the Pig, Poultry and Horticultural farm types, the presentation of average 'per ha' figures would not be useful. Detailed historic FBS data for the different pig, poultry, and horticulture systems found in England are published on line at the addresses given on page 4. For pigs, Askham Bryan: for poultry and horticulture, Reading, or go to www.farmbusinesssurvey.co.uk.

2.   RENTS

One of the main factors affecting the rental level of agricultural land is the type of tenancy it is let on. There are three main types of agricultural agreements for letting land in England and Wales: Full or Agricultural Holdings Act (AHA) 1986, Farm Business Tenancies (FBTs, under the 1995 Act) and Seasonal Lets of less than 1 year. Since the introduction of the 1995 Act no new AHA tenancies can be created.

The Basic Payment Scheme provisions also need to be taken into account when comparing rents. The situation will vary from farm to farm and differ between the different regions of the countries of the UK. The tenant is the only person who can claim the Basic Payment (BP). In seasonal lets (grazing agreements) the Licensor should be the claimant. In an AHA tenancy agreement the rental is struck independently of the Basic Payment in that the tenant will have been awarded the Single Payment entitlements in 2005 which will have been converted to Basic payment entitlements on 1st January 2015 and at the end of the tenancy the ownership remains with the tenant or his/her successors. With FBTs the assumption is that the tenant is claiming a 'full' BP, and if land becomes available without BP entitlements then rental levels will be lower than those shown below.

Unless otherwise stated the figures in this section relate to farms let with a combination of crops, grass and rough grazing in England; they include housing and buildings, as available.

Agricultural Holdings Act Tenancies:

Rents for land had been tending to fall up to 2007 but this was offset by higher rents for housing and buildings so that overall per hectare rents were stable. Since then improving commodity prices on cereals and general cropping farms have seen rents increasing year on year. The upturn in livestock prices, particularly in the beef sector has seen rents on grazing livestock farms improve quite considerably since 2009. But a difficult year in 2012 which had a knock on effect into 2013 saw a small impact on rents. The fall in the beef price since the first half of 2014 should lead to grassland rental prices stabilising and even falling.

The average rent for lowland, excluding woodland and rough grazing for farms under full Agricultural Tenancies is likely to be approximately £200 per ha, *£80 per acre*, in 2015/16. The levels on large mixed arable farms (i.e. including potatoes, sugar beet and/or vegetables) on very good soil, or well-equipped dairy farms, will tend to average £200 to £250 per hectare, *£80 to £101 per acre*. Rents on moderate, below average, quality farms, particularly with full repairing and insuring leases are likely to average £125 to £150 per hectare, *£50 to £60 per acre*.

Farm Business Tenancies:

On average FBT rents will remain higher than those above for AHA tenancies, although this is not always the case especially for lowland cattle and sheep land and dairy land. When reviewing AHA rents the scarcity value is ignored, but FBT rents reflect an open market and therefore the gap is wider. For cereals land of reasonable quality offers have tended to follow the price of a tonne of wheat per acre, but in recent years there has been very little on offer for under £495 per hectare (*£200 per acre*). However this may prove to have been a high point. The fall in commodity prices has led to prices stabilising, although rents for maize land and other alternatives destined for Anaerobic Digesters are putting a base in the market. Local markets for potato land can command high values and even cause agents to try and increase 3-5 year agreements on the back of this but it must be remembered there has to be a rotation.   A sensible rent for new agreements throughout 2015/2016 for arable land would be £370 per hectare (£150 per acre) although many are expected to be ahead of this, the range will be in the region of £370 to £495 per hectare, *£150 - £200 per acre*. Dairy land is expected to be in a similar range with rents for well-equipped dairy farms in excess of £495 per hectare, *£200* per acre.

Farm Business Survey 2013-14:

The following figures are the latest National Statistics produced by Defra showing the estimates of farm rents in England from the 2013/14 Farm Business Survey (FBS). Results from the 2013/14 Survey are referred to as the 2013 results. It should be borne in mind that rough grazing may be included in the figures given in the table below and the figures relate to the 2013/14 (Feb-Feb) year mainly covering 2013. Some farms are likely to be let at below competitive rates, for various reasons.

Average Rent by Type of Agreement:	£/ha	(acre)
Full Agricultural Tenancies	171	(69)
Farm Business Tenancies for 1 year and over......................	196	(79)
Seasonal Lets of less than one year.....................................	127	(51)

Full Agricultural Tenancies in England:

Average Rent by Farm Type: (£ per ha [acre])	2009	2010	2011	2012	2013
Cereals	148(60)	166 (67)	172 (70)	182 (74)	191 (77)
General Cropping	170 (69)	192 (78)	192 (78)	203 (82)	201 (81)
Dairy	155 (63)	180 (73)	186 (75)	193 (78)	195 (79)
Cattle & Sheep (LFA)	52 (21)	62 (25)	66 (27)	59 (24)	64 (26)
Cattle and Sheep (Lowland)	131 (53)	139 (56)	148 (60)	152 (62)	160 65)
All	139 (56)	152 (62)	159 (64)	163 (66)	171 (69)

Farm Business Tenancies – One year and over:

Average Rent by Farm Type: (£ per ha [acre])	2009	2010	2011	2012	2013
Cereals	167 (68)	176 (71)	192 (78)	211 (85)	221 (89)
General Cropping	225 (91)	249(101)	307(124)	264(107)	290(117)
Dairy	166 (67)	169 68)	184 (74)	195 (79)	206 (83)
Cattle & Sheep (LFA)	70 (28)	68 (28)	78 (32)	77 (31)	76 (31)
Cattle and Sheep (Lowland)	117 (47)	119 (48)	121 (49)	121 (49)	124 (50)
All	162 (66)	162 (66)	179 (72)	176 (71)	196 (79)

Source of Data

DEFRA (Farming Statistics): Farm rents 2013/14 – England. In the past DEFRA rental statistics were collected via the Tenanted Land Survey (TLS) and these were reported on in previous editions of the Farm Management Pocketbook. Following a review in early 2009 DEFRA decided that the Farm Business Survey (FBS) data should be the main source and the Tenanted Land Survey (TLS) should be discontinued. The FBS is an annual survey conducted by trained Interviewers. The FBS collects data at business level and collects data for up to 15 agreements per business, with a sample of around 1,900 farm businesses. The 2014-15 Survey is due to be published in March 2016.

RICS Rural Land Market Survey:

Previous editions of the Pocketbook have included average rental levels these are now available on the Pocketbook website at www.thepocketbook.co.uk

3.   LAND PRICES

SALE VALUE OF FARMLAND, ENGLAND AND WALES

Current Agricultural Land Prices

A CALP/RICS Farmland Price Index (England and Wales) began in 1995. It covers sales of vacant possession land in England and Wales, excluding residential value where more than 50% of total sale price; value of milk quota excluded. It is calculated by dividing total value of sales by total area sold. Figures for the most recent half-yearly periods are subject to revision as further information becomes available.

As can be seen from the table below, the volume of land traded in any year, and included in the Index, is low – probably only between 0.1%-0.2% of the total agricultural area of England and Wales. The relative scarcity of land for sale has helped contribute to the increases in prices seen since the early 2000's. Such a 'thin' market can also make the prices sensitive to a small number of large transactions. For this reason, in recent years, the RICS has moved away from the transaction-based figures presented below, to using opinion-based data as its headline land price figures.

Farmland prices have weathered the economic downturn of recent times far better than other asset classes. 'Lifestyle' purchasers were replaced by farmers keeping the demand and the price of land high as the economy faltered. Since 2009, very low rates of borrowing money and negligible returns for cash investments have fuelled farmland values. This has been coupled with tight supply of land and improved farm commodity prices. But the recent fall in commodity prices is expected to slow the pace at which prices have been rising over the last few years, however with supply tight and 'lifestyle' buyers coming back to the market, prices are expected to continue to increase. Land prices could drop back (along with other asset classes) when base rates rise, leading to higher costs of borrowing money and fixed interest investments start to generate a return. As always there is a wide variation in prices. Farmland prices for the period 1995 to 2000 can be found in previous editions of the Pocketbook or on the Pocketbook website at www.thepocketbook.co.uk

CALP/RICS Farmland Price Index 2005-2014 – Transaction based. (* Provisional)

		Number of Sales	Area sold '000		Weighted Average Price £		Index 1995
			Ha	(acres)	Ha	(acres)	=100
2007	H1	141	7.0	(17.3)	11,153	(4,513)	215
	H2	230	10.8	(26.7)	14,138	(5,721)	273
2008	H1	233	8.9	(21.9)	15,824	(6,404)	305
	H2	278	11.7	(28.9)	16,342	(6,713)	315
2009	H1	181	6.3	(13.8)	15,199	(6,151)	293
	H2	256	11.4	(28.2)	16,126	(6,526)	311
2010	H1	293	5.5	(14.0)	15,177	(6,142)	293
	H2	262	12.0	(29.6)	17,458	(7,065)	336
2011	H1	154	4.2	(10.6)	18,631	(7,540)	359
	H2	273	11.7	(28.9)	20,721	(8,386)	399
2012	H1	166	4.69	(11.6)	20,586	(8,331)	397
	H2	240	7.69	(19.0)	21,053	(8,520)	406
2013	H1				21,601	(8,742)	416
	H2	311	11.9	(29.4)	22,965	(9,294)	447
2014	H1	181	5.00	(12.4)	23,706	(9,595)	461
	H2*				24,876	(10,067)	484
2015	*Estimate*				*25,000*	*(10,117)*	*486*

Other Land Price Series

In past editions of the Pocketbook, Inland Revenue and Valuation Office (VO) land price returns have been published, covering 30 years up to 1996/97 and 1993-2004 respectively. These series contained detailed splits between vacant possession and tenanted land, farms (including houses and buildings) and bare land, and also by size, land class and region. This information is still available from past editions of the Pocketbook. Data in the VO series does not continue beyond 2004, although limited information is available on the website, www.voa.gov.uk. Previous editions also include the Oxford Institute/Savills (1) Series, 1937-2000. Much of the data included in this section is available from the RICS website – www.rics.org

SALE VALUE OF FORESTS AND WOODLANDS

Forests

The figures in this section relate to planted land sold (over 25 hectares) so that values include the value of the property (land) and the timber. They focus on properties that are predominantly conifer.

The decline in timber prices was reversed back in 2010 due to the high price of imported timber; a consequence of a weak Pound. Timber prices have risen since then and have continued to rise over the year as confidence in the market continues to grow. The forestry market remained active throughout the year, and although property sales did not break the record set in 2013 it was still the second busiest year since 1998, when records first started. During 2014, there were fewer large transactions as seen in 2013 and the quality was not as good. Properties in Scotland continue to dominate the market, with around 77% of total sales. Looking forward the industry is expecting another active year.

Forestry continues to be attractive to investors especially due to the tax benefits available to owning woodland. Income tax is not payable on timber sales. There is potentially 100% relief on Inheritance Tax (IHT) and any gains attributable to standing or felled timber are exempt from Capital Gains Tax (CGT). 2014 was again a good year for forestry delivering excellent returns and demand going forward is expected to remain high with more opportunities for woodland owners becoming available. As economies start to recover and movement in the development and construction sectors increase, demand for timber both as a material and for fuel should grow further. Woodlands often present opportunities for wind turbines and hydro-electric schemes, whilst biomass projects supported under the Renewable Heat Incentive are likely to boost demand for timber products. But as economies grow, those who invested for the first time during the financial crisis may exit the sector seeking better returns in the short term from other investments, which may see capital values reaching their peak.

In 2012 there was a move in the market towards larger, more commercial forests helped by more favourable grants being offered for these kinds of properties. This trend continued in 2013. But in 2014 the total area sold declined by 2.8% compared to 2013 to 13,390 hectares whereas the number of properties traded increased by 30% compared to year earlier levels to 103 resulting in a reduction in the average size of a property to 130 hectares, 25% less than in 2013 and the smallest size since 2006. The total market value of commercial forestry properties traded throughout GB in 2014 reduced by 15% compared to the highs of 2013 to £82.85m. .

The average value of a hectare of commercial conifer in the UK was down by 12% in the year to October 2014 compared to 2013 to £6,190 per stocked Ha. Although the average value is less than in 2013 (and 2012) looking back to 2002 the annualised average increase in property values per hectare has been 12.8%, performing considerably better than many other investments.

The figures below are for the UK and are predominantly upland with at least 50% coniferous content. Values vary with many factors and only size of block and age are recorded here, but yield class is also important.

Value of Forestland:

By Size Range (approx.)	2013	2014
	£/ha (£/acre)	£/ha (£/acre)
25 to 50 hectares............................	6,300 (2,550)	7,000 (2,833)
51 to 100 hectares..........................	6,200 (2,509)	6,000 (2,428)
101 to 200 hectares........................	8,500 (3,440)	6,400 (2,590)
Above 200 hectares	7,700 (3,116)	6,000 (2,428)

By Age Band	2013	2014
	£/ha (£/acre)	£/ha (£/acre)
Young (1 to 10 years)	4,800 (1,943)	4,500 (1,821)
Mid-rotation (11 to 20 years).........	4,700 (1,902)	6,625 (2,681)
Semi-mature (21 to 30 years).........	5,100 (2,064)	6,750 (2,732)
Mature (31 to 40 years).................	8,000 (3,238)	6,900 (2,792)
Mature (over 40 years)...................	8,100 (3,278)	5,750 (2,327)

Woodlands

The value for small woodland decreased in 2010 as demand from lifestyle buyers for less commercial, more amenity and sporting woodland was hit by the economic climate. As the economic climate picks up this is expected to reverse. Values remain at their highest adjacent to centres of population and for properties of high amenity value. Sales in the South of England are in the £8-12,000/ha range, whereas £2-5,000/ha is more typical for other locations or where amenity values are lower.

Source: UPM Tilhill, Forest Market Report (2014)

4.   PUBLIC LIABILITY INSURANCE

Public liability insurance is not a legal obligation. However, it is necessary if the general public is interacting with your business in any way, whether deliveries, visitors, etc. With a rising emphasis on encouraging the public to understand farming including visiting farms, this should be a necessity for all farms.

These figures are per year, per farm. Prices of some providers are the same for each band, as they calculate their quotes differently. Often public liability comes with product and environmental liability. These figures are solely for farming, and not other activities that might take place on a farm such a contract farming, other diversifications such as a shoot, livery or a farm shop.

	Mixed Farm (130 ha)	Dairy (130 ha)	Arable (250 ha)
£5m	£250	£250	£320
£10m	£450	£450	£500

5. BUILDINGS

BUILDING COSTS

Building costs are notoriously variable. Many factors influence a contractor's price, including distance from his yard, size of contract, site access, site conditions, complexity of work, familiarity with the type of work and his current work load. There will also be differences in efficiency and standard of work between contractors and, as is often the case with farm buildings, the absence of detailed specification by the client may mean different contractors will not have quoted for identical buildings. The number of extras that are found to be required after a contract has been agreed will also vary.

The costs given below are an approximate guide. They refer to new buildings, erected by contractor on a clear level site and exclude VAT and grants that may be available. More detailed information is available in the following publications. The books and journals giving general building cost information generally assume knowledge of how to take off quantities for building work.

Specialised Information on Farm Buildings

- Farm Building Cost Guide. Published by SAC Building Design Services, Aberdeen.

- Standard Costs. Published by the Scottish Government. Used when claiming government grants on a standard-cost basis. It can be found at www.scotland.gov.uk/Resource/Doc/158202/0042819.pdf

- The Farm Buildings Handbook. Published by the Rural and Industrial Design and Building Association, Stowmarket.

General Building Cost Information

Books are produced by a number of publishers with annual or more frequent new editions and updates. Examples are Laxton's Building Price Book, Spon's Architects' and Builders' Price Book, and Wessex Comprehensive Building Price Book. Regularly updated cost information is also given in several professional and trade journals.

Constituent Parts

Frame, Roof and Foundations   *per m² floor area*

1. Open-sided timber framed pole barn with round pole uprights on concrete bases, sawn timber rafters and purlins, high-tensile galvanised steel cladding to roof and gable ends above eaves, hardcore floor, eaves height 4.8 m, 9 m span, no side cladding, rainwater drainage to soakaways.   £80

2. Open-sided steel portal-framed building with fibre-cement or plastic coated steel cladding to roof and gables above eaves, hardcore floor, eaves height 4.8 m, no side cladding, rainwater drainage to soakaways.

9 m span	£135
13.2 m span	£125
18 m span	£115

3. Cost breakdown of 2 above;

Materials:		
	portal frame and purlins	26%
	foundations	3%
	roofing	16%
	rainwater and drainage	3%

	hardcore and blinding	2%
	Total Materials	50%
Erection:	portal frame and purlins	19%
	foundations	2%
	roofing	19%
	rainwater and drainage	5%
	hardcore and blinding	5%
	Total Erection	50%

Roof cladding *per m²*

1. Natural grey fibre-cement, 146 mm corrugations fixed with drive screws

Materials	£15.00	
Fixing	£12.50	
Total		£27.50

2. Extra for coloured sheet — £2.50
3. Deduct for translucent sheets — £0.55
4. Deduct for PVC-coated steel — £3.00
5. Deduct for high-tensile corrugated galvanised steel sheeting — £4.00

per m run

6. PVC 150 mm half-round gutter on fascia brackets, including stop-ends and outlets — £27.50
7. PVC 100 mm rainwater pipe with fixings, swan-neck and shoe — £45.00
8. Fibre-cement close-fitting ridge — £40.00
9. Fibre-cement ventilating ridge — £45.00

Walls and Cladding *per m²*

1. Concrete blockwork, fair faced and pointed both sides
   - 150 mm thick — £50.00
   - 215 mm thick — £70.00
   - 215 mm thick hollow blocks — £70.00
   - 215 mm thick hollow blocks, filled and reinforced — £90.00
2. Extra for rendering or roughcast to blockwork on one side — £25.00
3. Vertical spaced boarding 21x 145 mm with 19 mm gaps including horizontal rails, all pressure treated — £28.00
4. Fibre-cement vertical cladding, including rails — £43.00
5. Corrugated high-tensile steel side cladding, including rails — £37.50
6. Wall element: 215 mm thick blockwork, including strip foundation (base 750 mm below ground level), 2.5 m height above ground level — £180 per m run

Floors *per m²*

1. Concrete floor 100 mm thick, Gen 3 mix, on 150 mm hardcore, including excavation: — £36.50

Breakdown:
- (a)   excavate, level and compact — £3.50
- (b)   hardcore — £5.00
- (c)   blinding — £2.40
- (d)   damp-proof membrane — £2.10
- (e)   premixed concrete spread and compacted — £19.00
- (f)   float finish — £4.50

2.   Extra to above for
- (a)   150 mm instead of 100 mm — £6.00
- (b)   laying concrete to falls — £2.00
- (c)   broom or textured finish — £2.00
- (d)   Carborundum dust non-slip finish — £3.50
- (e)   insulating concrete — £12.50

3.   Reinforced concrete slatted floors for cattle
- (a)   cattle loading — £77.50
- (b)   tractor loading — £90.00

4.   Reinforced concrete slats for pigs — £60.00

5.   Insulating floor, including excavation and base
- (a)   27 mm expanded polystyrene, 38 mm screed — £52.50
- (b)   insulating concrete with lightweight aggregate — £45.00
- (c)   as (b) with 20 mm screed — £52.50

6.   Form channel in concrete — £5.00 per m run

7.   Excavate for cast 1 m3 in-situ concrete bases for stanchions — £140.00 each

Services and Fittings — *per m²*

1.   Drainage: 100 mm PVC pipe laid in trench, including 750 mm deep excavation and backfil — £29.00 per m run
Breakdown:
- (a)   excavate and backfill — £18.00
- (b)   100 mm PVC pipe laid — £10.00
Extras:
- (c)   add to (a) for 1 m deep — £4.00
- (d)   add to (b) for 150 mm pipe — £7.00

2.   Excavate soakaway and fill with stones — £120 each

3.   Trap and grid top, 100 mm PVC — £29.00 each

4.   Yard gully with heavy duty road grating 400 x 300 mm — £200 each

5.   Inspection chamber 900 mm deep, 450 x 600 mm opening and medium duty cast iron cover — £400 each

6.   Above-ground vitreous enamel slurry tank on concrete base, 1000 m³ — £55,000 each

7.   Reception pit, 20 m³ — £6,000 each

8.   Slurry channel beneath (not including) slats, 1.8 m deep, 3m wide — £500 per m run

9.   Lighting: 1.5 m 60W single fluorescent unit, including wiring and switch — £135 each
Extras:
- (a)   PVC conduit — £6.50
- (b)   screwed steel conduit — £12.00

10.	Power: 13A switched outlet	£24.00 each
11.	Diagonal feed fence, fixed, including posts (painted)	£135 per m run
12.	Tombstone feed fence, fixed, including posts (painted)	£145 per m run
13.	Feed bunker	£80 per m run
14.	Hay rack, wall fixing	£85 per m run
15.	Cubicle division, galvanised, fixed in place	£110 each
16.	Fencing: three-rail timber with posts, all pressure treated	£30.00 per m run
17.	Gate, 3 m wide, galvanised steel, including posts set in concrete	
	(a) medium duty	£250 each
	(b) heavy duty	£325 each
	Deduct for painted instead of galvanised finish	£30

Complete Buildings

Fully Covered and Enclosed Barn

Portal frame, 18 m span, 6 m bays, 6 m to eaves, 3 m high blockwork walls with sheet cladding above, 6 m sliding doors at either end, 150mm thick concrete floor	£210 per m² floor area

Cows and Cattle Housing

1.	Covered strawed yard, enclosed with ventilated cladding, concrete floor, pens only, with 4.0 m² per head floor area	£750 per head
2.	Extra to 1 for 4.0 m wide double-sided feeding passage, barrier and troughs	£300 per head
3.	Kennel building	£450 per head
4.	Portal framed building with cubicles	£1,500 per head
5.	Extra to 4 for feed stance, feeding passage, barriers and troughs	£625 per head
6.	Extra to 4 for slatting of cubicle passages	£640 per head
7.	Covered collecting yard, 1.1 m² per cow	£225 per head
8.	Milking parlour building, example: 5.5 x 11.5 m for 8/16 parlour	£20,000
9.	Parlour equipment, herringbone parlours:	
	(a) low level, 1 stall per point	£3,850 per point
	(b) pipeline	£3,150 per point
	(c) extra for meter and auto cluster removal	£2,150 per point
	(d) auto feed dispenser	£900 per point
10.	Dairy building	£335 per m² floor area
11.	Bulk tank and washer	£8.50 per litre
12.	Loose box, 16 m² floor area laid to falls, rendered walls	£350 per m² floor area
13.	Bull pen and open run	£13,500
14.	Cattle crush and 20 m race	£6,500
15.	Slatted floor cattle building for 120 growing cattle (1.7 m² pen space per head) with drive-through feed passage/troughs	£1,500 per head

Silage   *per tonne stored*

1. Timber panel clamp on concrete base with effluent tank   £80
2. Precast concrete panel clamp with effluent tank   £110
3. Glass-lined forage tower and unloader   £250

Waste Storage   *per m³ stored*

1. Lined lagoon with safety fence   £45.00
2. Glass-lined steel slurry silo
    small (400 m³)   £60.00
    medium (1,200 m³)   £55.00
    large (3,600 m³)   £50.00
3. GRP below-ground effluent tank, encased in concrete
    small (12 m³)   £500
    large (36 m³)   £450

Sheep Housing

1. Penning, troughs, feed barriers and drinkers installed in
    suitable existing building   £38 per ewe
2. Purpose-built sheep shed with 1.35 m² pen space per ewe
    concentrate troughs, feed passage and barrier for   forage
    feeding   £225 per ewe
    Extras:
    (a) softwood slatted floor panels, materials only   £10.00 per m²
    (b) slatted panels as (a), made up, plus supports   £31.50 per m²

Pig Housing   *per sow and litter*

1. Farrowing and rearing
    (a) Prefabricated farrowing pens with crates, side creep
         areas, part-slatted floors, including foundations,
         electrical and plumbing work   £3,500
    (b) Steel-framed farrowing house with insulated
         blockwork walls, part-slatted pens with side creeps
         in rooms of eight with off main passage   £3,950
    (c) Flat-deck rearing house 3-6 weeks with fully
         perforated floors to pens, 0.25 m² per pig pen area   £150 per weaner
    (d) Prefabricated veranda house including foundations,
         electrical and plumbing work, 0.3m² per pig internal
         lying area   £120 per weaner

2.   Finishing   *per baconer*

    (a) Prefabricated fattening house with part-slatted floors, trough feeding   £265

    (b) Prefabricated fattening house with part-slatted floors, floor fed   £255

    (c) Steel framed building with insulated blockwork walls, part-slatted floors, trough fed   £110

    (d) Automatic feeding systems for items (a), (b) and (c) above:

        dry-feed system with ad-lib hoppers   £675

        dry on-floor feeding   £16.00

        wet feeding   £23

3.   Dry sows and boars   *per sow*

    (a) Yards with floor feeding   £375

    (b) Sow cubicle system   £600

    (c) Yards with electronic feeders   £1,050

    (d) Yards with individual feeders   £1,250

    (e) Two-yard system with flat-rate feeding   £1,350

    (f) Boar pens as part of sow house   £2,750 each

4.   Complete pig unit

    Building costs calculated on basis of three-week weaning, 23 pigs per sow per year to bacon, excl. external slurry or dung storage, feed storage and handling/weighing facilities:

    (a) Breeding and rearing only   £2,100 per sow

    (b) Breeding with progeny to bacon   £3,750 per sow

Poultry Housing and Equipment   *per bird*

1.   Intensive enriched cages with automatic feeding and egg collection; (new traditional cages were banned from 1st January 2003;only enriched cages complete with nest box, perches and scratching area are now allowed)   £24.00-£28.00

2.   Perchery/barn   £22.00-£27.00

3.   Free Range: new sites stocked at 9 birds per m²,   £27.50-£35.00

    existing sites stocked at 11.7 birds per m²   £22.50-£29.00

    smaller mobile units will cost   £32.00 plus

4.   Broiler Breeders, deep litter, 0.167 m² per bird   £29.00

5.   Pullets (cage and floor reared)   £16.50

6.   Broilers, deep litter, 0.05 m² per bird   £9.50-£10.50

7.   Turkeys, 20,000 pole barn fattening unit (cost varies with size of unit and degree of automation)   £21.00-£28.00

Grain Storage and Drying   *per tonne stored*

1.   Intake pit, conveyor, elevator, overhead conveyor and catwalk, storage bins within existing building   £240

    extra for low volume ventilation of bins   £95

2.	As 1 in new building	£340
3.	Portable grain walling for on-floor storage in existing building	£55
4.	On floor grain storage in purpose-built building	£125
	Extras:	
	(a) low volume ventilation	£9.00-£10.00
	(b) on-floor drying with above-ground main duct and laterals	£135
	(c) add to (b) for below-ground laterals	£17.00
5.	Sealed towers for moist grain, including loading and unloading equipment	£165-£210

Potato Storage — *per tonne stored*

1.	Pallet-box store with recirculation fans	£240
	Pallet boxes, 1 tonne	£85
2.	Bulk store, building only	£225
	Ventilation system: fans, main duct, below-floor lateral ducts	£55

Roads and Fences — *per m length*

3.2 m wide hardcore road with drainage ditches using locally excavated material	£35.00
using imported hardcore (£6.15/m³)	£50.00
extra for bitumen macadam surfacing, two coats	£57.00
Traditional 7-wire stock fence	£8.50
High tensile 7-wire stock fence	£6.50

Construction Equipment Hire — *hourly rate, with driver*

Excavator	£30.00-£40.00
Tipping lorry	£40.00-£55.00
10-tonne crane	£50.00-£70.00

weekly rate

Concrete mixer, 100 litre (5/3)	£50
Compressor and heavy breaker	£140

STANDARD BUILDING COSTS

Standard costs were published by the Scottish Government on the basis of the cost of farm or casual labour and new materials. The last set of data issued was for 2002 and so the figures are no longer included in The Pocketbook.

STORAGE REQUIREMENTS

Bulk (cubic metres (feet) per tonne):

		M³/tonne	Ft³/tonne
Beans		1.2	(43)
Wheat, peas		1.3	(46)
Barley, rye, oilseed rape, linseed, fodder beet		1.4	(50)
Oats		1.9	(68)
Potatoes		1.6	(57)
Dry bulb onions		2.0	(71)
Concentrates:	meal	2.0	(71)
	cubes	1.6	(57)
Grass silage:	18% DM	1.3	(46)
	30% DM	1.6	(57)
Maize silage		1.3	(46)
Silage: large round bales		2.5	(88)
Wheat straw ⎱		13.0	(464)
Barley straw ⎰ small bales		11.5	(411)
Hay		6.0	(214)
Wheat straw ⎱		20.0	(714)
Barley straw ⎰ large round bales		18.0	(643)
Hay		8.0	(286)
Brewers' grains		0.9	(32)

(With straw and hay the storage requirement clearly depends on the packing density; the above are simply typical averages).

Boxes (floor area in square metres (feet) per tonne):

Potatoes:	0.5 tonne boxes, 5 boxes high	0.52	(5.6)
	1.0 tonne boxes, 4 boxes high	0.52	(5.6)
	1.0 tonne boxes, 5 boxes high	0.45	(4.8)

Bags (floor area in square metres (feet) per tonne):

Feedstuffs:	2 bags high	1.6	(17)
Fertiliser:	6 bags high	1.1	(12)
	10 bags high	0.7	(8)

VII.   TAXATION

Note: no responsibility can be taken for any errors or omissions in the information presented in this section or for any action taken on the basis of the information provided. Professional advice should always be sought before taking any decision that may affect your tax position.

1.   INCOME TAX

RATES OF INCOME TAX

	Tax Rate %	Income Band 2015-16	Income Band 2016-17	Dividend Tax Rate % 15-16	16-17
Basic rate	20	£0 - £31,785	£0 - £32,000	10	7.5
Higher rate	40	£31,786 - £150,000	£32,001 - £150,000	32.5	32.5
Additional rate	45	over £150,000	over £150,000	37.5	38.1

For 2015-16 a lower rate of 0% applies to other savings income (primarily bank and building society interest) up to a limit of £5,000. This 10% rate is not available if taxable non-savings income exceeds £5,000. This is likely to continue for 2016-17.

For 2016-17 a Dividend Tax Allowance will exempt the first £5,000 if dividend income from tax and then the rates shown in the table will apply to the excess.

ALLOWANCES AND RELIEFS

Personal Allowance

This is £10,600 for 2015-16. The basic personal allowance for income tax is gradually reduced to nil for individuals with adjusted net incomes in excess of £100,000. The reduction is £1 for every £2 over the limit. For 2016-17 the basic personal allowance will rise to £11,000.

The previous (higher) age related allowances have now been aligned with the basic personal allowance.

Married Couples Allowance

This was abolished from the tax year ended 6th April 2001 except for couples where at least one spouse was born before 6th April 1935. From 2005-06 the allowance has been available to couples in a civil partnership where at least one partner was born before 6th April 1935. The relief is given as a reduction in income tax restricted to the lower of 10% of the allowance (£835.50 for 2015-16) or the total tax liability.

Personal Pension Schemes

Tax relief is obtainable for contributions to a pension. There are limits on how much of the contribution is eligible for relief – both yearly and lifetime. The annual allowance is £40,000 for 2015-16. The lifetime allowance is £1m for 2015-16.

From 2016-17 the £40,000 annual limit will be progressively reduced for those earning above £150,000 per year.

2.   PRIVATE COMPANY TAXATION

RATES OF CORPORATION TAX

The rates set out in the table below apply to profits made in any financial year (FY) from 1st April to 31st March. FY15 therefore covers 1st April 2015 to 31st March 2016. Profits are chargeable at the following rates;

	FY15	FY16	FY17
All profits	20	20	19

The previous Small Companies rate and marginal relief rate were abolished for FY15.

COMPANY TAXATION – OTHER ISSUES

Capital Gains

Capital gains of companies are charged at the appropriate rate of Corporation Tax. The indexation allowance is still available to reduce capital gains made by Companies.

Distributions

Dividends are not deductible in arriving at the amount of Corporation Tax profit. However, the recipient of distributions will be credited with a tax payment of 10% of distributions received, which will be deemed to discharge the liability of basic rate (20%) taxpayers. Higher rate taxpayers are liable to pay tax at 32.5% on that part of their dividend income falling above the higher rate limit. Taxpayers with income in excess of £150,000 will be liable to tax on dividends at 37.5%.

Losses

Carry back of losses not set against other income is restricted to one year. Losses can be carried forward and offset against profits of the same trade.

3. AGRICULTURAL BUSINESSES: OTHER ITEMS

ASSESSING SELF-EMPLOYED PROFITS

Self-employed people are assessed for tax in any tax year on the basis of the profits recorded in the annual accounts which end in that tax year, i.e. on a 'current year basis'.

LIVESTOCK

Dairy cows or breeding livestock may be treated on the herd basis or on a trading stock basis;

Herd Basis

Under the herd basis valuation changes are not included in the trading account, nor are additions to the herd, but sales from the herd and replacements are. On the sale of all or a substantial proportion (normally taken as 20% or more) of the herd, no tax is paid on any profit over the original cost price, nor is there any relief for loss.

Trading Stock Basis

Purchases, sales and valuation changes are all included in the trading account. Under this method stock should be valued at the lower of cost (or cost of production) and net realisable value. Where animals are home-produced and it is not possible to ascertain actual costs from farm records the 'deemed' cost may be used. This is 60% of market value for cattle and 75% for sheep and pigs.

STOCK VALUATION: CROPS

Crops should generally be valued at the cost of production (or net realisable value, if lower). Costs which are directly attributable to buying, producing and growing the crops should be included. The deemed cost method allows 75% of market value to be used although this method should only be used where it is not possible to ascertain actual costs.

ALLOWANCES FOR CAPITAL EXPENDITURE

Machinery and Plant

1. The same rules apply whether the machinery and plant is new or second hand. An annual writing down allowance of 18% p.a. is available on a reducing balance basis on capital expenditure incurred on the provision of plant and machinery. Qualifying expenditure is added to the asset 'pool' and the writing down allowances are given on the residue of expenditure in that pool.

2. The Annual Investment Allowance ('AIA') gives 100% relief for the first £500,000 of qualifying expenditure per accounting period. The allowance will fall to £200,000 after the 31st December 2015 and stay at that level for the lifetime of the current Parliament. The limit is proportionally increased or decreased where the chargeable period is longer or shorter than a year. A group of companies can only receive a single allowance. Expenditure on cars does not qualify, although expenditure on long life assets, or on 'integral features' can be claimed.

3. An 8% rate applies to expenditure incurred on certain listed 'integral features' in a building and on long life assets. Expenditure brought forward will obtain the 8% rate.

4. 100% first year allowances can be claimed for expenditure incurred by any business on designated energy-saving plant and machinery and environmentally beneficial technologies and products. The lists of items which qualify can be found on the Government's Energy Technology Product lists, which is at www.eca.gov.uk.

Cars

For expenditure on motor cars purchased in or after April 2009, the regime is based on CO_2 emissions. For cars purchased after April 2015 those with CO_2 emissions exceeding 130gm/km are allocated to the 8% special rate pool. All other cars go into the general 18% rate pool apart from new cars with emissions of 75gm/km or less which get a special 100% first year allowance. For unincorporated businesses, cars have their own separate pools where there is an element of private use.

Machinery Leasing

Tax allowances for rental payments on financial leases are spread to reflect the commercial depreciation of the asset. This may mean that full tax relief for rental payments may not be gained in the years in which the payments are made.

Buildings

Farm buildings, fencing, drainage and other improvements (including up to one-third of farmhouses) used to qualify for a writing-down allowance of 4% annually, given equally over 25 years. These allowances have now been completely phased out.

LOSSES

Losses can normally be set against other income in the year they are incurred and in the prior year. If other income is insufficient in the year when the loss occurs and in the prior year, unrelieved losses can be carried forward and set off against future profits from the same trade. Special rules apply to prevent abuse of loss relief provisions by 'hobby' farmers who are not running their farms on a commercial basis with a view to producing a profit: normally losses are disallowed against other income after 5 consecutive years of loss. Trading losses may be set against capital gains in the same year as the loss.

PROFIT AVERAGING

This relief is to enable farmers, other than companies, to average their taxable profits over two consecutive years. Where the difference between the profits of two consecutive years is 30% or more of the higher profits, the total profits for the two years are equally divided between the two years. Marginal relief is available where the difference is less than 30% but more than 25% of the higher profits. Profit for the purposes of tax averaging calculations is after the deduction of capital allowances. There is a two year limit in which to make the claim.

There is a proposal to allow profit averaging over 5 years as from April 2016. Details were awaited at the time of writing.

4.   CAPITAL GAINS TAX

APPLICATION AND RATES

Applies to capital gains made by an individual. Capital gains accruing to companies are chargeable to Corporation Tax. A capital gain is the difference between the acquisition value and the sale price. The first £11,100 of capital gains (for the 2015-16 year) realised by an individual in a tax year are covered by their annual exemption.

Disposals of non-business assets attract capital gains tax of 18% for basic rate taxpayers or 28% for higher and additional rate taxpayers. The rate of CGT is 18% where total taxable gains and income, after taking into account all allowable deductions including losses, personal allowances and the CGT annual exemption, are less than the upper limit of the income tax basic rate band. The 28% rate will apply to gains or any parts of gains above this limit.

Exempt assets include a principal private residence (e.g. farm house, if non-exclusive business occupation applies) if occupied as such, normal life assurance policies, animals and tangible movable property (i.e. chattels) disposed of for £6,000 or less.

Capital Gains Tax is chargeable only on the disposal (including gifts) of assets. Capital Gains Tax is not payable on death. Payment of Capital Gains Tax is due on 31st January following the tax year of disposal.

RELIEFS

Losses

Should a transaction produce a loss, this may be set against any long term chargeable gains arising in the same year or, if these are insufficient, those accruing in subsequent years. Losses brought forward will be used only to the extent necessary to reduce untaxed gains for the year to £11,100.

Where a trading loss can be set against other income in the same or prior year for income tax purposes, any unused loss can be set against capital gains for those years.

Improvements

Spending that has increased the value of the asset can be offset against any gain. In the case of agricultural property, allowance would be made for any capital expenditure undertaken to improve the property.

Indexation and Taper Relief

Indexation and Taper relief for individuals has now been abolished for any disposals taking place on or after 6th April 2008. Indexation allowance is still available for capital gains arising in companies.

Entrepreneurs Relief

Entrepreneur's relief applies to certain disposals of business assets by an individual. The relief, which must be claimed, gives a reduced effective rate of Capital Gains Tax of 10% for eligible gains of up to £10m for disposals after 6th April 2011 (lower limits applied before this date). The limit is a lifetime limit per individual. The assets which qualify for entrepreneurs' relief are in line with those which qualified for business asset taper relief. This covers:

- a trading business carried on by an individual alone or in partnership;
- assets of such a trade following cessation;
- shares or securities in a trading company where the individual owns 5% or more and is an officer or employee

The conditions for the relief must have been satisfied throughout a qualifying period of a year before the disposal.

Editorial Note: *The rules for Entrepreneurs' relief are complex, particularly in cases of disposals of part of the business. The rules are similar to the previous Retirement Relief and are particularly tricky in cases of disposals of farmland and related assets and trade. It is recommended that professional advice is sought where it is anticipated claiming this relief, particularly as given the increase in the lifetime allowance combined with the increase in tax rate for non-business assets, the tax savings can be greatly increased.*

Rollover

Payment of tax may be deferred on gains accruing from the sale of business assets (including land and buildings occupied and used for trade purposes, fixed plant and machinery and from the sale of shares in a family business) if part or all of the proceeds are spent on acquiring new qualifying assets. The tax is deferred by deducting the gain from the acquisition price of the new asset. It can only be claimed if the new asset is acquired within 12 months before and 3 years after the disposal of the old assets. Disposal and acquisition dates for Capital Gains purposes are generally contract, not completion, dates.

Holdover

Payments of tax may be deferred where disposal is by gift. This relief only applies to gifts of business assets, land which qualifies for agricultural property relief at either the 100% or 50% rate under Inheritance Tax (see next section) and gifts which lead to an immediate charge to Inheritance Tax (e.g. gifts into a discretionary trust). The amount of the chargeable gain which would normally have accrued to the donor will be held over; the value at which the donee is deemed to acquire the asset will be its market value reduced by the amount of the donor's chargeable gain held over. Where deferral is not available, payment of tax by interest bearing annual instalments over 10 years will be allowed for gifts of land, controlling share holdings and minority share holdings in unquoted companies.

5. INHERITANCE TAX

APPLICATION AND RATES

This tax is charged on lifetime gifts and transfers on death. The rate for 2015-16 is 40%, on amounts chargeable to Inheritance Tax above the nil rate band of £325,000.

The nil rate band is potentially increased for surviving spouses or civil partners who died on or after 9th October 2007. From this date the nil rate band may be increased by the unused proportion of the deceased spouse or civil partners nil rate band.

From the 2017-18 year it is proposed to bring in a Main residence nil rate band. This will commence at £100,000 and rise to £175,000 by 2020-21. It will be in addition to the usual nil rate band but only be applicable to the main house of the deceased if transferred to a direct descendent. Any unused portion can be transferred between spouses.

Outright gifts to individuals are exempt from tax at the time of the gift. If the donor lives for a further seven years then the transfer is fully exempt. Gifts into accumulation and maintenance trusts and interest in possession trusts no longer receive special treatment - all other gifts will be taxed at half the above rates at the time of the transfer.

Tax is charged on the value of an individual's estate at death plus the value of all gifts made within seven years of death. Allowance is made for any tax paid on lifetime gifts included in the value of the estate on death. Relief is given for outright gifts made more than three years before death according to the following scale:

Years between gift and death	0-3	3-4	4-5	5-6	6-7
Percentage of the full tax charge	100%	80%	60%	40%	20%

Exemptions include: transfers between husband and wife; the first £3,000 of gift made by a donor in the income tax year and separately up to £250 per year to any number of persons; gifts made out of income which form part of normal expenditure; marriage gifts within limits of £5,000 for a parent, £2,500 for a lineal ancestor and £1,000 for other donors.

RELIEFS

Agricultural Property Relief

Relief may be available for agricultural land. Subject to a general rule that the agricultural land must have been occupied by the transferor (or by his controlled company) for two years, or owned by the transferor for 7 years and occupied for agricultural purposes by someone else before any relief is granted. The relief is at two different rates. If the basis of valuation is vacant possession (or there is the right to obtain it within 12 months), the taxable value of the land is reduced by 100%. If the basis of valuation is tenanted value, the taxable value of the land is reduced by 50% of that tenanted value. Ownership and occupation periods normally include prior periods of ownership or occupation by husbands and wives. From 1st September 1995, 100% relief applies to new lettings of agricultural land as Farm Business Tenancies. Agricultural Relief includes agricultural land in the European Economic Area (EEA).

Editorial Note: There has been much publicised activity and tax cases concerning APR claims, particularly attempts by the Inland Revenue to reduce or deny the relief on claims for farmhouses. Care must be taken to protect the relief particularly where the attached land is either let out on a Farm Business Tenancy or under a contract farming arrangement.

Business Property Relief

Relief is also available in respect to 'business property' transferred during lifetime or on death. The relief extends to the business assets of a proprietor and the interest of a partner or controlling shareholder in the business capital of a company. The value of such property, providing certain tests are satisfied (e.g. it has been owned by the transferor for two years preceding transfer), is reduced by 100%. Where a partner or controlling shareholder owns assets (e.g. land) that the business uses, the value will be reduced by 50%. Shareholdings in unquoted companies receive a 100% reduction in market value.

Lifetime gifts of property eligible for Agricultural and Business Property Relief have to be retained (or replaced by similar property) until the death of the donor (or earlier death of the donee) if those reliefs are to be available when the tax (or additional tax) becomes payable subsequent to the donor's death

In the case of the transfer of property eligible for APR and BPR, the tax can be paid by annual instalments over ten years free of interest.

6.   STAMP TAXES

Stamp Duty is charged at 0.5 per cent of consideration paid (purchase by cash, other stocks or shares) on the transfer of shares and securities.

Stamp Duty Land Tax is charged on the transfer of an interest in land; both sales and leases. With sales of property the tax is levied on a percentage of the sale value of the property. Note that for residential property, it is the value that falls into each bracket that is charged at the prevailing rate. For non-residential property, SDLT is charged on the total value at whatever band is reached. The rates applicable to transactions since March 2014 are:

Residential property	Rate	Non-residential and mixed use	Rate
Value up to £125,000............	nil	Value up to £150,000..............	nil
£125,001 to £250,000	2%	£150,001 to £250,000..............	1%
£250,001 to £925,000	5%	£250,001 to £500,000..............	3%
£925,001 to £1,500,000	10%	£500,001 or more....................	4%
£1,500,001 or more..............	12%		

Purchased of property other than individuals with a value of over £500,000 are subject to a 15% rate as from March 2014.

Stamp Duty Land Tax is payable on leases calculated according to the net present value of the rent payable over the term of the lease.

7.   VALUE ADDED TAX

Agricultural businesses with a turnover of taxable goods and services in excess of £82,000 per annum must register for VAT. Businesses with a turnover below this figure can voluntarily register. Those with sales of less than £80,000 may apply for de-registration. The standard VAT rate has been 20% since January 2011. Most agricultural products are zero rated for VAT purposes. VAT has to be paid on certain inputs. Registered businesses are eligible to reclaim the tax paid where the goods or services purchased have been used in the production of zero-rated supplies.

A flat rate scheme is available to farmers as an alternative to registering for VAT. Farmers under the flat rate scheme do not have to submit tax returns or account for VAT and consequently cannot reclaim tax. They can, however, charge (and keep) a flat rate addition of 4% when they sell to VAT registered customers goods and services which qualify. This addition is not VAT but acts as compensation for losing input tax on purchases. The registered person paying the flat rate amount to the farmer can recover it as if it were VAT, subject to the normal rules for reclaiming. The local VAT office may refuse to issue a certificate to participate in the flat rate scheme if this would mean the farmer would recover substantially (£3,000) more than through the normal system.

A flat rate scheme operates for small businesses generally and is an alternative that farmers can use if they have taxable supplies of no more than £150,000 and a total business income of no more than £187,500. This scheme operates in a different way to the flat rate scheme for farmers in that a business charges the normal rate of VAT on sales. However, the VAT which the business has to remit to Customs and Excise is calculated by multiplying the value of gross sales by a rate specified for each particular trade sector. The rate for agriculture is 6.5% since January 2011 except for businesses supplying agricultural services, when the rate is 11%.

Editorial Note*: Farmers and landowners must always consider the VAT implications when considering any new or more farming activities on the land or within the buildings,* *particularly where supplies are made the public who cannot recover any VAT which may be charged on the service or goods provided from the farm.*

8.   NATIONAL INSURANCE

The tables below set out the National Insurance contributions for the 2015-16 year;

Class 1 (not contracted out)

Employee's weekly earnings	Employee
£155 or less..	Nil
£155.01 to £815................................	12%
Over £815..	2%

Employer contributions are 13.8% on weekly earnings over £156

Class 2

Self-employed flat rate	£2.80 a week

Class 3

Non-employed (voluntary) flat rate	£14.10 a week

Class 4

Self-employed. On profits or gains

between £8,060 and £42,385	9%
over £42,385...	2%

VIII.   FARM BUSINESS MANAGEMENT

1.   DEFINITIONS OF FARM MANAGEMENT TERMS

VALUATIONS AND CAPITAL

Valuations

Valuation is essentially a process of estimation. Various methods are possible, according to the purpose intended. The basis should be consistent throughout the period or any series of figures.

1. *Saleable crops in store.* At estimated market value less costs still to be incurred, e.g. for storage and marketing. Both may be estimated either at the expected date of sale or at the date of valuation.

2. *Growing crops.* Preferably at variable costs to the date of valuation, although estimated total cost can alternatively be used.

3. *Saleable crops ready for harvesting* but still in the ground. Preferably as valued in point 1 above, less estimated harvesting costs, although they can alternatively be treated as described in point 2 above.

4. *Fodder stocks (home-grown).* Normally at variable costs when calculating gross margins although this can be misleading for management purposes. Estimated market value (based on hay-equivalent value according to quality for example) includes the opportunity cost of the fodder in the livestock margin. Fodder crops still in the ground, e.g. kale, treated as point 2 above.

5. *Stocks of purchased materials (including fodder).* Priced at cost (net of discounts).

6. *Machinery and equipment.* Original cost (net of grants and discounts), less accumulated depreciation to date of valuation – this gives a valuation on the 'historic' cost basis. Alternatively at estimated market value.

7. *Livestock.* At current market value, less cost of marketing. Fluctuations in market value expected to be temporary should be ignored.

Capital

Tenant's Capital. The estimated total value of capital on the farm, other than land and fixed equipment. There is no easy way of determining this sum precisely and estimates are made in several ways depending on the information available and the purpose for which the estimate is required. One method is to take the average of the opening and closing valuations (at either market value or cost) of livestock, crops, machinery and stores (feed, seed, fertilisers). See also pages 248 (following section).

Landlord's Capital. Value of the land and fixed equipment (including buildings).

OUTPUT TERMS

Revenue (or Income). Receipts adjusted for debtors at the beginning and end of the accounting period. Items such as CAP support, revenue grants, contract receipts and wayleaves are included.

Returns. Revenue adjusted for valuation changes (add closing, deduct opening, valuation).

Gross Output. Returns plus the value of produce consumed in the farmhouse or supplied to workers for which no payment is made, less purchases of livestock, livestock products and other produce bought for resale.

Enterprise Output. The total value of an enterprise, whether sold or retained on the farm. It therefore equals Gross Output of the enterprise plus the market value of any of the products kept on the farm (transfers out). The Basic Payment should not be apportioned to individual enterprises. Products transferred from another enterprise to be used in the production of the enterprise whose output is being calculated are deducted at market value (transfers in). Instead of the accounting year the "harvest year" can be used for crops which means valuations may not be relevant.

(Enterprise) Output from Forage. Primarily the sum of the enterprise outputs of grazing livestock, but includes keep let and occasional sales, e.g. of surplus hay, together with an adjustment for changes in the valuation of stocks of home-grown fodder. However, fortuitous changes in stocks caused by yield variations due to the weather, the severity or length of the winter, or minor changes in livestock numbers or forage area can be either ignored (if small in relation to total annual usage) or included in miscellaneous output.

Adjusted Forage (Enterprise) Output. Output from Forage less rented keep and purchases of bulk fodder.

Standard Output. The average enterprise output per hectare of a crop or per head of livestock calculated from average yield data and either national or local average price.

INPUT TERMS

Expenditure. Payments adjusted for creditors at the beginning and end of the accounting period. Capital expenditure is not included.

Costs. Expenditure adjusted for valuation changes (add opening, deduct closing, valuation), with the following adjustments: Add; depreciation on capital expenditure including machinery, any loss made on machinery sales (add to depreciation) and the value of payments in kind to workers if not already included in their earnings. Deduct; purchases of livestock, livestock products and other produce bought for resale, any profit made on machinery (deduct from depreciation), allowance for private use of farm vehicles (deduct from machinery costs), the value of purchased stores used in the farmhouse (e.g. electricity) or sold off the farm (deduct from the relevant item).

Inputs. Costs with the following adjustments, made in order to put all farms on a similar basis for comparative purposes. Add: the value of unpaid family labour, including the manual labour of the farmer and his wife, and, in the case of owner-occupiers, an estimated rental value (based on average rents of similar farms in the area), less any cottage rents received. Deduct: any mortgage payments and other expenses of owner-occupation, interest payments and the cost of paid management. A proportion of the rental value of the farmhouse may also be deducted.

Fixed Costs. See pages from 218 whole Farm Fixed Costs.

Variable Costs. See page 1.

MARGIN TERMS

Management and Investment Income. Gross Output less Inputs. It represents the reward to management and the return on tenant's capital invested in the farm, whether borrowed or not. It is mainly used for comparative purposes, all farms having been put on a similar financial basis by the adjustments made to costs in calculating Inputs.

Net Farm Income. Management and Investment Income, less paid management, plus the value of the manual labour of the farmer and his wife. It represents the return to all tenant's type capital and the reward to the farmer for his manual labour and management.

Profit (or Loss). Gross Output less Costs. This represents the surplus or deficit before imputing any notional charges such as rental value or unpaid labour. In the accounts of owner-occupiers it includes any profit accruing from the ownership of land.

Farm Business Income. This term is increasingly being used in FBS costings, and is similar to 'Profit' above. It represents the return to all unpaid labour and to all their own capital in the farm business including land and farm buildings.

Gross Margin. See page 1.

Net Margin. A term sometimes used to denote Gross Margin less direct labour and machinery costs charged to an individual enterprise. This is not, however, nationally accepted terminology. Increasingly Net Margin in the enterprise context is being used to denote the profit of an enterprise by taking its gross output less its 'complete enterprise costs', but see page 2.

AREA TERMS

Total Hectares. All hectares comprising the farm.

Hectares. Total hectares less areas of woods, waste land, roads, yards, buildings, etc.

Adjusted Hectares. Hectares reduced by the conversion of rough grazing into the equivalent hectares of average quality grassland. This is the figure often used for lowland farms when calculating "per hectare" results.

Forage Hectares. Total hectares of forage crops grown, less any hectares exclusively used by pigs or poultry and the area equivalent of any home-grown fodder fed to livestock reared in cereal systems. Also, the area of rough grazing is converted to its grassland equivalent (see Adjusted Hectares). Forage crops are all crops including grass, rough grazing, maize and whole crops grown specifically for grazing livestock, but excluding catch crops and crops harvested as grain and pulses.

Adjusted Forage Hectares. Forage hectares adjusted as follows. Add area equivalent of keep rented, deduct area equivalent of keep let; deduct the area equivalent of occasional sales of fodder, e.g. surplus hay, and seed cuts (note: hay and seed grown regularly for sale should be regarded as cash crops, not forage crops); add or deduct the area equivalent of planned changes in the valuation of stocks of home-grown fodder (fortuitous changes in stocks resulting from weather conditions may be ignored); convert rough grazing into their grassland equivalent if not already done. The following adjustments also may be made: add the area equivalent of catch crops and of grazing from cash crops of hay or seed: add the area equivalent of purchased fodder.

In calculations such as Gross Margins per Forage Hectare, Adjusted Forage Hectares are usually used. If the area equivalent of purchased fodder has been added, the cost of purchased fodder must not be charged as a variable cost: this is probably the best calculation for comparative purposes. Alternatively, when considering all the grazing enterprises taken together, purchased fodder can be deducted as a variable cost and no addition made for its area equivalent.

2. CAPITAL REQUIREMENT AND RETURN

TENANT'S CAPITAL

1. *Machinery.* Costs of new machinery are given on pages 190. Written-down values in 2016 are likely to average £345-£800 per hectare (£140-£324/acre) of actively farmed land (excluding fallow and rough grazing) taking all farm types together. Average values for different farm types are given on the next page.

2. *Breeding Livestock.* The 2016 average of breeding livestock value per hectare can be anything up to £1,800 (£730/acre) for an intensive (outdoor) dairy/livestock farm. Intensive (housed) pig and poultry units will be substantially more but a meaningless figure. Approximate average market values of various categories of breeding livestock (of mixed ages in the case of adult stock) are as follows (actual value will vary according to average age and weight, quality, breed and market conditions):

Average market values of various breeding livestock

	Breeding Herd		
	Newly calved	Average	Cull**
Holstein/Friesian Dairy Cows	£1,350	£1,000	£400
Channel Island Dairy Cows	£965	£570	£180
Suckler Beef Cows:	£1,150*	£775	£550
Pure-bred Beef Cows	£1,700*	£1,125	£550

* Calf at Foot < 3 months

	Replacements		
	Holstein Friesians	Ayrshires and C.I. Breeds	Beef Cattle
In Calf Heifers	£1,250	£965	£1,000
1-2 years	£950	£700	£750
6-12 months	£600	£450	£500
Under 6 months	£300	£225	£250

Other Livestock	
Ewes (2 ½ years old / one lamb crop)	£145
Rams (2 ½ years old / one mating season)	£480
Sows and In-Pig Gilts	£210
Boars	£750

3. Working Capital. This is defined as the current assets of a business less its current liabilities. It is the liquid capital needed to finance the cash flow through the production cycle, the length of which varies considerably between different crop and livestock enterprises and different combinations of these enterprises. It can include the cost of purchased fattening stock, feed, seed, fertilisers, regular labour, machinery running costs, general overhead costs, rent and living expenses. This capital will vary between farm business types. Specialist root crop and vegetable farm businesses will have significantly higher working capital requirements than livestock and combinable cropping businesses. The only accurate way to estimate working capital requirement is to complete a full cash flow estimate for the production cycle of the business.

Average Tenants Capital per Hectare

Average Tenant's Capital for different English farm types for 2016:

Farm Type Group	Average No. Hectares	Breeding Livestock ***	Crops and Stores	Machinery and Equipment*	Total Tenant's Capital	
**		£/ha	£/ha	£/ha	£/ha	£/acre
Mainly Dairying:						
under 75 ha	60	1,185	194	1059	2,438	*987*
75 to 125 ha	85	1,307	251	1,192	2,750	*1,113*
Over 125 ha	170	1,596	332	1,180	3,108	*1,258*
Average	150	1,536	316	1,025	2,877	*1,165*
Mainly Cereals:						
under 185 ha	170	30	633	900	1,563	*633*
185 to 320 ha	270	37	690	820	1,547	*626*
over 320 ha	550	41	656	838	1,535	*621*
Average	290	38	672	870	1,580	*640*
General Cropping:						
under 150 ha	125	21	594	914	1,529	*619*
150 to 225 ha	185	-	586	869	1,455	*589*
over 225 ha	450	64	619	831	1,514	*613*
Average	280	45	582	814	1,442	*584*
Mainly Sheep/Cattle (Lowland):						
Under 100 ha	80	452	132	613	1,197	*485*
100 to 150 ha	125	446	135	522	1,103	*447*
Over 150 ha	240	483	135	489	1,107	*448*
Average	130	459	132	531	1,122	*454*
Mainly Sheep/Cattle (Upland LFA):						
under 130 ha	100	478	59	471	1,008	*408*
130 to 230 ha	140	527	61	376	964	*390*
over 230 ha	300	485	55	302	842	*341*
Average	175	446	52	339	837	*339*

*   Based on current (i.e. replacement) costs.

**   Size range estimated from survey data

***   Trading Livestock or crops in store are not included as they are not assets of production and will vary according to marketing styles and time of year

The above (deliberately rounded) data is based on Farm Business Survey results for England compiled annually by University/Colleges (as listed on page 4). The value of Basic Payment entitlements is excluded as are other assets not named above, such as debtors.

RETURN ON CAPITAL

Return on Tenant's Capital

Return on tenant's capital is calculated by taking the management and investment income (MII) of a business as a percentage of the tenant's capital (see definitions in section VIII.1). Because MII is before deduction of any interest, this return is 'gross', i.e. before allowing for cost of finance. However, it should be borne in mind that MII includes no charge for management but that a rental value for owner-occupied land and the value of the unpaid labour of the farmer and wife have been deducted.

Return on Landlord's Capital

The return on landlord's capital is calculated by taking the rental income, less any ownership expenses (mortgage, insurance, repairs etc.), expressed as a percentage of the land value. With farmland in 2016 averaging, possibly £23,500 per hectare (£9,500 per acre) (see page 225) with vacant possession (assuming no special amenity or house value), an average lowland existing rent of, say, £350 per hectare (£140 per acre) (see page 223), and assuming ownership expenses at £87 per hectare (£35 per acre), the (net) return of £263 per hectare (£106 per acre) averages 1%. This takes no account of land valuation change.

Return on Capital to Individual Enterprises

On a mixed farm it is difficult to ascertain the return on enterprise capital, except perhaps for a full-time pig or poultry enterprise. It would also be of limited use. It would require the arbitrary allocation both of costs and capital inputs that are common to several, or all, of the enterprises on the farm.

What is relevant and important is the extra (net) return from an enterprise either to be introduced or expanded, as calculated by a partial budget, related to the extra (net) capital needed. The 'net' in brackets relates to the additional returns to gross margins less any additional (or plus any reduction in) 'fixed' costs, bearing in mind that another enterprise may have to be deleted or reduced in size; and, regarding capital, to the fact that deletion or reduction of another enterprise may release capital.

In most cases of 'marginal' substitution, it is differences in the value of breeding livestock and differences in variable costs that are particularly relevant, but the timing of both inputs and sales are also obviously very important.

'Marginal' Capital Requirements

These are for small changes in crop areas or livestock numbers and can be estimated as follows:

- Crops: variable costs until payment of sale.
- Dairy Cows and Egg Production: value of the cow* or hens, plus food until payment of product.
- Other Breeding Livestock: average value of stock*, plus variable costs to sale (payment) of the progeny (e.g. lambs) – or their transfer to another enterprise (e.g. weaners to the pig fattening enterprise).
- Rearing Breeding Livestock (e.g. heifers, shearlings, gilts, pullets): cost of the calf, lamb, weaner or chick, plus variable costs until they produce their first progeny/milk/eggs.
- Fattening Livestock and Production of Stores: cost of stock, plus variable costs till sale.

* Value of breeding stock, including dairy cows: either the average value over their entire breeding or milk producing life (see table on page 248) or their value when they first produce progeny can be taken. The latter will give the lower return on (marginal) capital and is thus the severer test.

Home-reared stock: where stock to be used for milk or egg production, breeding or fattening are home-reared, there are two possibilities:

(a) either they can be valued at variable costs of production when they are transferred from the rearing to the 'productive' enterprise; in this case the return on (marginal) capital will be estimated over the combined rearing and 'productive' enterprise.

(b) or they can be valued at market value at point of transfer. This is the procedure if one wishes to work out a return on (marginal) capital for the rearing and the 'productive' enterprises separately.

Return on 'Marginal' Capital

This is sometimes expressed as the gross margin less fuel and repair costs of the enterprise expanded as a percentage of the 'marginal', or extra capital. However, two points have to be remembered:

(a) If another enterprise has had to be reduced in size to enable the enterprise under consideration to be expanded, the capital released and the gross margin forfeited by reducing the size of the first enterprise must be brought into the calculation in estimating the net result of the change.

(b) All the above statements on 'marginal' capital refer to small changes. If the change is large enough to cause changes in labour, machinery or building requirements, the capital changes brought about may be considerably greater.

Return on Investments in Medium-Term and Long-Term Capital

This calculates the Rate of Return and the Discounted Yield.

Example: If a £5,000 investment results in an annual net return of £500 (after deducting depreciation, but ignoring interest payments) and with no capital salvage value:

$$\text{Rate of Return on Initial Capital} = \frac{500}{5,000} \times 100 = 10\%$$

$$\text{Rate of Return on Average Capital} = \frac{500}{2,500} \times 100 = 20\%$$

Care has to be used when using the return on *'average'* capital as the capital has still been spent, it is just that half has been written off. It is more accurate to calculate the *'Discounted Yield'*, which is the discount rate that brings the present value of the net cash flows (which means ignoring depreciation) to the value of the investment. The tables on pages 257 may be used.

'Short-Cut' Estimates of the Discounted Yield on Depreciating Assets

The Discounted Yield falls between the simple Rates of Return on Initial and Average Capital. In fact, for investments lasting 5 to 15 years, when the Rate of Return on Initial Capital is 10 per cent and on Average Capital 20 per cent, the Discounted Yield will be almost exactly halfway between, i.e. about 15 per cent. However, this is only so providing the anticipated annual net cash earnings are fairly constant — or fluctuate unpredictably around a fairly constant level.

There are three circumstances when the Discounted Yield will get closer to the Rate of Return on Initial Capital (i.e. the lower per cent return) and further from the Rate of Return on Average Capital:

(a)   The longer the life of the investment.

(b)   The higher the Rate of Return.

(c)   The higher the net cash flow is in the later years of the investment compared with the earlier years.

When the opposite circumstances occur, the Discounted Yield will be closer to the Rate of Return on Average Capital (i.e. the higher per cent return).

There are varying degrees of estimation and uncertainty in calculating future net annual earnings of investments. The following short-cuts might reasonably be used where the annual net cash earnings are expected to be fairly constant - or fluctuate unpredictably (e.g. through weather effects on yields) around a fairly constant level. (W.O. period = write-off period; R.R.I.C. = rate of return on initial capital).

1. Where

   (i)   the W.O. period is 5 years or less,

   (ii)   the W.O. period is 6 - 10 years and the R.R.I.C. is 15 per cent or less,

   (iii)   the W.O. period is 11 - 20 years and the R.R.I.C. is 10 per cent or less,

   calculate the Return on Capital as being approximately midway between the Rates of Return on Initial and Average Capital, i.e. by calculating the Rate of Return on 2/3 of the original investment.

   For example, following the earlier example above:

$$\frac{500}{3,333} \times 100 = 15\%.$$

2. Where

   (i)   the W.O. period is 6 to 10 years and the R.R.I.C. exceeds 15 per cent,

   (ii)   the W.O. period is 11 to 20 years and the R.R.I.C. is between 10 per cent and 25 per cent,

   (iii)   the W.O. period exceeds 20 years and the R.R.I.C. is 10 per cent or less,

   calculate the Return on Capital on 80 per cent of the original investment.

   For example, again following the earlier example:

$$\frac{500}{4,000} \times 100 = 12.5°\%.$$

3. Where

   (i)   the W.O. period is 11 to 20 years and the R.R.I.C. exceeds 25 per cent,

   (ii)   the W.O. period exceeds 20 years and the R.R.I.C. exceeds 10 per cent, take the Return on Capital to be the R.R.I.C.

In borderline cases, use method 1 rather than 2, or 2 rather than 3 if there is a tendency for the cash flow to be higher in the earlier years, e.g. because of tax allowances on machinery. Take 2 rather than 1, and 3 rather than 2, if the likelihood is that the cash flow will be lower in earlier years and increase in later years.

However, where the annual cash flow is expected to vary (apart from unpredictable fluctuations) it is safer to make the full D.C.F. calculation. This is particularly so where the variation is both up and down and where further periodic investments are to be made during the life of the project.

3. INTEREST RATES

Rate of interest on Bank Loans

Typically 3.0% to 3.5% above Base Rate. Main range is 1.5% above to 4.0% above. Extremes are likely to be 0.8% above and 7% above. Particularly low margins over base have become rare, especially for new lending agreements. Annual arrangement fees based on the total facility can add substantially to the cost of borrowing. At the time of writing, base rate is at an all-time low since 2009 at 0.5%, but the Bank of England had started preparing borrowers for a rate rise at some point, possibly during 2016. It would be prudent for budgeting purposes to allow an additional 0.5% by the end of 2016.

Fixed Rate Mortgages

The table gives typical mortgage rates on domestic dwellings. Note that this is taken from the current mortgage marketplace. Each offering is different with varying retention clauses, booking fees or early redemption costs. The lowest interest rate is not necessarily the best mortgage.

Typical Fixed Rates on Residential Mortgages

Fixed Rate	95% LTV*	75%	60% LTV*
2-year	4.0%	1.5%	1.2%
5-year	4.8%	2.5%	2.2%
10-year	n/a	3.9%	3.2%

* LTV = Loan to Value (the percent the financier loans against the capital value)

Annual Percentage Rate (APR)

This is the effective rate of interest calculated on an annual basis and should be used when seeking to make a true comparison between interest charges on money borrowed from different sources. The APR allows for the fact that when interest is applied to accounts at half yearly, quarterly or monthly intervals an element of compounding will arise.

For example, £100 borrowed for one year at a quoted annual nominal interest rate of 6% (e.g. 5.5% over base rate of 0.5%) with interest charged quarterly, will lead to an accumulated interest charge of £6.136 (i.e., giving an APR of just under 6.14%). The higher the annual nominal interest rate and the more frequently the interest charges are applied to the account, the more pronounced the compounding element becomes. For example, an annual nominal interest rate of 10% produces an APR of 10.25% with half yearly charging, 10.38% with quarterly charging and 10.47% with monthly charging.

In the case of some loans and hire purchase agreements, interest charges may be quoted as a flat rate on the original amount borrowed. The APR will be considerably greater than the flat rate if the loan is repaid by equal periodic instalments, comprising part capital and part interest, so that the borrowing is completely repaid by the end of the agreed term. For example, the APR for a loan at a flat rate of interest of 8% repaid by monthly instalments over 5 years will be 15%. The shorter the repayment period, and the more frequent the payments, the higher is the APR compared with the flat rate.

The Real Rate of Interest.

When preparing profit and loss budgets to estimate how worthwhile an investment in a fixed asset (machinery, buildings, land) is, it is usual to price inputs and outputs at present-day values even when most costs and returns are expected to rise due to inflation over the life of the investment. Where this real terms approach is adopted a more realistic estimate of the effect on profitability can be gained by basing charges for capital on the real rate of interest rather than the APR.

The real rate of interest is the APR adjusted for the annual rate at which prices relevant to the investment are expected to increase. A crude estimate of the real rate of interest can be obtained by simply subtracting the expected rate of price increase from the APR; for example, if the APR were 8% and the expected rate of inflation 3%, the real rate of interest would be $8 - 3 = 5\%$.

4. FINANCIAL RATIOS

Common Ratios

The following ratios are standard guidelines using '*normalised*' output prices, i.e. those in an average year:

% of Gross Output	Arable	Dairy	Mixed	Upland
Variable Costs	32	39	37	47
Labour+	12	15	21	17
Machinery	18	17	19	14
Sundry Fixed Costs	9	9	10	12
Rent & Interest	12	13	9	8
Profit *	17	17	4	2
Basic Payment Support	14	5	14	19

+ *including drawings*
* *to cover, tax, capital repayments, reinvestments*

It has to be borne in mind that these are indeed only rough guidelines and need to be considered with great care. Values vary with type of farming and size of farm. It is often unclear how some items are being measured, especially whether unpaid manual labour of the farmer and family has been included or whether a rental value has been allowed for owner-occupied land. In the table above, variable costs of about 30% would be found on cereals type farms, leaving 40% for labour, machinery and sundry fixed costs. On intensive livestock farms variable costs of 40% would be expected, leaving only 30% for fixed costs. Higher rent and finance can be justified on more profitable farm systems.

The Basic Payment as a percentage of output is also included to compare against profit. Being greater than total farm profit in some cases, it identifies the dependence of several farm businesses to direct subsidy.

Farm Survey Ratios

The following are rounded averages based on farm surveys in recent years on a large sample of all types of farm, assuming a Management and Investment Income (see page 246) of 10% of Total Output is made. It is to be noted that Total Output includes the market value of any production retained for use/consumption on the farm (e.g. cereals for feed or seed). Unpaid labour (value of manual labour by the farmer and spouse) is included. Rent includes the rental value of owner-occupied land and interest charges are not included in the costs. Casual labour and all contract work are included in fixed costs. Costs are a lower proportion and the margin a higher proportion in profitable years (and on more profitable farms), and *vice-versa* in low profit years.

Average Financial Ratios from Farm Business Survey (England)

	% Total Output	% Total Gross Margin	% Total Fixed Costs
Gross Margin (*inc. SPS*)	62		
Variable Costs:			
(excl. casual labour and contract)	36	60	63
Fixed Costs:			
Labour: Paid (inc. unpaid)	17	28	29
Power & Machinery (inc. contract)	18	29	29
Rent/Rental Value	17	24	32
General Overheads	7	10	11
Total Fixed Costs	59	90	100
Margin	**5**	**10**	**8**

Lending Criteria

Another set of standards widely used by lending and leasing institutions looks at total Finance Charges (rent, interest, leasing charges, etc.), as a percentage of Gross Output and Gross Margin;

Finance as a % of Gross Output	Finance as a % of Gross Margin	Lending Criteria
0-10%	0-15%	Normally very safe
11-15%	16-22.5%	Common range, should be safe
15%	25%	Average Farm in 2013/14*
16-20%	23-29%	Care required
20% plus	30% plus	Potentially dangerous

* *Interpretation from Farm Business Survey data*

As lenders will be well aware, these ratios must be regarded with caution and in conjunction with the farm's level of net worth (% equity) and its trend in recent years, recent trends in its profitability and the potential borrower's record of expenditure both on and off the farm, together with his or her character and potential. Also, some enterprises and types of farming are more risky than others.

DISCOUNTING TABLE

Discount Factors for Calculating the Present Value of Future (irregular) Cash Flows

Year	2%	3%	4%	5%	6%	7%	8%	9%	10%	11%	12%	13%	14%	15%	16%	18%	20%	25%
									Percentage									
1	0.980	0.971	0.962	0.952	0.943	0.935	0.926	0.917	0.909	0.901	0.893	0.885	0.877	0.870	0.862	0.847	0.833	0.80
2	0.961	0.943	0.925	0.907	0.890	0.873	0.857	0.842	0.826	0.812	0.797	0.783	0.769	0.756	0.743	0.718	0.694	0.64
3	0.942	0.915	0.889	0.864	0.840	0.816	0.794	0.772	0.751	0.731	0.712	0.693	0.675	0.658	0.641	0.609	0.579	0.51
4	0.924	0.888	0.855	0.823	0.792	0.763	0.735	0.708	0.683	0.659	0.636	0.613	0.592	0.572	0.552	0.516	0.482	0.41
5	0.906	0.863	0.822	0.784	0.747	0.713	0.681	0.650	0.621	0.593	0.567	0.543	0.519	0.497	0.476	0.437	0.402	0.33
6	0.888	0.837	0.790	0.746	0.705	0.666	0.630	0.596	0.564	0.535	0.507	0.480	0.456	0.432	0.410	0.370	0.335	0.26
7	0.871	0.813	0.760	0.711	0.665	0.623	0.583	0.547	0.513	0.482	0.452	0.425	0.400	0.376	0.354	0.314	0.279	0.21
8	0.853	0.789	0.731	0.677	0.627	0.582	0.540	0.502	0.467	0.434	0.404	0.376	0.351	0.327	0.305	0.266	0.233	0.17
9	0.837	0.766	0.703	0.645	0.592	0.544	0.500	0.460	0.424	0.391	0.361	0.333	0.308	0.284	0.263	0.225	0.194	0.13
10	0.820	0.744	0.676	0.614	0.558	0.508	0.463	0.422	0.386	0.352	0.322	0.295	0.270	0.247	0.227	0.191	0.162	0.11
11	0.804	0.722	0.650	0.585	0.527	0.475	0.429	0.388	0.350	0.317	0.287	0.261	0.237	0.215	0.195	0.162	0.135	0.09
12	0.788	0.701	0.625	0.557	0.497	0.444	0.397	0.356	0.319	0.286	0.257	0.231	0.208	0.187	0.168	0.137	0.112	0.07
13	0.773	0.681	0.601	0.530	0.469	0.415	0.368	0.326	0.290	0.258	0.229	0.204	0.182	0.163	0.145	0.116	0.093	0.06
14	0.758	0.661	0.577	0.505	0.442	0.388	0.340	0.299	0.263	0.232	0.205	0.181	0.160	0.141	0.125	0.098	0.078	0.04
15	0.743	0.642	0.555	0.481	0.417	0.362	0.315	0.275	0.239	0.209	0.183	0.160	0.140	0.123	0.108	0.084	0.065	0.04
20	0.673	0.554	0.456	0.377	0.312	0.258	0.215	0.178	0.149	0.124	0.104	0.087	0.073	0.061	0.051	0.037	0.026	0.01
25	0.610	0.478	0.375	0.295	0.233	0.184	0.146	0.116	0.092	0.074	0.059	0.047	0.038	0.030	0.024	0.016	0.010	.004
30	0.552	0.412	0.308	0.231	0.174	0.131	0.099	0.075	0.057	0.044	0.033	0.026	0.020	0.015	0.012	0.007	0.004	.001

Example: The Present Value of £2,000 received 10 years from now, at 8 per cent discount rate of interest = 2,000 x 0.463 = £926.

Conversely, £926 invested now, at 8 per cent compound interest, will be worth £2,000 in 10 years' time.

ANNUITY / DISCOUNTING TABLE B

Discount Factors for Calculating the Present Value of Future Annuity (i.e. Constant Annual Cash Flow) Receivable in Year 1 to n inclusive.

Year	2%	3%	4%	5%	6%	7%	8%	9%	10%	11%	12%	13%	14%	15%	16%	18%	20%	25%
									Percentage									
1	0.980	0.971	0.962	0.952	0.943	0.935	0.926	0.917	0.909	0.901	0.893	0.885	0.877	0.870	0.862	0.847	0.833	0.80
2	1.942	1.913	1.886	1.859	1.833	1.808	1.783	1.759	1.736	1.713	1.690	1.668	1.647	1.626	1.605	1.566	1.528	1.44
3	2.884	2.829	2.775	2.723	2.673	2.624	2.577	2.531	2.487	2.444	2.402	2.361	2.322	2.283	2.246	2.174	2.106	1.95
4	3.808	3.717	3.630	3.546	3.465	3.387	3.312	3.240	3.170	3.102	3.037	2.974	2.914	2.855	2.798	2.690	2.589	2.36
5	4.713	4.580	4.452	4.329	4.212	4.100	3.993	3.890	3.791	3.696	3.605	3.517	3.433	3.352	3.274	3.127	2.991	2.69
6	5.601	5.417	5.242	5.076	4.917	4.767	4.623	4.486	4.355	4.231	4.111	3.998	3.889	3.784	3.685	3.498	3.326	2.95
7	6.472	6.230	6.002	5.786	5.582	5.389	5.206	5.033	4.868	4.712	4.564	4.423	4.288	4.160	4.039	3.812	3.605	3.16
8	7.325	7.020	6.733	6.463	6.210	5.971	5.747	5.535	5.335	5.146	4.968	4.799	4.639	4.487	4.344	4.078	3.837	3.33
9	8.162	7.786	7.435	7.108	6.802	6.515	6.247	5.995	5.759	5.537	5.328	5.132	4.946	4.772	4.607	4.303	4.031	3.46
10	8.983	8.530	8.111	7.722	7.360	7.024	6.710	6.418	6.145	5.889	5.650	5.426	5.216	5.019	4.833	4.494	4.192	3.57
11	9.787	9.253	8.760	8.306	7.887	7.499	7.139	6.805	6.495	6.207	5.938	5.687	5.453	5.234	5.029	4.656	4.327	3.66
12	10.58	9.954	9.385	8.863	8.384	7.943	7.536	7.161	6.814	6.492	6.194	5.918	5.660	5.421	5.197	4.793	4.439	3.73
13	11.35	10.635	9.986	9.394	8.853	8.358	7.904	7.487	7.103	6.750	6.424	6.122	5.842	5.583	5.342	4.910	4.533	3.78
14	12.11	11.296	10.563	9.899	9.295	8.745	8.244	7.786	7.367	6.982	6.628	6.302	6.002	5.724	5.468	5.008	4.611	3.82
15	12.85	11.938	11.118	10.380	9.712	9.108	8.559	8.061	7.606	7.191	6.811	6.462	6.142	5.847	5.575	5.092	4.675	3.86
20	16.35	14.877	13.590	12.462	11.470	10.594	9.818	9.129	8.514	7.963	7.469	7.025	6.623	6.259	5.929	5.353	4.870	3.95
25	19.52	17.413	15.662	14.094	12.783	11.654	10.675	9.823	9.077	8.422	7.843	7.330	6.873	6.464	6.097	5.467	4.948	3.99
30	22.40	19.600	17.292	15.372	13.765	12.409	11.258	10.274	9.427	8.694	8.055	7.496	7.003	6.566	6.177	5.517	4.979	4.00

Example: The Present Value of £500 a year for the next 10 years, at 12 per cent discount rate of interest = 500 x 5.650 = £2,825. This is the same answer that would be obtained by multiplying 500 by each discount factor (at 12 per cent) in Table A for each year from 1 to 10, and adding together the ten resulting figures.

To obtain the Discounted Yield of a constant annual net cash flow, divide this into the original investment and look up the resulting figure in the table above, against the number of years. Example: an investment of £1,000 is estimated to produce £80 a year additional profit over 10 years (before charging interest). Add £100 depreciation a year = £180 annual net cash flow. 1000 /180 = 5.56. This equals just over 12 per cent (the 10 years /12 per cent figure being 5.650).

257

COMPOUNDING TABLE

The Future Money Value of £1 after n Years with no additional payments made

Rate of Interest

Year	2%	3%	4%	5%	6%	7%	8%	9%	10%	11%	12%	13%	14%	15%	16%	18%	20%	25%
1	1.02	1.03	1.04	1.05	1.06	1.07	1.08	1.09	1.10	1.11	1.12	1.13	1.14	1.15	1.16	1.18	1.20	1.25
2	1.04	1.06	1.08	1.10	1.12	1.14	1.17	1.19	1.21	1.23	1.25	1.28	1.30	1.32	1.35	1.39	1.44	1.56
3	1.06	1.09	1.12	1.16	1.19	1.23	1.26	1.30	1.33	1.37	1.40	1.44	1.48	1.52	1.56	1.64	1.73	1.95
4	1.08	1.13	1.17	1.22	1.26	1.31	1.36	1.41	1.46	1.52	1.57	1.63	1.69	1.75	1.81	1.94	2.07	2.44
5	1.10	1.16	1.22	1.28	1.34	1.40	1.47	1.54	1.61	1.69	1.76	1.84	1.93	2.01	2.10	2.29	2.49	3.05
6	1.13	1.19	1.27	1.34	1.42	1.50	1.59	1.68	1.77	1.87	1.97	2.08	2.19	2.31	2.44	2.70	2.99	3.81
7	1.15	1.23	1.32	1.41	1.50	1.61	1.71	1.83	1.95	2.08	2.21	2.35	2.50	2.66	2.83	3.19	3.58	4.77
8	1.17	1.27	1.37	1.48	1.59	1.72	1.85	1.99	2.14	2.30	2.48	2.66	2.85	3.06	3.28	3.76	4.30	5.96
9	1.20	1.30	1.42	1.55	1.69	1.84	2.00	2.17	2.36	2.56	2.77	3.00	3.25	3.52	3.80	4.44	5.16	7.45
10	1.22	1.34	1.48	1.63	1.79	1.97	2.16	2.37	2.59	2.84	3.11	3.39	3.71	4.05	4.41	5.23	6.19	9.31
11	1.24	1.38	1.54	1.71	1.90	2.10	2.33	2.58	2.85	3.15	3.48	3.84	4.23	4.65	5.12	6.18	7.43	11.64
12	1.27	1.43	1.60	1.80	2.01	2.25	2.52	2.81	3.14	3.50	3.90	4.33	4.82	5.35	5.94	7.29	8.92	14.55
13	1.29	1.47	1.67	1.89	2.13	2.41	2.72	3.07	3.45	3.88	4.36	4.90	5.49	6.15	6.89	8.60	10.70	18.19
14	1.32	1.51	1.73	1.98	2.26	2.58	2.94	3.34	3.80	4.31	4.89	5.53	6.26	7.08	7.99	10.15	12.84	22.74
15	1.35	1.56	1.80	2.08	2.40	2.76	3.17	3.64	4.18	4.78	5.47	6.25	7.14	8.14	9.27	11.97	15.41	28.42
20	1.49	1.81	2.19	2.65	3.21	3.87	4.66	5.60	6.73	8.06	9.65	11.52	13.74	16.37	19.46	27.39	38.34	86.74
25	1.64	2.09	2.67	3.39	4.29	5.43	6.85	8.62	10.83	13.59	17.00	21.23	26.46	32.92	40.87	62.67	95.40	264.7
30	1.81	2.43	3.24	4.32	5.74	7.61	10.06	13.27	17.45	22.89	29.96	39.12	50.95	66.21	85.85	143.4	237.4	807.8

COMPOUNDING TABLE B

The Future Money Value of £1 after n Years

Year									Rate of Interest									
	2%	3%	4%	5%	6%	7%	8%	9%	10%	11%	12%	13%	14%	15%	16%	18%	20%	25%
1	1.02	1.03	1.04	1.05	1.06	1.07	1.08	1.09	1.10	1.11	1.12	1.13	1.14	1.15	1.16	1.18	1.20	1.25
2	2.06	2.09	2.12	2.15	2.18	2.21	2.25	2.28	2.31	2.34	2.37	2.41	2.44	2.47	2.51	2.57	2.64	2.81
3	3.12	3.18	3.25	3.31	3.37	3.44	3.51	3.57	3.64	3.71	3.78	3.85	3.92	3.99	4.07	4.22	4.37	4.77
4	4.20	4.31	4.42	4.53	4.64	4.75	4.87	4.98	5.11	5.23	5.35	5.48	5.61	5.74	5.88	6.15	6.44	7.21
5	5.31	5.47	5.63	5.80	5.98	6.15	6.34	6.52	6.72	6.91	7.12	7.32	7.54	7.75	7.98	8.44	8.93	10.3
6	6.43	6.66	6.90	7.14	7.39	7.65	7.92	8.20	8.49	8.78	9.09	9.40	9.73	10.07	10.41	11.1	11.92	14.1
7	7.58	7.89	8.21	8.55	8.90	9.26	9.64	10.03	10.44	10.86	11.30	11.76	12.23	12.73	13.24	14.3	15.50	18.8
8	8.75	9.16	9.58	10.03	10.49	10.98	11.49	12.02	12.58	13.16	13.78	14.42	15.09	15.79	16.52	18.1	19.80	24.8
9	9.95	10.46	11.01	11.58	12.18	12.82	13.49	14.19	14.94	15.72	16.55	17.42	18.34	19.30	20.32	22.5	24.96	32.3
10	11.17	11.81	12.49	13.21	13.97	14.78	15.65	16.56	17.53	18.56	19.65	20.81	22.04	23.35	24.73	27.8	31.15	41.6
11	12.41	13.19	14.03	14.92	15.87	16.89	17.98	19.14	20.38	21.71	23.13	24.65	26.27	28.00	29.85	33.9	38.58	53.2
12	13.68	14.62	15.63	16.71	17.88	19.14	20.50	21.95	23.52	25.21	27.03	28.98	31.09	33.35	35.79	41.2	47.50	67.8
13	14.97	16.09	17.29	18.60	20.02	21.55	23.21	25.02	26.97	29.09	31.39	33.88	36.58	39.50	42.67	49.9	58.20	86.0
14	16.29	17.60	19.02	20.58	22.28	24.13	26.15	28.36	30.77	33.41	36.28	39.42	42.84	46.58	50.66	60.0	71.04	109
15	17.64	19.16	20.82	22.66	24.67	26.89	29.32	32.00	34.95	38.19	41.75	45.67	49.98	54.72	59.93	71.9	86.44	137
20	24.78	27.68	30.97	34.72	38.99	43.87	49.42	55.76	63.00	71.27	80.70	91.47	103.8	117.8	133.8	173	224.0	429
25	32.67	37.55	43.31	50.11	58.16	67.68	78.95	92.32	108.2	127.0	149.3	175.8	207.3	244.7	289.1	404	566.4	1318
30	41.38	49.00	58.33	69.76	83.80	101.1	122.3	148.6	180.9	220.9	270.3	331.3	406.7	500.0	615.2	933	1418	4034

* Equal payments made at the beginning of each year.

AMORTISATION TABLE

Annual Charge to write off £1,000

Write-off Period	Rate of Interest																
	2	3	4	5	6	7	8	9	10	11	12	13	14	15	16	18	20
5 years	212	218	225	231	237	244	250	257	264	271	277	284	291	298	305	320	334
6	179	185	191	197	203	210	216	223	230	236	243	250	257	264	271	286	301
7	155	161	167	173	179	186	192	199	205	212	219	226	233	240	248	262	277
8	137	142	149	155	161	167	174	181	187	194	201	208	216	223	230	245	261
9	123	128	134	141	147	153	160	167	174	181	188	195	202	210	217	232	248
10	111	117	123	130	136	142	149	156	163	170	177	184	192	199	207	223	239
11	102	108	114	120	127	133	140	147	154	161	168	176	183	191	199	215	231
12	95	100	107	113	119	125	133	140	147	154	161	169	177	184	192	209	225
13	88	94	100	106	113	120	127	134	141	148	156	163	171	179	187	204	221
14	83	89	95	101	108	114	121	128	136	143	151	159	167	175	183	200	217
15	78	84	90	96	103	110	117	124	131	139	147	155	163	171	179	196	214
16	74	80	86	92	99	106	113	120	128	136	143	151	160	168	176	194	211
17	70	76	82	89	95	102	110	117	125	132	140	149	157	165	174	191	209
18	67	73	79	86	92	99	107	114	122	130	138	146	155	163	172	190	208
20	61	67	74	80	87	94	102	110	117	126	134	142	151	160	169	187	205
25	51	57	64	71	78	86	94	102	110	119	127	136	145	155	164	183	202
30	45	51	58	65	73	81	89	97	106	115	124	133	143	152	162	181	201
40	37	43	51	58	66	75	84	93	102	112	122	131	141	151	160	180	200

Example: £30,000 is borrowed to erect a building. The annual charge to service interest and capital repayment on the £30,000, repayable over 10 years at 12%, is 30 x £177 = £5,310. Where the write-off period of the building (10 years) is equal to the repayment period of the loan, then the average annual depreciation plus interest will equal £5,310.

The proportion of the total annual charge representing the average amount of capital repaid per annum can be readily determined by dividing the sum borrowed by the number of years of the loan: (in the above example this is £30,000 ÷ 10 = £3,000/year). The remainder is clearly the average amount of interest paid per annum: (in the above example, £5,310 — £3,000 = £2,310/year). The year to year variations between the two items (i.e. capital repaid and interest) are shown in the Mortgage Repayment Data tables (2 pages further on) , which demonstrate the way the capital repayment part increases and the interest part decreases over time.

SINKING FUND TABLE

The sum required to be set aside at the end of each year to make £1,000

Rate of Interest

No. of Years	2	3	4	5	6	7	8	9	10	11	12	13	14	15	16	18	20
5	192	188	185	181	177	174	170	167	164	161	157	154	151	148	145	140	134
6	159	155	151	147	143	140	136	133	130	126	123	120	117	114	111	106	101
7	135	131	127	123	119	116	112	109	105	102	99	96	93	90	88	82	77
8	117	112	109	105	101	97	94	91	87	84	81	78	76	73	70	65	61
9	103	98	94	91	87	83	80	77	74	71	68	65	62	60	57	52	48
10	91	87	83	80	76	72	69	66	63	60	57	54	52	49	47	43	39
11	82	78	74	70	67	63	60	57	54	51	48	46	43	41	39	35	31
12	75	70	67	63	59	56	53	50	47	44	41	39	37	34	32	29	25
13	68	64	60	56	53	50	47	44	41	38	36	33	31	29	27	24	21
14	63	59	55	51	48	44	41	38	36	33	31	29	27	25	23	20	17
15	58	54	50	46	43	40	37	34	31	29	27	25	23	21	19	16	14
16	54	50	46	42	39	36	33	30	28	26	23	21	20	18	16	14	11
17	50	46	42	39	35	32	30	27	25	22	20	19	17	15	14	11	9
18	47	43	39	36	32	29	27	24	22	20	18	16	15	13	12	10	8
19	44	40	36	33	30	27	24	22	20	18	16	14	13	11	10	8	6
20	41	37	34	30	27	24	22	20	17	16	14	12	11	10	9	7	5
25	31	27	24	21	18	16	14	12	10	9	7	6	5	5	4	3	2
30	25	21	18	15	13	11	9	7	6	5	4	3	3	2	2	1	1
40	17	13	11	8	6	5	4	3	2	2	1	1	1	1	—	—	—

MORTGAGE REPAYMENT DATA

Items per £1000 invested; where I = Interest, P = Principal repaid, L = Loan outstanding

Loan of	3%			4%			5%			6%			8%			10%		
5 years	I	P	L	I	P	L	I	P	L	I	P	L	I	P	L	I	P	L
1	30	188	812	40	185	815	50	181	819	60	177	823	80	170	830	100	164	836
2	24	194	618	33	192	623	41	190	629	49	188	635	66	184	645	84	180	656
3	19	200	418	25	200	424	31	200	424	38	199	435	52	199	447	66	198	458
4	13	206	212	17	208	216	21	210	220	26	211	224	36	215	232	46	218	240
5	6	212	0	9	216	0	11	220	0	13	224	0	19	232	0	24	240	0
10 years																		
1	30	87	913	40	83	917	50	80	920	60	76	924	80	69	931	100	63	939
2	27	90	823	37	87	830	46	83	837	55	80	844	75	75	856	94	69	868
3	25	93	730	33	90	740	42	88	749	51	85	758	69	81	776	87	76	792
4	22	95	635	30	94	646	37	92	657	46	90	668	62	87	689	79	84	709
5	19	98	537	26	97	549	33	97	561	40	96	572	55	94	595	71	92	617
6	16	101	436	22	101	448	28	101	459	34	102	471	48	101	494	62	101	516
7	13	104	332	18	105	342	23	107	353	28	108	363	39	110	384	52	111	405
8	10	107	224	14	110	233	18	112	241	22	114	249	31	118	266	40	122	282
9	7	111	114	9	114	119	12	117	123	15	121	128	21	128	138	28	134	148
10	3	114	0	5	119	0	6	123	0	8	128	0	11	138	0	15	148	0

MORTGAGE REPAYMENT DATA (CONTINUED)

Loan of	3%			4%			5%			6%			8%			10%		
	I	P	L	I	P	L	I	P	L	I	P	L	I	P	L	I	P	L
20 years																		
1	30	37	963	40	34	966	50	30	970	60	27	973	80	22	978	100	17	983
5	25	42	802	34	39	818	43	37	833	53	34	847	72	30	872	92	26	893
10	19	49	573	26	48	597	33	47	620	41	46	642	58	44	683	76	41	722
15	11	56	308	15	58	328	20	60	347	26	61	367	38	64	407	51	66	445
20	2	65	0	3	71	0	4	76	0	5	82	0	8	94	0	11	107	0
25 years																		
1	30	27	973	40	24	976	50	21	979	60	18	982	80	14	986	100	10	990
5	27	31	854	36	28	870	45	25	884	55	23	897	75	19	920	95	15	938
10	22	36	686	30	34	712	38	33	736	47	31	760	66	27	802	86	24	838
15	16	41	490	22	42	519	29	41	548	37	41	576	54	40	629	72	39	677
20	9	48	263	13	51	285	18	53	307	23	55	330	35	59	374	48	62	418
25	2	56	0	2	62	0	3	68	0	4	74	0	7	87	0	10	100	0

MORTGAGE REPAYMENT DATA (CONTINUED)

Loan through	4%			5%			6%			8%			10%			12%		
	I	P	L	I	P	L	I	P	L	I	P	L	I	P	L	I	P	L
30 years																		
1	40	18	982	50	15	985	60	13	987	80	9	991	100	6	994	120	4	996
5	37	21	903	47	18	917	57	16	929	77	12	948	97	9	963	118	7	974
10	32	25	786	42	23	811	51	21	833	71	18	872	92	14	903	113	11	927
15	27	31	643	35	30	675	44	29	706	63	26	760	83	23	807	104	20	846
20	20	38	469	27	38	502	34	38	535	51	38	596	69	37	652	88	36	701
25	12	46	257	17	49	282	21	51	306	33	56	355	46	60	402	61	63	448
30	2	56	0	3	62	0	4	69	0	7	82	0	10	96	0	13	111	0
40 years																		
1	40	11	989	50	8	992	60	6	994	80	4	996	100	2	998	120	1	999
5	38	12	943	48	10	954	58	8	964	79	5	977	99	3	986	119	2	992
10	36	15	874	45	13	896	56	11	915	76	8	944	97	5	964	118	4	977
15	32	18	789	42	16	821	52	15	850	73	11	895	94	9	928	115	6	951
20	28	22	687	37	21	726	47	20	762	67	17	823	88	14	871	110	11	906
25	24	27	562	32	27	605	40	26	645	59	24	718	80	22	778	102	20	826
30	18	33	410	24	34	450	31	35	489	48	36	563	66	36	628	86	35	685
35	11	40	225	15	43	252	20	47	280	31	53	335	45	58	388	60	61	437
40	2	49	0	3	56	0	4	63	0	6	78	0	9	93	0	13	108	0

Note—All figures rounded to nearest £.

6.   FARM RECORDS

The following records should be kept for management purposes:

BASIC WHOLE FARM FINANCIAL POSITION

1. Cash Analysis Book, fully detailed.

2. Petty Cash Book.

3. Annual Valuation, including physical quantities of

   i.   Harvested crops in store

   ii. Livestock (breeding and fattening) at (near) market value, less any variable costs yet to be borne.

   iii. Fertilisers, seeds, sprays, casual labour or contract work applied to growing crops should be recorded, but "cultivations" and manure residues can be ignored for management purposes.

   iv. Fertiliser, seed, sprays and other sundry direct items in store,

4. Debtors and creditors at the end of the financial year.

OTHER FINANCIAL AND PHYSICAL RECORDS

5. Output (quantities and value) of each crop and livestock enterprise for the "harvest year" (or production cycle). It may be possible to get information of sales from a fully detailed cash analysis book (although, for crops, the financial year figures will then have to be allocated between crops from the current harvest and those from the harvest in the previous financial year, in order to check on the accuracy of the opening valuation of crops in store; this is particularly a problem with Michaelmas ending accounts). The following records of internal transfers and consumption will also be required:

   (a) Numbers and market value of livestock transferred from one livestock category to another, e.g. dairy calves to dairy followers or beef enterprise, or dairy heifers to dairy enterprise.

   (b) Quantity and market value of cereals fed on farm and used for seed.

   (c) Quantity and market value of milk and other produce consumed by the farmer or his employees, used on the farm (e.g. milk fed to calves), or sold direct.

6. A monthly record of livestock numbers; preferably reconciled with the previous month according to births, purchases, deaths, sales and transfers.

7. Costs and quantities of concentrate feed to each category of livestock, including home-grown cereals fed on the farm.

8. Allocation of costs of seed, fertiliser, sprays, casual labour and contract work specific to an enterprise. This is in order to calculate gross margins, where required.

9. Breeding record for cows, including bulling dates, date(s) served, type of bull used, pregnancy testing, estimated calving date, actual calving date, and date when dried off.

10. For each crop, total output and yield per hectare, in both quantity and value. Include each field where the crop has been grown and its approximate yield, where this can be satisfactorily obtained.

11. For each field, keep one page to cover a period of say, ten years. Record on this, each year, crop grown, variety sown, fertiliser used, sprays used, date sown, date(s) harvested, approximate yield (if obtainable), and any other special notes that you feel may have significance for the future.

12. A rotation record. On a single page, if possible, list each field down the side and say, ten years along the top. Colour each field-year space according to the crop grown, e.g. barley yellow, potatoes red, etc.

13. It is important to note that other farm records are required for legislative and cross compliance purposes including:

      i. Livestock movements, identification, flock and herd records etc.

      ii. Nitrate Vulnerable Zone (NVZ) records and calculations including livestock loadings, manure storage, fertiliser plans and usage etc.

      iii. Pesticide application and storage records, risk assessments

      iv. Farm waste storage and disposal records and necessary exemptions / permits / transfer certificates

      v. Integrated Pollution and Prevention Controls (IPPC) records (for pig and poultry units)

      vi. Soil Protection reviews and risk assessments

      vii. Financial (HMRC) records including VAT, PAYE, NI etc.

IX.   MISCELLANEOUS DATA

1.   CONSERVATION COSTS

Note: Costs vary widely, depending on geographical location and the type and size of the job. Markets for such services can be highly localised, sparse in some areas, competitive in others.

Hedges

Hedge Cutting. Flailing £34.80/hour to £48/hour for sawblade cutting. Average of 3 miles per day (refer also to contracting charges on page 196).

Hedge Laying (Making hedges stock proof and rejuvenated by selective cutting and positioning). Depends on hedge thickness (single or double), amount of timber to clear, access to hedge, style of hedge and varieties in hedge.   Manual hedge laying approximately 20m/day at £15.00/metre (contract charge).

Hedge Planting. Single row = 3-4 plants per metre, double row 6 plants per metre

- Plants average £52p - £1.30 each (mixed species); spiral guards 38p; canes 14p.

- *As per 'Fencing' below*

- Labour: Planting up to £2.75-£3.75/metre, professional contractor up to 100-150 metres/day. Preferably October/March.

- Overall from   £3.20/metre; unfenced, single width, self-planted;
    to   £28.50/metre; double width & double rabbit fenced, contract planted.

Hedge Coppicing. By hand: 2 men and a chain saw, £6.00-7.00 per metre plus burning debris. Contractor: tractor mounted saw, driver and 2 men, 12.5 metres per hour, £42.00/hour.

Devon Hedges. Maintenance, flailing annually and occasional mechanical recasting banks when eroded. Flailing costs as above and recasting with Backhoe excavator £26.00/hr.

Fencing

Fencing (labour and materials): stock proof post and 4-barb £5.00/metre, rabbit proof (dug in) up to £6.90/metre (per side). Post and 3 rails £13.75/metre

Dry Stone Walls

Dry Stone Walling. This is one of the most variable costs depending on stone type, stone grading availability, structure, vehicular access to site and local competition (people pay more for private walls in gardens than fields). As a guide, the following figures apply: Cost of graded stone approximately £145/tonne, varying regionally and depending on local stone, type and availability. Cost of wall building is (normally quoted per square meter but grants awarded per linear meter) from as low as £40 (highlands) to £200 (Cotswolds) per square metre. Most are around £87-100/m^2. Partial grants might be available in some areas e.g. within National Parks.

Trees

Amenity tree planting; (half acre block or less)

- Transplants average £1.10; shelter plus stake and tie £1.35; stake 57p; whip 83p. rabbit spiral guard 37p; netlon guard 55p; cane 16p.
- Trees per man day: farmer 200, contractor 400; (large-scale, 33 man days/ha). Optimal time November to April.

Shelter Belts; Per 100 metre length

- 100 large species (oak, lime, etc.) £56; 66 medium species (cherry, birch, etc.) £48; 100 shrubs, £39;
- 166 tree stakes, shelters and ties, £295;

  (site preparation, weed control, labour and fencing extra)

Woodland Establishment.

- Conifers £230/1,000 (2m spacing), broadleaves £450/1000 (3m spacing).
- To supply and plant transplants; conifer £3.30/tree, oak or beech £4.00-£4.50 each, (2-3ft tall) in tubes dependent on shelter size and species.
- Rabbit fencing £6.90/metre (dug in), deer fencing £8.70/metre, deer and rabbit fencing £10.70/metre
- Contract planting labour: Conifers at 2m £1,640/ha; broadleaves at 3m £1,125/ha; forest transplants £315/1,070.

Forestry, General.

- 2-man tree surgery team £560/day
- Contract labour: chain sawing £25/hr,
- brush cutting £15.30/hr,
- extracting timber/pulp £5.40-£12.25/tonne,
- chemical spot weeding 11p-15p/tree, or £326/hectare
- Rhododendron control range from £700-£2,650/hectare dependant on stem diameter (largest over 7cm) and accessibility.

Pollarding and Tree Surgery.

- Pollard: £100/mature tree; Pollarding: 2 or 3 trees/day. Pollard every 20-40 years.
- Tree surgery from £185/tree. Dependant on size and number. Best in winter.

Ponds and Ditches

Pond Construction. Butyl lining (0.75mm) £6.10/m^2; other linings up to £4.30/m^2. Contract labour: 150 Komatsu £32/hr.; bulldozer D6 LGP £51/hr, 13t 360° excavator £44/hr (excluding haulage), Flail-mowers from £19.40/hr (machine only). Autumn (dry ground conditions).

Pond Maintenance. Hymac £45/hr.; Backhoe £24.50/hr. 100 m^2/day (contractor). Timing: probably winter; time depends on ground condition and species whose life cycles may be disturbed. Every 15 to 50 years.

Ditch Maintenance. Backhoe excavator £24.50/hr; 13t 360° excavator £44/hr (excluding haulage), labour £13.00/hr. preferably in winter. Every 3 to 7 years on rotation.

Grassland

Permanent Grass Margins at Field Edges. To provide wildlife benefits and help control pernicious weeds, reducing herbicides at the field edge. (A sterile strip provides virtually no wildlife benefit and the initial establishment costs may be offset by savings in maintenance costs in future years.)

Seed costs per 100 metres of seeds as follows.

- 2m grass margins, £2.80-£3.10;

- 6m grass margins, £8.60-£9.30;

- beetle banks, £6.90 (6m wide) (£4.60/kg, 25kg/ha).

Establishment of Wildlife Grassland Meadow. £190-300/ha for ground preparation, depending on weed burden and total area, more for heavy land or exceptional weed burden. Seed costs very variable, but as a guide:

- Native Perennial wild flowers and grasses, £17.00/kg, 25kg/ha = £425/ha

- Pollen and Nectar mix for bumble bees and butterflies £6.00/kg, 20kg/ha = £120/ha

- Bird Seed sward £5.00/kg, 12kg/ha = £60/ha for single year crop, £4.00/kg, 50kg/ha = £200 for longer sward.

- Single species native grass seeds vary from £3.40/kg (e.g. Creeping Red Fescue) to £60/kg (Sweet Vernal).

- Single species native perennial wild flower seeds vary from £57/kg (Ribwort Plantain) to £490/kg (Cowslip)

- Buffer strip grass margin mix for cross compliance, ELS and HLS (possibly CSS) compliance, £4.00/kg drilled at 25kg/ha = £100/ha. Costs of ground preparation and drilling are usually higher than the seed.

Acknowledgement: Thanks to Cotswold Seeds, 0800 252 211 and the Forestry Commission http://www.forestry.gov.uk/forestresearch

2.   GRASS, FORAGE AND ENVIRONMENTAL SEEDS

Seed Prices (for 2016) and Seed Rates

Crop	Price £/Kg	Seed Rate Kg/Ha	Cost £/Ha
Grass Leys			
1 year Westerwolds	£2.40	35	84
2 year leys	£2.70	35	95
3-4 year leys	£3.70	35	130
4-6 year leys	£3.95	35	138
Long-term ley	£4.40	37.5	165
Permanent Grass	£4.75	32.5	155
Drought Resistant	£6.00	32.5	195
Mixed and Clover Leys			
White Clover ley	£4.00	30	120
Red Clover ley	£3.90 – 5.20	30	117 - 145
Timothy/M. Fescue ley	£4.68	31	145
Fodder Crops			
Fodder Kale	£9.80-13.50	5	49-68
Swedes	£43	Precision drill 0.7	30
		seed drill 4.00	172
Stubble Turnips	£3.80	3.75 kg drilled,	14.25
		5.0 kg broadcast	19
Maincrop Turnips	£11.25	3.75 kg drilled,	42
		5.0 kg broadcast	56
Rape	£2.80	10	28
Rape/Kale hybrid	£8.00	7.50	60
Mustard	£2.00	20	40
Rape and Turnip mix	£5.00/kg mix	1.25 kg rape	
		3.75 kg turnips	18
Kale, Swede & Turnips	£14.50/kg mix	1.5 kg kale,	
		0.5 kg swede	
		1.75 kg turnips	56
Cover Mixes, Environmental and Equine			
Game Cover mixture	£4.08	25	106
Game Maize	£3.50	27.5	98
Forage Maize: Silage			175
Vetch	£1.60	75	120
Quinoa & Kale mix	£10.0	7.5	75
Field Corner mixture	£12.70	25	317
Horse grazing	£5.70	35	200
Gallop mixture	£4.00	125	500

Crop	Price £/Kg	Seed Rate Kg/Ha	Cost £/Ha
Individual Varieties			
Westerwold Ryegrass	£2.40	35	84
Italian Ryegrass	£2.50	35	88
Perennial Ryegrass	£3.90	25 to 40	97 - 156
Hybrid Ryegrass	£3.60	35	125
Cocksfoot	£4.20	20 to 25	84 - 105
Red Clover ley	£8.20	15	123
White Clover ley	£8.90	7	62
Timothy	£4.80		
Meadow Fescue	£6.20		
Sweet Vernal	£60.00		
Reed Canary Grass	£18.00	7.5	135
Lucerne	£7.40 (inoculated)	20	148
Sainfoin	£2.65	87	232
Millet	£2.40	25	60
Sunflower	£4.40	25	110
Sorghum	£3.70	20	72

Acknowledgement: Particular thanks to - Cotswold Seeds 0800 252 211

3.   FERTILISER PRICES

Compounds	Analysis			Price Per Tonne
	N	**P_2O_5**	**K_2O**	**£**
	0	26	26	303
	0	24	24	281
	0	18	36	293
	0	20	30	280
	0	30	15	282
	0	30	20	304
	5	24	24	316
	8	24	24	337
	10	26	26	373
	11	15	20	278
	13	13	20	278
	15	15	20	306
	16	16	16	302
	22	4	14	253
	20	10	10	262
	25	5	5	241
	26	0	15	258

Straights	Price per tonne £
Ammonium Nitrate: UK (34.5% N)	240
Ammonium Nitrate: Imported (34.5% N)	230
NS grade: UK (27% N, 30% SO_3)	232
Sulphate of Ammonia (21% N, 60% SO_3)	235
Urea (46% N.): granular/ prills	320
Liquid Nitrogen (26% N, 5% SO_3)	188
Triple Superphosphate (TSP) (46% P_2O_5)	315
DAP (18/46/0)	401
Muriate of Potash (MOP) (60% K_2O)	265

Average price (p) per kg:			
	N :	69.6	(UK AN)
	P_2O_5 :	68.5	(TSP)
	K_2O :	44.2	(MOP)

The prices above are for fertiliser delivered in 600kg bags; delivery in bulk averages £7.00/tonne less; collection of bags by farmers £8/tonne less. They are based on forward prices in October 2015 and spring 2016; they vary according to area and bargaining power. They assume delivery in 25-27 tonne loads; add approximately £3.70/tonne for 10 tonne loads, £8.50 for 6-9 tonne loads, £20 for 4-5 tonne loads.

4. MANURE VALUE OF SLURRY

Nutrient Values of Common Farm Yard Manure Types

	Dry Matter %	(kg N/t)		(kg P$_2$O$_5$/t)		(kg K$_2$O/t)	
		Total N	Available N	Total P	Available P	Total K	Available K
Cattle FYM *	25	6.0	0.6	3.2	1.9	8.0	7.2
Pig FYM	25	7.0	1.0	6.0	3.6	8.0	7.2
Sheep FYM	25	7.0	0.7	3.2	1.9	8.0	7.2
Duck FYM	25	6.5	1.0	5.5	3.3	7.5	6.8
Horse FYM	30	7.0	N/a	5.0	3.0	6.0	5.4
Layer Hen	28	6.4		2.0		4.0	

*For manure stored for 3 months or more. FYM = Farmyard Manure

Note: these nutrient contents are for guidance only and will vary between different livestock systems and storage methods. Analysis should be performed to understand the specific values of manure.

Manure Output per Head during the Housing Period

	Undiluted Excreta t or m^3	Total Kg		
		N	P$_2$O$_5$	K$_2$O
1 dairy cow ~ *6,000 to 9,000 litres milk yield*	11.6	60	26	46
1 beef cow ~ *>500 kg*	8.2	41	15.5	33
1 finishing pig ~ *per place* ~ 86% *occupancy*	1.6	10.6	5.6	5.6
1,000 broiler hens ~ *per hen place* ~ 85% *occupancy*	19	330	220	340

Note: These figures should not be used for calculating NVZ compliance as they only allow for the time spent in the buildings and therefore exclude manure deposited in fields during grazing. Refer to the DEFRA NVZ guidance booklets for NVZ calculation methodology and annual manure output tables.

Lime

Prices average around £22 delivered and spread per tonne with an application rate of 6 tonnes per hectare per application, typically every 4 years, or 1.25 tonnes per hectare of arable land per year.

Lime price varies according to type of dressing, grade of mineral (such as particle size and consistency), location and ease of spreading. And could be as low as £2 per tonne ex quarry to £20 ex quarry. A short haul would cost about £5.50 and spreading approximately £4.50 per tonne, adding £10 to the ex-quarry cost.

Biosolids (Sewage Sludge)

Biosolids act as good soil conditioner and fertiliser to farmers, whilst providing the most environmentally favourable method for water companies to dispose of the sludge. Biosolids vary in nutritional composition depending on processing and location, but RB209 describes its content as follows:

Biosolid Key Composition

	Digested Cake	Thermally Dried Pellets	Lime Stabilised
Dry Matter	25%	95%	35%
Total Nitrogen *kg/t*	*11*	*40*	*8.5*
Total Phosphate (P2O5)	*18*	*75*	*26*
Total Potash	*0.6*	*2*	*0.8*
Available N *kg/t*	1.6	2	0.9
Available P$_2$O$_5$ *kg/t*	9	35	13
Available K$_2$O *kg/t*	0.5	1.8	0.7
Available SO$_3$ *kg/t*	6	23	8.5
Guideline Price £/t applied	£4.00	£35	£3.75

Nutrient data taken from Fertiliser Manual RB209 (2010)

Application rates vary according to terrain, soil analysis and plant need, but an application of 25 tonnes dry solids per hectare is the typical maximum rate. Thermally dried and lime stabilised cakes are far less common than digested cake. A biosolids Assurance Scheme coming into use in coming months is expected to make the product considerably more acceptable for use on land used to grow grains for high-value processing which has not been the case in many firms to now.

5.   AGROCHEMICAL COSTS

Only the names of the active ingredients are given below, with their principal use. These materials should only be applied in accordance with the manufacturers' recommendations.

Application rates vary and there are differences between the prices of various proprietary brands. The list is not intended to be exhaustive and there is no implied criticism of materials omitted.

The variation in costs per hectare is because of varying application rates rather than price variation between suppliers. It is priced on the purchase of chemical alone, i.e., not the agronomy service.

Crop	Function		Material	Cost £/ha per application
Cereals	Herbicides	General	Mecoprop-P	5.90-13.50
			Ioxynil+Bromoxynil	5.50-15.00
			Metsulfuron-methyl	17.60
			Mesosulfuron + Iodosulfuron	35.00
			Diflufenican	4.20 - 7.00
		Cleavers	Fluroxypyr	5.90 - 7.80
			Amidosulfuron	9.20 – 13.80
			Florasulam (Placeholder1)m + Fluroxypyr	12.40-18.60
		Wild Oats	Pinoxaden	20.00-52.00
		Wild Oats & Blackgrass	Clodinafop-propargyl	31.25
			Fenoxaprop-P-ethyl	20.00-30.00
			Flurasulam + Pyroxsulam	27.50
	Growth Regulator		Chlormequat	3.40
			2-chloroethylphosphonic acid	6.80-13.80
			2-chloroethylphosphonic acid + Mepiquat Chloride	11.50-23.00
			Trinexapac-ethyl	6.90-13.80
	Fungicides		Azoxystrobin	31.00
			Fenpropimorph	20.00-26.50
			Epoxiconazole	20.40
			Tebuconazole	10.20
			Prothioconazole	18.90-37.70
			Chlorothalonil	5.60
			Epoxiconazole & Boscalid	28.00
			Pyraclostrobin	34.00
			Prothioconazole & bixafen	33.60 - 41.80
			Epoxiconazole & Fluxapyroxad	30.50 – 38.20
			Epoxiconazole & isopyrazam	30.60 – 40.80
			Chlorothalonil & propiconazole	11.20 – 22.40

Crop	Function		Material	Cost £/ha per application
		Seed Dressing	Fuberidazole + Triadimenol	6.60-10.50
			Fuberidazole + Triadimenol + Imidacloprid	11.70-18.70
			Prothioconazole + Clothianidin	12.20-19.40
			Silthiofam	24.50-38.80
			Imidacloprid + Tebuconazole + Triazoxide	13.10-21.20
			Fluquinconazole	13.20 – 21.40
			Fludioxonil + Tefluthrin	13.30 - 22.40
			Triticonazole + Prochloraz	6.60 – 10.70
			Manganese	6.60 – 10.90
	Aphicide		Pirimicarb	9.45
			Chlorpyrifos	7.20-14.40
			Lambda-Cyhalothrin	3.70
	Slug Killer		Metaldehyde	8.50
			Ferric-Phosphate	20.00
Oilseed Rape	Herbicides		Propyzamide	27.30
			Metazachlor	22.50-37.50
			Clomazone	20.00
	Insecticide		Deltamethrin	4.90
			Pirimicarb	9.50-14.30
			Lambda-Cyhalothrin	5.50
	Fungicide		Iprodione + Thiophanate-methyl	26.50-40.00
			Tebuconazole	5.10-10.20
			Metconazole	21.20
			Boscalid	17.30 – 34.50
	Dessicant		Glyphosate	8.55
Potatoes	Herbicides:		Metribuzin	18.80-37.50
			Linuron	19.00-35.70
			Diquat	8.50-17.00
			Clomazone	23.00
	Blight Control		Cymoxanil + Mancozeb	10.60
			Cymoxanil + Famoxadone	13.20-18.50
			Fluazinam	9.20
			Mancozeb + Metalaxyl	29.00
	Insectaicides		Oxamyl	45.70-68.60
	Haulm Dessicant		Diquat	35.00
Sugar Beet				
	Herbicides:	Pre-emergence	Chloridazon:	11.60-27.2
		Post-emergence	Phenmedipham:	3.60-6.00

Crop	Function	Material	Cost £/ha per application
		Triflusulfuron-methyl	23.00
	Insecticide	Oxamyl	45.70-68.60
		Pirimicarb	9.60
Beans	Herbicide	Bentazone	70.40
		Pendimethalin	16.80-20.10
		Clomazone	20.00
	Fungicide	Chlorothalonil	16.80
		Tebuconazole	10.20
		Azoxystrobin	30.60
Peas and Beans			
	Herbicide	Pendimethalin + Imazamox	42.00
	Insecticide	Pirimicarb	9.45
		Lambda-Cyhalothrin	5.60
Maize	Herbicide	Nicosulfuron	21.00 - 32.00
		Bromoxynil	23.00
		Mesotrione	34.00
Brassicas	Herbicides	Metazachlor	36.00
		Pyridate	78.00
Broadleaved Grass weeds and volunteer Crops			
	Cereals	Fluazifop-P-butyl	25.00 - 37.50
		Propaquizafop	12.60 – 27.00
		Cycloxydim	25.50 - 42.50
Grassland	Herbicides	MCPA	9.60 - 16.00
		Dicamba +Mecoprop-P + MCPA	21.00-26.00
General	Weed and Grass Killer		
	Couch Grass Control	Glyphosate	8.00 - 11.00
		Clopyralid + Fluroxypyr + MCPA	30.00 - 60.00

The above prices are based on retail prices paid by farmers (August 2015) and reflect the discounts available where there are competing products from several manufacturers. The range in prices per hectare reflects the varying application rates. This is the price for the product, not including the agronomic advice that often comes with it.

Average rates for agronomy only are £12.75/ha for cereals or maize only and rising to £21-£32/ha for potatoes and other vegetable and perishable crops.

Acknowledgement: Thanks to Frontier 01767 680 351

6. AGROCHEMICAL RATES

This table summarises the agrochemical spend for the main crops in Chapter 1, with a breakdown of what each figure is comprised from. Clearly the variation can be considerable between soil-types, regions, farms and even fields, but this offers a starting point from which individual costings can be derived.

Agrochemical Breakdown (excluding seed treatments) £/ha

	Herb-icides	Fung-icides	Insect-icides	PGR	Other	Total Ag-chemical
Feed Wheat	95	112	7	17	5	236
Milling Wheat	95	117	7	17	8	245
Second F. Wheat	105	117	7	17	5	252
Spring Wheat	60	51	7	17	5	140
Red Wheat	66	92	7	17	28	210
Feed Barley	75	77	7	17	5	181
Malting Barley	75	77	7	17	5	181
S. Malting Barley	60	51	7	17	5	140
Winter Oats	55	43	7	17	5	127
Spring Oats	35	33	7	8	5	88
Winter Rape	105	74	7	17	14	217
Spring Rape	50	53	7	17	14	141
Winter Beans	60	46	7	0	9	122
Spring Beans	60	41	10	0	9	120
Blue Peas	75	51	10	0	9	146
Marrowfats	65	90	10	0	16	181
Maincrop Potatoes	30	184	46	0	466	726
Sugar Beet	160	46	10	0	16	232

7. SEED ROYALTY RATES

Seed Royalty rates for autumn 2015 and spring 2016

	£/ha	£/tonne
Wheat	7.75	44.34
Winter Barley	7.43	43.43
Spring Barley	9.13	48.56
Oats	5.34	36.35
Peas	9.23	38.85
Beans	12.36	56.11
Oilseed Rape	9.81	2,229
Linseed	8.25	156.86
Triticale	7.86	46.68

Seed purchased from a merchant includes a royalty for the seed breeder. Farmers who save seed from the previous season (farm saved seed) are legally obliged to pay the royalty. If seed is cleaned and dressed, the royalty is taken at this point (per tonne), if not, the farmer is responsible for paying (per hectare). Some older varieties no longer have royalty charges. It is illegal to sell or buy seed (such as between farmers) unless licensed. View eligible varieties at www.bspb.co.uk .

8.　HOME SAVED SEED COSTS

	Value of Old Crop £/t	Cleaning & Dressing £/t	Testing £/t	Royalty £/t	Total Cost £/t
Feed Wheat	135	75	1.10	44	**255**
Milling Wheat	156	75	1.10	44	**276**
Spring Wheat	156	80	1.00	44	**281**
Winter Feed Barley	125	80	2.20	43	**251**
Winter Malting Barley	141	80	2.20	43	**267**
Spring Malting Barley	151	80	2.20	49	**282**
Winter Oats	125	83	4.40	36	**249**
Spring Oats	125	83	4.20	36	**249**
Winter Rape	280	4,450	70.6	2229	**7,030**
Spring Rape	280	4,450	130	2229	**7,089**
Winter Beans	185	55	2.30	56	**298**
Spring Beans	195	55	2.30	56	**308**
Blue Peas	200	50	2.90	39	**292**
Marrowfats	270	60	3.90	83	**416**

The old crop seed is the value of sales not made from 2015 harvest. Cleaning and dressing figures are based on costs for a mobile cleaner on a 350 hectare farm, and likely amounts of seeds required for each crop (the lower the tonnage, the higher the cost). Single purpose or basic seed treatments included. Testing costs assume a single test (one variety) per species (Germination only; £34/test). Royalty rates as above.

9.　SEED DRILLING RATES

		35	38	41	44	47	50	53	56	59	62	65	68	71
		\multicolumn{13}{}{Thousand Grain Weight (g/1000 grains)}
Seeds Planted per m²	150	53	57	62	66	71	75	80	84	89	93	98	102	107
	175	61	67	72	77	82	88	93	98	103	109	114	119	124
	200	70	76	82	88	94	100	106	112	118	124	130	136	142
	225	79	86	92	99	106	113	119	126	133	140	146	153	160
	250	88	95	103	110	118	125	133	140	148	155	163	170	178
	275	96	105	113	121	129	138	146	154	162	171	179	187	195
	300	105	114	123	132	141	150	159	168	177	186	195	204	213
	325	114	124	133	143	153	163	172	182	192	202	211	221	231
	350	123	133	144	154	165	175	186	196	207	217	228	238	249
	375	131	143	154	165	176	188	199	210	221	233	244	255	266
	400	140	152	164	176	188	200	212	224	236	248	260	272	284
	425	149	162	174	187	200	213	225	238	251	264	276	289	302
	450	158	171	185	198	212	225	239	252	266	279	293	306	320

Measured in Kg/Ha

10. FEED PRICES

			£/tonne
Cattle	Dairy:	High Energy Parlour	230
		Dairy Concentrate	200
		Medium Energy Blend	220
	Beef	Pellets (16% CP)	205
		Concentrate	170
	Calf	Milk Substitute (bags)	1,750
		High Fat replacer (bags)	1,170
		Calf Weaner Pellets.	255
		Calf Rearer Nuts	250
Sheep		High Energy Lamb Pellets.	220
		Medium energy sheep	210
		Sheep/lamb cake	210
		Ewe cake	220
Horses		Horse and Pony Pencils/Cubes (bags)	325
Goats		Goat Nuts	250
Pigs		Piglet Weaner	285
		Sow Nuts	235
		Early Grower Pellets (20-24% protein)	295
		Grower/Finisher Pellets (17-21% protein)	250
		Sow Concentrate	345
		Grower Concentrate	350
Poultry		Chick and Rearer Feeds	230
		Layers Feeds	240
		Broiler Feeds	295
		Turkey Feeds	250
Straight Feeds		Fishmeal (66/70% CP)	1,100
		Soya Bean Meal (Hipro; 50% CP)	305
		Rapeseed Meal (34-36% CP)	205
		Palm Kernel Meal/Cake (17% CP)	115
		Sunflower Seed (30/33% CP)	180
		Citrus Pulp Nuts/Pellets	175
		Wheatfeed Meal (14-18% CP)	125
		Wheatfeed Pellets (14-18% CP)	130
		Maize Gluten (19-20% CP)	155
		Molasses (Cane) (5% CP)	180
		Sugar Beet Pulp (Molassed Nuts/Pellets)	150
		Brewers' Grains	55
		Distillers Wheat Grain	200
		Distillers Barley Grain	195
		Distillers Maize Grains	185
		Feed Wheat (Delivered)	145
		Feed Wheat (Home Grown)	135
		Feed Barley (Home Grown)	125

Compound feed prices are from July 2015; there will be a range incorporating differences in the ingredients and delivery destinations on any occasion. Market prices will also move (possibly considerably) throughout the year. These are delivered prices for hauls over 10 miles in 25 tonne loads. The additional farm delivered cost for bags ranges from £22.00 to £30.00 per tonne.

11.   FEEDSTUFF NUTRITIVE VALUES

Typical Energy and Protein Contents of Some Common Feeds and cost per unit

Type of Feeds	£/T	Dry Matter g/kg	ME MJ/kg DM	CP g/kg DM	p/kg DM	p/MJ ME	p/g CP
Forages:							
Barley Straw	65	860	7	10	7.56	1.08	0.76
Grass Silage (typical clamp)	25	250	10.8	150	10.19	0.94	0.07
Hay (typical meadow)	62	850	8.8	100	7.26	0.83	0.07
Maize Silage	20	300	11	90	6.51	0.59	0.07
Pasture (rotational grazed)	6	180	11.5	160	3.07	0.27	0.02
Whole-crop Wheat (fermented)	36	350	10.5	95	10.38	0.99	0.11
Cereals:							
Barley (home grown *)	125	860	13.2	120	14.53	1.10	0.12
Oats (home grown *)	125	860	12.5	120	14.53	1.16	0.12
Wheat (home grown *)	135	860	13.6	130	15.70	1.15	0.12
Maize	155	880	13.8	90	17.61	1.28	0.20
Roots:							
Fodder Beet	7	180	12	60	3.80	0.32	0.06
Potatoes	30	200	13.3	100	15.00	1.13	0.15
Wet By-Products:							
Brewers Grains	55	260	11.5	250	21.15	1.84	0.08
Straights:							
Cane Molasses	180	750	12.7	40	24.00	1.89	0.60
Distillers Barley Grains	195	900	12.2	260	21.67	1.78	0.08
Distillers Maize Grains	185	900	14	310	20.56	1.47	0.07
Distillers Wheat Grains	200	900	13.5	340	22.22	1.65	0.07
Dried Citrus Pulp	175	900	12.6	70	19.44	1.54	0.28
Dried Molassed Sugar Beet Pulp	150	900	12.5	100	16.67	1.33	0.17
Field Beans	165	880	13.3	290	18.75	1.41	0.06
Maize Gluten Feed	155	880	12.8	210	17.61	1.38	0.08
Palm Kernel Meal	115	900	11.4	200	12.78	1.12	0.06
Wheat-feed	130	880	11.3	190	14.77	1.31	0.08

*   Home grown feed should be costed to the livestock enterprise at the value the grain
    could otherwise be sold at, i.e. the opportunity cost of the crop.

12. AGRISTATS

These basic agricultural statistics relate to the UK farming and food sectors. The main source of data is the Defra Publication 'Agriculture in the UK 2014'. This can be found online at - www.defra.gov.uk/statistics/foodfarm/cross-cutting/auk/. All figures are for the UK and relate to the 2014 year unless otherwise stated.

INDUSTRY STRUCTURE

Agriculture's Economic Contribution	UK	England	Wales	Scotland	N.I.
Gross Output (£m)............................	25,800	19,314	1,551	3,049	1,886
Total Income from Farming* (£m)...	5,379	4,197	212	688	283
Agriculture's Share of the Economy**	0.62%	0.58%	0.62%	0.94%	1.43%
Agriculture's Share of Employment .	1.43%	1.06%	4.19%	2.45%	5.77%

*   *Total Income from Farming (TIFF) is essentially the profit of the farming sector. These are provisional figures (and considered high by the Editor, thought likely to fall in next update).*

** *Based on agriculture's share of gross value-added – 2013 data.*

The wider agri-food sector (including farming, food manufacturing, wholesaling, retailing and catering) contributed £103.0bn or 7.6% to national gross value-added in 2013, and employed 13% of the total UK workforce (13% in 2012).

Agricultural Workforce (2014)	2012	2013	2014
Regular Full-time....................................	*65,000*	*63,000*	64,000
Regular Part-time*.................................	*41,000*	*39,000*	40,000
Seasonal, Casual and Gang....................	67,000	61,000	66,000
Salaried Managers	11,000	11,000	11,000
Total Employees.....................................	184,000	174,000	181,000
Farmers, Partners Directors and Spouses			
Full-time..	141,000	138,000	140,000
Part-time*...	158,000	152,000	155,000
Farmers, Partners Directors & Spouses .	298,000	290,000	294,000
Total Labour Force	481,000	464,000	476,000

*   *Part-time is less than 39 hours in England and Wales, less than 38 hours in Scotland and less than 30 hours in Northern Ireland.*

UK Farmed Areas '000 Hectares

Crop Areas (June) – '000 Hectares

	2010	2012	2013	2014	2015 est.
Wheat	1,939	1,992	1,615	1,936	1,868
Barley	922	1,003	1,213	1,080	1,110
Oats	124	122	177	137	131
Mixed Corn, Triticale, Rye	29	26	24	26	27
Total Cereals (excl. maize)	**3,014**	**3,143**	**3,029**	**3,179**	**3,136**
Oilseed Rape	642	756	716	675	630
Linseed	44	28	34	15	20
Peas (harvested dry)	42	24	29	32	43
Field Beans	166	96	118	107	147
Potatoes	138	149	139	141	138
Sugar Beet	118	120	117	116	97
Veges & Salad grown in open	119	124	116	116	126
Top & Soft Fruit	34	33	33	33	35
Other Horticulture	14	15	15	15	15
Maize	164	158	194	183	185
Other Arable Crops	102	102	123	109	115
Bare Fallow	174	153	255	160	185
Total Tillage	**4,771**	**4,901**	**4,918**	**4,881**	**4,871**
Temporary Grass (<5 years)	1,232	1,357	1,390	1,396	1,385
Total Arable	**6,003**	**6,258**	**6,308**	**6,277**	**6,256**
Permanent Grass (>5 years)	5,925	5,799	5,802	5,824	5,850
Total Grass*	7,157	7,156	7,192	7,220	7,235
*Total Tillage & Grass**	**11,928**	**12,057**	**12,110**	**12,101**	**12,106**
Sole Right Rough Grazing	4,055	3,926	3,940	3,930	3,940
Common Rough Grazing	1,228	1,200	1,197	1,199	1,200
Total Rough Grazing	**5,283**	**5,126**	**5,137**	**5,129**	**5,140**
Land for Outdoor Pigs	10	7	9	8	8
Utilisable Agric.l Area (UAA)	**17,221**	**17,190**	**17,256**	**17,238**	**17,254**
Woodland	774	827	865	897	875
Other Land on agric.l holdings	274	332	324	318	325
Total Agricultural Area	**18,269**	**18,349**	**18,445**	**18,453**	**18,454**

*   *Excluding Rough Grazing*

**   *2014 Estimate provided by The Andersons Centre*

The Utilisable Agricultural Area (UAA) comprises around 71% of the total UK land area. Of the remaining 29%, 4% is woodland and other land on agricultural holdings. The 25% of 'non-agricultural' land broadly splits equally between forest land, urban areas and 'other' land uses. The latter category includes villages, small towns, transport infrastructure, non-urban wasteland, and inland water. The total UK land area is approximately 24.3 million hectares.

Livestock Numbers (June)

'000 Head	2005	2012	2013	2014	2015*
Total Cattle and Calves...............	10,770	9,952	9,844	9,837	9,825
of which: Dairy Cows	1,998	1,796	1,782	1,841	1,850
Beef Cows.............	1,751	1,666	1,611	1,569	1,525
Total Sheep and Lambs	35,416	32,215	32,856	33,743	34,500
of which .... Female Breeding	16,935	15,229	15,561	16,026	16,100
Total Pigs	4,862	4,481	4,885	4,815	4,850
of which Female Breeding ...	470	426	421	406	390
Poultry Broilers..................	111,475	1052,558	104,576	110,374	115,000
Laying Flock	29,544	46,633	47,025	48,404	49,000
Other Poultry.........	10,928	10,870	11,008	10,907	11,000
Farmed Deer...............................	33	31	32	32	32
Goats	96	98	98	100	100

* *2015 Estimate provided by The Andersons Centre*

Size Distribution of Holdings - 2014

By Area on Holding	Holdings - '000	Area - '000 Ha	% of Holdings	% of Area
Under 20 hectares	95	694	44.8	4.0
20 to 50 hectares..............................	41	1,364	19.5	7.9
50 to 100 hectares............................	33	2,389	15.7	13.8
100 hectares and over	42	12,810	19.9	74.2
Total	212	17,257	100	100

Average Size of Enterprises

Hectares	2005	2011	Number	2005	2011
Cereals (excl. maize)	49.4	59.0	Dairy Cows	68	80
Oilseed Rape..............	34.4	46.6	Beef Cows.......... ...	27	28
Potatoes	11.6	15.2	Breeding Sheep	217	218
Sugar Beet	20.3	23.6	Breeding Pigs.........	80	72
			Broilers	37,953	42,692

Data not updated since 2011.

Age of Farm Holders

	2000	2005	2007	2010	2013
Under 35 years	5	3	3	3	3
35-44 years	18	14	12	11	10
45-54 years	26	23	23	25	25
55-64 years	26	29	29	29	28
65 years and over	25	31	33	3332	34
Median age	56	58	59	59	59

DEFRA data. Does not measure amount of farming controlled by each age group, or who the active decision maker is.

FINANCE

Total Income From Farming (TIFF)

	Real Terms 2014		Current Values	
	TIFF (£ million)	TIFF per AWU (£)	Gross Output	Total Income from Farming (£ million)
1985	3,478	12,700	31,897	1,414
1986	3,898	14,300	31,223	1,655
1987	4,351	16,200	30,111	1,942
1988	3,992	15,100	29,106	1,888
1989	4,095	15,700	29,148	2,092
1990	3,311	12,900	27,584	1,830
1991	3,334	13,100	26,554	1,963
1992	4,389	17,300	26,648	2,668
1993	6,050	24,100	28,128	3,774
1994	6,597	26,600	28,769	4,166
1995	7,591	31,100	30,587	4,909
1996	6,678	27,700	29,776	4,496
1997	3,855	16,100	25,972	2,658
1998	2,611	11,100	23,528	1,827
1999	2,687	11,800	22,552	1,901
2000	1,897	8,600	20,674	1,375
2001	1,939	9,000	20,837	1,421
2002	2,542	12,100	20,616	1,912
2003	3,259	15,800	21,000	2,504
2004	2,921	14,400	21,229	2,310
2005	2,707	13,500	18,182	2,201
2006	2,624	13,200	17,569	2,191
2007	2,808	14,200	18,521	2,410
2008	4,358	22,300	22,572	3,853
2009	4,466	23,200	21,703	4,024
2010	4,182	21,800	22,117	3,888
2011	5,446	28,000	24,934	5,172
2012	4,890	25,100	25,031	4,723
2013	5,626	29,100	26,394	5,530
2014	5,379	27,800	25,800	5,379

* *TIFF per full-time entrepreneur equivalent*

TIFF is the business profits plus remuneration to farmers, partners and directors and others with an entrepreneurial interest in the business. It is calculated on a calendar year basis and is the main aggregate measure of UK farming's income (profitability). There are no imputed charges (such as a rental value for owned land or value of the farmer's own labour).

TIFF Accounts - Inputs and Outputs *(2014 Provisional)*

Inputs	£m	Outputs	£m	%
Animal Feed	5,012	Wheat	2,472	*9.6*
Seeds	708	Barley	896	*3.5*
Fertilisers	1,440	Oats and other cereals	105	*0.4*
Pesticides	946	Oilseed rape	684	*2.7*
Hired Labour	2,459	Potatoes	684	*2.7*
Depreciation: equipment	1,728	Sugar beet	315	*1.2*
Depreciation: buildings	953	Fresh vegetables	1,220	*4.7*
Depreciation: livestock	1,379	Fruit	622	*2.4*
Maintenance: materials	945	Plants and flowers	1,166	*4.5*
Maintenance: buildings	585	Other crops	1,073	*4.2*
Fuels	967	Cattle	3,514	*13.6*
Electricity	405	Sheep	1,388	*5.4*
Agricultural services	1,063	Pigs	1,275	*4.9*
Veterinary expenses	461	Poultry	2,481	*9.6*
Net rent	525	Milk	4,602	*17.9*
Interest and Finance Fees	410	Eggs	679	*2.6*
Other goods and services	3,253	Other livestock	330	*1.3*
		Other agricultural	1,063	*4.1*
	____	Non-ag income	1,210	*4.7*
Total Inputs	**23,240**	**Total Gross Output**	**25,780**	*100.0*
Total Income From Farming	5,379	Single Payment & subsidies	2,954	
	28,619	**Total Output**	**28,734**	
		Total crops	6,229	*24.2*
		Total horticulture	3,008	*11.7*
		Total livestock	8,889	*34.5*
		Total livestock products	5,380	*20.9*
		Other	2,273	*8.8*

Average English Farm Business Income (FBI) (Real Terms 2014/15 Prices)

Farm Type	2011/12	*2012/13*	*2013/14*	*2014/15 (prov.)*
Dairy	91,400	54,600	89,600	*78,000*
Grazing Livestock (LFA)	30,800	19,400	14,800	*16,500*
Grazing L'stock (Lowland)	33,800	16,700	15,400	*16,000*
Cereals	98,900	70,300	50,600	*51,000*
General Cropping	106,100	92,600	69,000	*56,500*
Specialist Pigs	40,200	43,300	66,500	*51,500*
Specialist Poultry	49,000	93,700	160,400	*140,500*
Mixed	78,200	38,700	30,200	*25,500*

FBI is the main farm-level measure of farming income (profitability). It is similar to TIFF but is based on a March to February year. *There has been a change in methodology of the series which means data prior to 2011/12 is not strictly comparable to more recent years. UK data is not currently available.*

Balance Sheet of UK Agriculture (2013 – latest data)			£m	£m
Assets:	Fixed:	Land	216,347	
		Buildings, plant and machinery ...	31,928	
		Breeding livestock	8,225	
		Total Fixed Assets:............................		*256,500*
	Current	Trading livestock	4,172	
		Crops and stores ......:.................	3,976	
		Debtors and cash deposits...........	6,241	
		Total Current Assets:		*14,388*
	Total Assets:	....		**270,889**
Liabilities:	Long &	Bank and Building Society loans.	6,574	
	Med-term:	AMC and SASC	1,761	
		Other (inc. family loans).............	636	
		Total Long and Medium Term Liabilities........		*8,971*
	Short-term	Bank overdrafts	2,799	
		Trade credit	2,475	
		Hire purchase and leasing............	1,307	
		Other..	54	
		Total Short-term Liabilities:............................		*6,636*
	Total Liabilities:...................................			**15,607**
Net Worth:				**255,282**

% Equity (Net worth as a % of Total Assets):	94.2%

Total Income from Farming (TIFF) 2013 as % of	a) Net Worth:	2.1%
	b) Total Assets:	2.0%
	c) Tenants Cap'	10.1%

Note: no charge has been made for farmers' own labour or management

PRODUCTIVITY

UK Crop Yields	average (harvest year)						*Average*
(tonnes per hectare)	2009	2010	2011	2012	2013	2014	09-14
Wheat	7.9	7.7	7.8	6.7	7.4	8.6	7.7
Barley (all).............	5.8	5.7	5.7	5.5	5.9	6.4	5.8
Winter Barley	6.4	6.4	6.1	6.4	6.4	7.2	6.5
Spring Barley.......	5.5	5.2	5.4	5.0	5.7	5.9	5.5
Oats	5.8	5.5	5.6	5.1	5.5	6.0	5.6
Oilseed Rape	3.4	3.5	3.9	3.4	3.0	3.6	3.5
Linseed	2.0	1.6	2.0	1.5	1.8	2.7	1.9
Field Beans	3.7	3.0	3.4	3.3	3.2	4.2	3.5
Dried Peas	3.6	3.5	4.1	2.4	3.7	4.0	3.6
Potatoes (all)..........	44.3	43.8	42.3	31.3	40.8	42.0	40.8
Early Potatoes......	15.5	29.0	35.0	26.0	27.0	34.0	27.8
Maincrop Potatoes	47.7	45.5	44.0	32.0	43.3	43.0	42.6
Sugar Beet*	74.0	55.1	75.4	60.7	72.1	80.1	69.6

* *Adjusted to 16% sugar*

UK Livestock Output

(kg unless stated)	2009	2010	2011	2012	2013	2014	Average 09-14
Milk Yield (litres/cow)*	7,031	7,303	7,563	7,477	7,543	7,916	7,472
Beef Carcase Wgt**	342	347	345	347	342	350	346
Lamb Carcase Wgt Δ....	18.8	18.9	19.0	19.1	19.0	19.0	19.0
Pig Carcase Wgt ♦	77.8	78.1	78.0	78.0	79.0	81.0	78.7

columns header: average (harvest year)

* litres per annum   ** steers, heifers & young bulls
Δ clean sheep and lambs   ♦ clean pigs

FOOD

Self Sufficiency* (%)

	2003	2013		2003	2013
All Food........................	64	60	Indigenous-type Food	77	73
Crops:...........................			Livestock:		
Wheat	124	83	Beef and Veal.........	70	83
Barley	120	110	Mutton and Lamb...	86	100
Oats	124	95	Pig-meat.................	49	61
Total Cereals.................	113	85	Poultry-meat..........	91	90
Oilseed Rape	108	114	Milk	102	103
Potatoes	82	75	Hen Eggs...............	87	87
Sugar	76	60			
Fresh Vegetables	63	55			
Fresh Fruit	8	10			

* ratio of UK production to UK human consumption

Food Spending*

	2008	2009	2010	2011	2012	2013
Household Expenditure	23.00	23.86	24.50	24.92	25.98	26.62
Eating-Out Expenditure	8.16	8.26	8.54	8.79	8.95	9.29
All Expenditure	31.17	32.12	33.04	33.71	34.93	35.92

* expenditure on Food and Non-alcoholic Drinks (£ per person per week) DEFRA

Producers Share*

	1990	2000	2010	2011	2012	2013	2014
Basket of Goods....	43	35	37	39	39	38	40
Wheat (bread)........	16	10	8	11	11	11	9
Potatoes	31	27	20	22	22	22	17
Carrots	31	38	41	46	47	44	34
Apples	51	40	42	40	44	37	34
Milk	35	28	32	34	35	31	39
Beef	57	44	48	53	54	58	50
Lamb	57	43	56	57	53	53	52
Pork	55	47	39	39	40	36	40
Chicken.................	44	37	38	39	39	40	39
Eggs......................	36	29	27	26	31	34	32

* farmer's share of retail price (per cent) DEFRA.

13. RATE OF INFLATION; PRICE AND COST INDICES

INFLATION DATA

Calendar Year	RPI*: % yearly change	RPI: Index 1987=100	CPI** % yearly change	CPI Index 2005=100	Agricultural Prices Index, 2010 = 100	
					Outputs	Inputs
1988..............	4.9	107	-	-	69.4	53.0
1989..............	7.8	115	5.2	67	74.0	55.8
1990..............	9.5	126	7.0	72	75.3	58.4
1991..............	5.9	134	7.5	77	74.1	60.5
1992..............	3.7	139	4.3	80	74.1	62.1
1993..............	1.6	141	2.5	82	78.2	64.7
1994..............	2.4	144	2.0	84	78.8	64.8
1995..............	3.5	149	2.6	86	85.9	66.3
1996..............	2.4	153	2.5	88	83.7	69.9
1997..............	3.1	158	1.8	90	73.1	68.1
1998..............	3.4	163	1.6	91	68.4	65.3
1999..............	1.5	165	1.3	92	65.6	65.1
2000..............	3.0	170	0.8	93	63.6	66.3
2001..............	1.8	173	1.2	94	68.8	68.2
2002..............	1.7	176	1.3	95	65.7	67.8
2003..............	2.9	181	1.4	97	70.1	69.0
2004..............	3.0	187	1.3	98	71.6	72.9
2005..............	2.8	192	2.1	100	69.6	75.3
2006..............	3.2	198	2.3	102	72.3	78.1
2007..............	4.3	207	2.3	105	82.2	84.8
2008..............	4.0	215	3.6	109	98.9	103.2
2009..............	-0.5	214	2.2	111	95.0	95.9
2010..............	4.6	224	3.3	115	100.0	100.0
2011..............	5.2	235	4.5	120	113.1	112.2
2012..............	3.2	243	2.8	123	118.7	113.8
2013..............	3.0	250	2.0	126	125.5	117.0
2014..............	2.4	256	1.5	128	114.1	112.2
2015 (so far)..		259 (May)		128 (May)	107.6	108.6

* Retail Price Index

** Consumer Price Index

Inflation of food-based Component of CPI

Per Cent	2000	2005	2010	2011	2012	2013	2014	2015 to May
CPI (Overall Index)	2.1	3.3	4.5	4.5	2.8	2.6	1.5	0.4
All goods	0.3	3.1	4.6	4.6	2.3	2	0.6	-1.8
All Services	4.1	3.6	4.3	4.3	3.5	3.2	2.5	2.2
Food & non-alcoholic drinks	15	3.4	5.5	3.2	1.9	1.9	-0.2	-1.8
Food	1.7	3	5	3.1	2.1	2.1	-0.3	-1.8
Bread & Cereals	1.3	2.1	6.4	2.2	3.3	3.3	-0.6	-2.1
Meat	0.7	0.9	5.4	3.7	2.5	2.5	0.6	-2.4
Fish	1.6	6.6	9.2	3.6	5.2	5.2	2.6	-4.1
Milk, Cheese & Eggs	2.7	0.2	2.6	0.9	1.8	1.8	0.5	-3.2
Oils & Fats	-2.2	6.7	11.8	2.4	0.9	0.9	-0.6	-3.2
Fruit	1.2	7.9	3.7	1.7	-0.1	-0.1	0.3	1
Vegetables Inc. potatoes	3	2.9	3.4	3.3	2.3	2.3	-4.7	-1.9
Sugar, Jam & Sweets	2.8	5.6	7.5	5.0	0.1	0.1	1.8	1.5
Food Products	-0.5	0.7	3.2	5.0	2.9	2.9	0.6	-5.8

Weighting of food-based Component of CPI

parts per 1000	2000	2005	2010	2011	2012	2013	2014	2015
CPI (Overall Index)	1000	1000	1000	1000	1000	1000	1000	1000
All goods	591	536	549	561	555	534	540	532
All Services	409	464	451	439	445	466	460	468
Food & non-alcoholic drinks	121	106	108	118	112	106	112	110
Food	109	93	96	103	98	93	99	97
Bread & Cereals	19	15	16	17	17	16	17	16
Meat	27	23	22	22	22	21	22	22
Fish	5	4	4	4	4	4	4	4
Milk, Cheese & Eggs	14	13	14	15	14	13	14	14
Oils & Fats	2	2	2	2	2	2	2	2
Fruit	9	8	9	12	9	9	10	10
Vegetables Inc. potatoes	18	14	15	16	15	14	15	14
Sugar, Jam & Sweets	12	12	11	12	12	11	12	12
Food Products	3	2	3	3	3	3	3	3

DETAILED AGRICULTURAL PRICE AND COST INDICES

Producer Prices	2009	2010	2011	2012	2013	2014
Feed Wheat	89.5	100.0	141.7	144.3	151.9	121.3
Feed Barley	86.3	100.0	150.3	160.9	154.4	119.2
All Cereals	89.6	100.0	144.8	149.7	153.1	120.6
Oilseed Rape	91.5	100.0	143.3	139.1	127.0	99.7
Potatoes (all)	86.6	100.0	107.1	121.9	156.1	103.7
Sugar Beet	99.0	100.0	99.9	104.3	105.7	106.4
Desert Apples	96.6	100.0	107.0	118.0	117.1	104.0
All Fresh Vegetables	87.8	100.0	92.7	108.6	110.2	96.1
All Fresh Fruit	95.6	100.0	98.7	103.7	104.8	97.6
All Crop Products	*89.1*	*100.0*	*117.8*	*124.1*	*128.6*	*107.8*
Milk	96.1	100.0	111.0	113.8	128.2	127.7
Cattle	104.9	100.0	116.4	129.3	137.7	123.2
Sheep	91.1	100.0	112.3	105.1	102.0	106.1
Wool	47.1	100.0	121.6	75.5	101.0	155.9
Pigs	103.1	100.0	102.1	106.3	116.7	111.7
Poultry	99.5	100.0	102.9	105.0	109.3	105.9
Eggs	105.7	100.0	99.9	124.0	130.8	122.2
All Animal Products	*99.3*	*100.0*	*109.5*	*114.7*	*123.2*	*118.6*
All Products	*95.0*	*100.0*	*113.0*	*118.6*	*125.4*	*114.1*
Input Prices						
Seeds	105.0	100.0	105.8	98.5	110.2	98.1
Fertilisers	102.3	100.0	130.4	125.2	113.1	106.5
Agro-chemicals	102.8	100.0	100.7	102.0	97.7	102.6
Energy and Lubricants	88.3	100.0	118.2	122.4	123.4	119.1
Animal Feeding Stuffs	95.4	100.0	120.7	128.5	139.4	120.7
Plant Maint' & Repair	95.8	100.0	104.9	106.5	108.3	110.3
Machinery & Equip'	99.7	100.0	103.6	101.7	102.9	108.7
Building Maintenance	93.8	100.0	107.4	109.8	110.1	110.9
General Expenses	93.3	100.0	106.0	107.2	109.6	110.6
All Inputs	*95.9*	*100.0*	*112.2*	*114.0*	*116.9*	*112.2*

(2010 = 100)

14. METRIC CONVERSION FACTORS

Metric to Imperial   *Imperial to Metric*

Area

1 hectare (10,000m²).... 2.471 acres   1 acre .... 0.405 ha

                                      1 square mile .... 259 ha

1 square km .... 0.386 sq. mile   1 square mile .... 2.590 sq. km

1 square m .... 1.196 sq. yard   1 square yard .... 0.836 sq. m

1 square m .... 10.764 sq. feet   1 square foot .... 0.093 sq. m

(m = metre, km = kilometre)

Length

1 mm............................. 0.039 inch   1 inch. .... 25.4 mm

1 cm............................. 0.394 inch   1 inch .... 2.54 cm

1 m................................ 3.281 feet   1 foot................................... 0.305 m

1 m............................... 1.094 yard   1 yard .... 0.914 m

1 km........................... 0.6214 mile   1 mile .... 1.609 km

(mm = millimetre, cm = centimetre)

Volume

1 millilitre.............. 0.0352 fluid oz   1 fluid oz .... 28.413 ml

1 litre .... 35.2 fluid oz   1 fluid oz............................. 0.028 litre

1 litre .... 1.76 pints   1 pint.................................. 0.568 litre

1 litre .... 0.22 gallon   1 gallon .... 4.546 litres

1 cubic m .... 35.31 cu feet   1 cubic foot .... 0.028 cu m

1 cubic m .... 1.307 cu yard   1 cubic yard........................ 0.765 cu m

1 cubic m .... 220 gallons   1 gallon .... 0.005 cu m

1 ha of 10mm water . 22,000gallons   1 acre-inch .... $102.75m^3$

Weight

1 gram............................. 0.0353 oz   1 oz .... 28.35 gm

1 kg................................. 35.274oz

1 kg................................. 2.205 lb   1 lb.. 0.454 kg

50 kg................................ 0.984 cwt

1 tonne (1,000 kg)........... 19.68 cwt   1 cwt. .... 50.80 kg

1 tonne........................... 0.984 ton   1 ton .... 1.016 tonne

Milk

1 litre 1.03kg

1kg................................. 0.971 litre

1 litre .... 1.709 pints   1 pint....................................... 0.585kg

I tonne..................... 213.63 gallon   1 gallon 4.681kg

Yields and Rates of Use

1 tonne/ha. ....0.398 ton/acre	1 ton/acre ....2.511 tonnes/ha
1 tonne/ha. ....7.95 cwt/acre	1 cwt/acre.................... 0.125 tonne/ha
1 gram/ha..................0.014 oz/acre	1 oz/acre............................ 70.053 g/ha
1 kg/ha.......................0.892 lb/acre	1 lb/acre .... 1.121 g/ha
1 kg/ha....................0.008 cwt/acre	1 cwt/acre............................ 125.5 g/ha
1 kg/ha (fert.)..........0.797 unit/acre	1 unit/acre .... 1.255 kg/ha
1 litre/ha.................0.712 pint/acre	1 pint/acre ....1.404 litre/ha
1 litre/ha..................0.089 gal/acre	1 gal/acre....................... 11.24 litres/ha

Power, Pressure, Temperature

1 kW .... 1.341 hp	1 hp ....0.746 kW
1MW 1,000kW	
1 kilojoule.......................0.948 Btu	1 Btu ....1.055 kilojoule
1 therm ....10,000 Btu	1 Btu ....0.0001 therm
1 lb f ft........................... 1.356 Nm	1 Nm ....0.738 lb f ft
1 bar......................14.705 lb/sq.in.	1 lb/sq.in ....0.068 bar
°C to °F.......................... x1.8, + 32	°F to °C .... -32, ÷ 1.8

15. INDEX